**Y0-DNM-162**

Our sections are color-coded for your convenience.

**Distinctive Dining**

**Casual & Family Dining**

**Fast Food & Carryout**

**Activities & Attractions**

**Local Retail & Services**

**National Retail & Services**

**Entertainment on Vacation®**

**National Travel & Hotels**

Your Entertainment® Membership is packed with $1000s in savings on fine and casual dining, local attractions, travel, shopping, and much more! Your book coupons are just the beginning. The free mobile app and Entertainment.com® contain the same great book savings, PLUS use the app to access local savings in over 100 major cities throughout the U.S. and Canada. It's like getting all Entertainment® editions on your phone!

For over 50 years, Entertainment® has been the premier provider of unbeatable local discounts throughout the U.S. and Canada. Consumers enjoy doing more for less cost while supporting local businesses in the community. We proudly help raise MILLIONS of dollars for schools, charities and community groups every year through our fundraising sales.

# Weekend Getaway. Family Trip. Dream Vacation.

Check out the Travel section and save money with these popular brands.

## Special Travel Deals

You'll save even more on these top destinations:

- Las Vegas
- Orlando
- San Diego
- Chicago
- Atlanta
- and more

# Distinctive Dining Index

DISTINCTIVE DINING INDEX

# Get More

**Get thousands more discounts to use at home or when traveling.**

Download the mobile app now, included with this membership. Search for "Entertainment® Coupons" in your app store.

# How to Use Your Dining Offers

## Buy One, Get One Free Offers

The least expensive entrée or meal ordered is complimentary up to the maximum value stated on the offer.

### Maximum Value

### EXAMPLE A
Member's Order:

1 Steak Entrée... $25.00
1 Pasta Entrée... $18.00

Save the cost of the LEAST expensive entrée

$18.00

### EXAMPLE B
Member's Order:

1 Steak Entrée... $25.00
1 Fish Entrée... $22.00

Save the MAXIMUM value

$20.00

## Remember:

- Present your coupon or mobile offer before the bill is totaled.
- Calculate your tip on the total bill before the discount is deducted.
- Refer to the Rules of Use in the back of your book for complete program details. Refer to each individual offer for specific offer information, conditions and restrictions.
- Many of the dining offers found in your book, and more, are redeemable via the mobile app!

# Celebrate.

## *Delizioso.*

Banquets • Catering • Dine In • To Go • Delivery
bucadibeppo.com

---

# We're in your neighborhood.

**ARIZONA**
**PHOENIX**
Arrowhead, Chandler, Mesa, Scottsdale

**CALIFORNIA**
**LOS ANGELES**
Claremont, Encino, Farmers Market, Pasadena, Redondo Beach, Santa Monica, Thousand Oaks, Universal CityWalk, Valencia
**ORANGE COUNTY**
Anaheim, Brea, Huntington Beach
**SACRAMENTO**
Roseville, Sacramento
**SAN DIEGO**
Carlsbad, Mira Mesa, San Diego
**SAN FRANCISCO**
Campbell, Palo Alto, San Francisco, San Jose

**COLORADO**
**DENVER**
Broomfield

**DISTRICT OF COLUMBIA**
**WASHINGTON, D.C.**

**FLORIDA**
**JACKSONVILLE**
**MIAMI**
Coral Springs, Davie
**NAPLES**
Fort Myers, Naples

**ORLANDO**
Florida Mall, Maitland
**TALLAHASSEE**
**WEST PALM BEACH**
Boynton Beach

**GEORGIA**
**ATLANTA**
Alpharetta
**AUGUSTA**
**MACON**

**HAWAII**
**HONOLULU**

**ILLINOIS**
**CHICAGO**
Lombard, Orland Park, Wheeling

**INDIANA**
**INDIANAPOLIS**
Castleton Square, Downtown Indianapolis, Greenwood

**KENTUCKY**
**FLORENCE**
**LOUISVILLE**

**MARYLAND**
**BALTIMORE**
**GAITHERSBURG**
**WALDORF**

**MICHIGAN**
**DETROIT**
Livonia, Utica

**MINNESOTA**
**MINNEAPOLIS**
Burnsville, Eden Prairie, Maple Grove, Minneapolis, St. Paul

**MISSOURI**
**KANSAS CITY**
Kansas City - Plaza

**NEVADA**
**LAS VEGAS**
Excalibur Hotel & Casino, Las Vegas - Bally's, Las Vegas - Paradise, Summerlin

**NEW MEXICO**
**ALBUQUERQUE**

**NEW YORK**
**ALBANY**
**NEW YORK CITY**
Times Square

**NORTH CAROLINA**
**CHARLOTTE**
Pineville

**OHIO**
**CINCINNATI**
**CLEVELAND**
Strongsville, Westlake
**COLUMBUS**
Downtown Columbus, Worthington

**PENNSYLVANIA**
**PHILADELPHIA**
Exton, Reading, Whitehall
**PITTSBURGH**
Robinson Town Centre, Station Square

**TENNESSEE**
**NASHVILLE**
Cool Springs

**TEXAS**
**AUSTIN**
Austin, Cedar Park
**DALLAS**
Dallas, Frisco, Southlake
**HOUSTON**
Buffalo Speedway, The Woodlands

**UTAH**
**SALT LAKE CITY**
Fort Union, Salt Lake City
**ST. GEORGE**

**VIRGINIA**
**WINCHESTER**

**WASHINGTON**
**SEATTLE**
Lynnwood, Seattle

**WISCONSIN**
**APPLETON**
**MILWAUKEE**
Greendale, Milwaukee

19484-7002-8020

www.bucadibeppo.com

Valid at participating Buca di Beppo® locations.

Valid for Dine In or Buca To Go. Expires 12/31/17.

49784321

3663 Las Vegas Blvd. S.
(In Miracle Mile Shops at the Planet Hollywood Hotel & Casino)
Las Vegas, NV
(702) 737-0444

*Blondies offers fun and great food for everyone. Delicious appetizers, salads, subs and sandwiches. Pizzas, burgers, ribs, seafood and specialties like our 16 oz. Cowboy Cut Steak, Beer Can Chicken and the "Drunken Bird." Save room for one of our sinful desserts including our famous Smores. Catering services available. Book our VIP room. Full bar available. Open daily.*

**UP TO $27 VALUE**

*Enjoy one complimentary LUNCH OR DINNER ENTREE when a second LUNCH OR DINNER ENTREE of equal or greater value is purchased – maximum discount $27.*

Dine in only.

## PRE-GAME SHOW

**XXL onion rings**     **$6.75**
Beer-battered onions deep-fried to a
golden brown, served with ranch dressing.

**The wing thing**
Let your taste buds take flight. Choose traditional or boneless, mild, medium or hot.
1 doz. **$9.95**      2 doz. **$17.95**

**Blondies sampler**     **$15.95**
Chicken tenders, jalapeno poppers,
onion rings and hot wings, served with
a variety of sauces.

## THE GREENS

**Caesar salad**     **$10.95**
Crisp romaine lettuce tossed with croutons,
parmesan cheese and our signature Caesar
dressing. Add sliced chicken breast or
blackened salmon for $2.95

## 7TH INNING STRETCH

**Philly cheese steak**     **$9.95**
USDA chopped steak topped piled high
on a big hoagie roll with American, jack
or whiz cheese. Yo!

**Turkey club sandwich**     **$9.95**
Tender turkey breast and American cheese piled high
with lettuce, tomatoes and bacon. Served on sourdough
or wheat bread.

## 2ND QUARTER PIZZAS

*Hand-tossed 12" personal pizzas*

**BBQ chicken pizza**     **$14.95**
BBQ chicken, Hawaiian onions and
cilantro on a thin layer of sweet bbq
sauce, smothered with mozzarella cheese.

## THE MAIN EVENT

**Cowboy cut steak**     **$26.95**
The good, the big and the juicy. Tender, flavorful 16 oz.
bone-in rib eye, served with vegetables and French fries.

Menu Sampler - Prices and menu subject to change.

---

3663 Las Vegas Blvd. S.
(In Miracle Mile Shops at the Planet Hollywood
Hotel & Casino)
Las Vegas, NV
(702) 737-0444

| | | | |
|---|---|---|---|
| How was service? | ☐ Excellent | ☐ Good | ☐ Poor |
| How was your food? | ☐ Excellent | ☐ Good | ☐ Poor |
| How was the atmosphere? | ☐ Excellent | ☐ Good | ☐ Poor |
| Was this your first visit? | ☐ Yes | ☐ No | |
| Do you plan to return? | ☐ Yes | ☐ No | |

Birthday: _____

Anniversary: _____

Name: _____

Email Address*: _____
*In the event we send news and information about upcoming events and products via email.

*Tipping should be 15% to 20% of the total bill before discount.*

35216

# ❋Hokkaido
## Teppanyaki Steak House

www.hokkaidolv.com

3555 S. Town Center Dr., Ste. 101
(just off the 215 on Town Center Dr. in Summerlin)
Las Vegas, NV

(702) 487-5555

*We are a Japanese steak house serving quality steak and seafood, with an entertaining dining experience. Come try our specialty sake, imported beers and wines. Check out our sushi bar. Make sure you save room for our wide variety of delicious desserts!*

*We are open Monday-Sunday for dinner from 5 p.m.–10 p.m.*

---

# ❋Hokkaido
## Teppanyaki Steak House

### ALL TEPPAN - YAKI ENTREES

All teppan entrees are served with miso soup, ginger salad,
steam rice, shrimp appetizer, and seasoned vegetables.

| | | COMBINATIONS | |
|---|---|---|---|
| VEGETABLE | 15.95 | CHICKEN AND SHRIMP OR SCALLOP | 23.95 |
| CHICKEN | 16.95 | FILET MIGNON AND CHICKEN | 28.95 |
| NEW YORK STEAK | 21.95 | NEW YORK STEAK AND CHICKEN | 26.95 |
| FILET MIGNON | 24.95 | FILET MIGNON AND SHRIMP OR SCALLOP | 29.95 |
| SCALLOP | 22.95 | NEW YORK STEAK AND SHRIMP OR SCALLOP | 28.95 |
| SHRIMP | 20.95 | LOBSTER AND NEW YORK STEAK | 32.95 |
| SEA BASS | 25.95 | LOBSTER AND FILET MIGNON | 35.95 |
| LOBSTER TAIL | 35.95 | | |

#### NOW HAVE A FULL SUSHI BAR

### SASHIMI 4PC / SUSHI 8PC

SALMON SASHIMI
TUNA SASHIMI
CALIFORNIA ROLL
SPICY TUNA ROLL
SPICY SALMON ROLL
SHRIMP TEMPURA ROLL
DRAGON ROLL
TIGER ROLL
SPIDER ROLL
RED ROCK ROLL

### KIDS ENTREES
(10 YEARS OLD AND UNDER)

| | |
|---|---|
| CHICKEN | 9.95 |
| SHRIMP | 14.95 |
| NEW YORK STEAK | 15.95 |
| FILET MIGNON | 16.95 |

### SIDES

| | | | |
|---|---|---|---|
| FRIED RICE | 2.95 | MUSHROOM | 5.95 |
| SCALLOP | 9.95 | SHRIMP | 8.95 |

*A GREAT PLACE TO HAVE GOOD QUALITY FOOD
AND AN ENTERTAINING DINING EXPERIENCE!*

Menu Sampler - Prices and menu subject to change.

---

# ❋Hokkaido
## Teppanyaki Steak House

3555 S. Town Center Dr., Ste. 101
(just off the 215 on Town Center Dr. in Summerlin)
Las Vegas, NV

(702) 487-5555

www.hokkaidolv.com

| | | | |
|---|---|---|---|
| How was service? | ☐ Excellent | ☐ Good | ☐ Poor |
| How was your food? | ☐ Excellent | ☐ Good | ☐ Poor |
| How was the atmosphere? | ☐ Excellent | ☐ Good | ☐ Poor |
| Was this your first visit? | ☐ Yes | ☐ No | |
| Do you plan to return? | ☐ Yes | ☐ No | |

Birthday: _____

Anniversary: _____

Name: _____

Email Address*: _____

*In the event we send news and information about upcoming events and products via email.

*Tipping should be 15% to 20% of the total bill before discount.*

www.pureindiancuisinevegas.com

1405 East Sunset
Road, Suite 200
Las Vegas, NV

(703) 897-5555

*Get mesmerized with the taste of authentic Indian cuisine right here at Pure Indian Cuisine. We offer a wide selection of vegan, vegetarian, non-vegetarian and now introducing South Indian cuisine. Located just minutes away from the south end of the Las Vegas Strip, we have the best views of the strip right from our restaurant.*

---

## DAL MAKHANI $14
Lentil delicacy flavored with onions, tomatoes, ginger, garlic & cream

## TADKA DAAL $13
Delicately spiced yellow lentils

## MALAI KOFTA $15
Cheese & vegetable balls in an aromatic gravy

## PUNJABI CHICKEN CURRY $16
Tender chicken cooked in a blend of onions, tomatoes & spices

## CHICKEN VINDALOO $16
Tender chicken cooked in a hot spicy sauce with diced potatoes

## LAMB ROGAN JOSH $16
Kashmiri delicacy cooked with intensely hot & fragrant spices

## BALTI SHRIMP CURRY $17
Fish of the day simmered in a blend of onions, tomatoes & spices

## GOAN FISH CURRY $19
Fish of the day simmered in coconut milk & exotic spices

Menu Sampler - Prices and menu subject to change.

---

1405 East Sunset Road, Suite 200
Las Vegas, NV

(703) 897-5555

www.pureindiancuisinevegas.com

| | | | |
|---|---|---|---|
| How was service? | ☐ Excellent | ☐ Good | ☐ Poor |
| How was your food? | ☐ Excellent | ☐ Good | ☐ Poor |
| How was the atmosphere? | ☐ Excellent | ☐ Good | ☐ Poor |
| Was this your first visit? | ☐ Yes | ☐ No | |
| Do you plan to return? | ☐ Yes | ☐ No | |

Birthday: _____

Anniversary: _____

Name: _____

Email Address*: _____

*In the event we send news and information about upcoming events and products via email.

*Tipping should be 15% to 20% of the total bill before discount.*

## Steiner's

### Oasis Annie's Soups and Salads

**EUREKA, SOUP OF THE DAY**    $6.29 BOWL / $4.29 CUP
Our nationally known chef brings you the great flavors of the world– a variety of beef, chicken, seafood, and vegetable based soups reflective of the season, inspiration and availability

**OASIS, COBB SALAD**    $11.49
You'll think you found heaven– crisp iceberg and romaine greens with rows of diced chicken, avocado, bleu cheese, bacon, tomato and a halved hard boiled egg

### U.S. 93 Sandwiches

**LAKE MEAD, NEVADA DIP**    $8.49
You're taste buds will be swimming in ecstasy!– Succulent roast beef sliced thin to melt in your mouth served with steiner's special au jus, for your skinny dippin' pleasure!

**LOVELOCK, KING OF CLUBS**    $10.59
You are going to love locking your jaws around this king– real roasted fresh turkey breast, crisp bacon, lettuce ,tomato, avocado and swiss cheese and mayo on your choice of toast

### Tahoe Territory Specialties

**RED ROCK GRILLED STEAK SANDWICH**    $11.49
We'd hike every trail for this perfect nevada style steak sandwich. A 6oz. Usda prime flat iron steak served on a toasted hoagie roll with melted jack cheese, 3 crispy onion rings, lettuce, and sliced tomato

**PARADISE, CARNITAS STYLE PORK STACKER**    $9.99
Badges, we don't need no stinkin' badges. A touch of south america! Citrus and chile simmered shredded pork shoulder piled high on a sweet sourdough bun, with grilled pineapple salsa, and house pickled red onions

### Drake's Pioneer Country Chicken Sandwiches

**ORLEANS**    $9.79
The bayou is within your reach — a blackened breast with crisp bacon, melted crumbled bleu cheese, and roasted red peppers

**WILD WILD WEST**    $8.29
Dress it up the way you like it    add $.50 each item

### Peyton's Cowboy Country Burgers

**CAESAR'S TROJAN BURGER**    $9.89
Who needs the bcs-this is the national championship burger! From the "griddled iron" topped with roasted poblano chiles, sliced avocado, frizzled onions, and cheddar cheese. Served with a smoky chipotle mayoon a whole grain bun with your choice of steiner's sides

**KOBE (NOT BRYANT) BURGER (A LA CARTE)**    $13.99
Try a special burger from beer fed, hand massaged and sake brushed beef– served on a sweet sourdough bun with maui onions and aged white cheddar cheese, heirloom tomato and leaf lettuce. Don't snicker-they get $47 for this in new york city! –

### Silver State "Basket" Dinners (Available 24 hours a day!)

**FRIED CHICKEN IN A BASKET**    $10.99
Served with our brew city fries and cole slaw (upon request)

**FISH AND CHIPS BASKET**    $10.99
Icelandic cod dipped in beer batter and fried golden brown served with fries, tartar sauce, lemon wedges, and cole slaw (upon request)

### Laurich Silver State Dinners

**\*BABY BACK RIBS**    $19.99 WHOLE / $15.99 HALF
We've taken the most succulent ribs and smoked them to perfection and topped them off with our house guajillo bourbon barbecue sauce

**BROILED SALMON FILLET (NO BONES BABY!)**    $17.99
10 Oz. Pacific salmon char grilled with an extraordinary lemon butter and spices

**\*TWELVE OUNCE USDA CHOICE N.Y. STEAK**    $21.99
Char-grilled masterpiece topped with sautéed mushrooms and garlic butter

### Parker's Pastas (4pm to 11 pm daily)

**ANGEL HAIR ARABIATA**    $13.99 WITH CHICKEN / 9.99 PLAIN
"Iffa you lika pasta you a gotta a try a mea" angel hair pasta with a spicy marinara sauce, topped with shredded parmesan cheese-also great with grilled diced chicken

**SHRIMP SCAMPI ANGEL HAIR**    $17.99
6 Big shrimp tossed with fire roasted tomatoes, and then sautéed in a light lemon oil, garlic, basil, cream and butter sauce served over angel hair pasta

---

Menu Sampler - Prices and menu subject to change.

---

1750 N. Buffalo, Ste. 115 (NE Corner at Vegas Dr.)
Las Vegas, NV, (702) 304-8084
8168 S. Las Vegas Blvd. (SE Corner at Windmill)
Las Vegas, NV, (702) 214-6700
8410 W. Cheyenne Ave., Ste. 107 (NE Corner at Durango)
Las Vegas, NV, (702) 395-8777

www.steinerspub.com

| | | | | | |
|---|---|---|---|---|---|
| How was service? | ☐ Excellent | ☐ Good | ☐ Poor | | |
| How was your food? | ☐ Excellent | ☐ Good | ☐ Poor | Birthday: _____ | |
| How was the atmosphere? | ☐ Excellent | ☐ Good | ☐ Poor | | |
| Was this your first visit? | ☐ Yes | ☐ No | | | |
| Do you plan to return? | ☐ Yes | ☐ No | | Anniversary: _____ | |

Name: _____

Email Address*: _____

*In the event we send news and information about upcoming events and products via email.

*Tipping should be 15% to 20% of the total bill before discount.*    0000000131

# india palace
## Fine Indian Cuisine

**Panner Tikka Masala ~ $12.95**
Tender chunks of marinated cheese simmered in a creamy
tomato sauce

**Tandoori Fish ~ $17.95**
Boneless pieces marinated in yogurt & exotic spices

**Lamb Seekh Kebab ~ $16.95**
Minced lamb w/ onions, herbs & spices, molded on skewers

**Chicken Tikka Masala ~ $14.95**
Tandoori white chicken marinated in yogurt
& spices simmered in a creamy tomato sauce

**Karahi Chicken ~ $14.95**
Tender chicken strips stir-fried with bell pepper, onion,
tomatoes & spices

**Lamb Rogan Josh ~ $15.95**
Kashmiri delicacy cooked w/ intensely hot & fragrant spices

**Karahi Goat ~ $15.95**
Diced goat stir-fried w/ bell peppers, onions & spices.

*Menu Sampler - Prices and menu subject to change.*

---

## india palace
### Fine Indian Cuisine

505 E. Twain Ave.
Las Vegas, NV
(702) 796-4177

www.indiapalacelv.com

| | | | |
|---|---|---|---|
| How was service? | ☐ Excellent | ☐ Good | ☐ Poor |
| How was your food? | ☐ Excellent | ☐ Good | ☐ Poor |
| How was the atmosphere? | ☐ Excellent | ☐ Good | ☐ Poor |
| Was this your first visit? | ☐ Yes | ☐ No | |
| Do you plan to return? | ☐ Yes | ☐ No | |

Birthday: _____

Anniversary: _____

Name: _____

Email Address*: _____

*In the event we send news and information about upcoming events and products via email.

*Tipping should be 15% to 20% of the total bill before discount.*

000000026CL

## LEGACY ROLLS

**HELLO KITTY ROLL** 9
Coconut, crab stick tempura, cream cheese roll with tempura flakes and eel sauce on top

**HIT AND RUN** 12
Spicy tuna and cucumber roll topped with white tuna, avocado

**MORTAL COMBAT** 10
Deep fried spicy tuna and cream cheese roll topped with albacore

**STICKY ICKY** 12
Peanut butter, shrimp tempura and crab roll topped with coconut flakes

**MAUI ROLL** 11
Cream cheese, coconut and shrimp tempura topped with salmon and avocado

**JENNY ROLL** 10
Crab, avocado and cream cheese roll baked with salmon

## LUNCH SPECIALS
(all specials come with steamed rice,ginger salad and miso soup*)

Teriyaki Chicken, 3pc Vegetable Tempura, 4pc California Roll 7.99

Teriyaki Salmon, 3pc Vegetable Tempura, 4pc California Roll 9.99

Sushi Lunch - 5pcs of Sushi and 8pc California Roll 9.99

## DINNER SPECIALS

Teriyaki Chicken, 6pc Vegetable Tempura, 4pc California Roll 9.99

Teriyaki Salmon, 6pc Vegetable Tempura, 4pc California Roll 11.99

Sushi Dinner 7 pcs of Sushi and 8pc California Roll 11.99

*miso soup not included on take-out orders*

---

Menu Sampler - Prices and menu subject to change.

---

10040 W. Cheyenne Ave., Ste. 150
Las Vegas, NV

(702) 228-8758

TSHLV.com

| | Excellent | Good | Poor | |
|---|---|---|---|---|
| How was service? | ☐ Excellent | ☐ Good | ☐ Poor | |
| How was your food? | ☐ Excellent | ☐ Good | ☐ Poor | Birthday: _____ |
| How was the atmosphere? | ☐ Excellent | ☐ Good | ☐ Poor | |
| Was this your first visit? | ☐ Yes | ☐ No | | |
| Do you plan to return? | ☐ Yes | ☐ No | | Anniversary: _____ |

Name: _____

Email Address*: _____

*In the event we send news and information about upcoming events and products via email.

*Tipping should be 15% to 20% of the total bill before discount.*

## SEAFOOD SKEWERS (a la carte single skewer)

**Gulf Shrimp** ............................................................................................ $10.95
Large shrimp grilled with honey-lime butter (6 each)

**New England Lobster Tail** ........................................................................ $13.95
A tender sweet lobster tail smothered with fresh butter and lemon

**Pacific Scallops** ...................................................................................... $10.95
Scallops sautéed with white wine, shallots and finished with fresh butter

## DINNER RODIZIOS

**ULTIMATE SURF AND TURF RODIZIO $51.95**
Tempt your taste buds with unlimited servings of shrimp glazed with garlic butter, tender scallops, grilled salmon and fresh catch of the day. Grilled meats include beef tenderloin dusted with parmesan cheese, picanha, tri-tip roast beef, BBQ pork, grilled chicken, smoked ham and pineapple, lamb, Brazilian sausage and turkey wrapped in bacon, all hand carved at your table in true Brazilian fashion. Help yourself to unlimited samplings from our side bar which features over 40 hot and cold sides and salads to complete your experience

**SEAFOOD RODIZIO $46.95**
Enjoy unlimited servings of shrimp glazed with garlic butter, tender scallops, grilled salmon and fresh catch of the day. Choose from a wide variety of sides and salads to compliment your rodizio

**MEAT RODIZIO $41.95**
Take part in our parade of meats including; beef tenderloin dusted with parmesan cheese, picanha, tri-tip roast beef, BBQ pork, grilled chicken smoked ham and pineapple, lamb, Brazilian sausage and turkey wrapped in bacon. Choose from a wide variety of sides and salads to compliment your rodizio

## DINNER ENTRÉE

**Rib Eye Steak** ......................................................................................... $39.95
Rib eye steak, grilled with blackened cajun-style seasonings

**Beef Tenderloin** ...................................................................................... $40.95
Filet mignon, grilled and served with madeira glaze

**New York Steak** ...................................................................................... $39.95
New york steak, grilled with roasted wild mushrooms

**Skirt Steak** ............................................................................................. $34.95
Tender skirt steak seasoned with chimichurri sauce served with rice and black beans

**Brazilian Bouillabaisse** ........................................................................... $37.95
Lobster, shrimp, salmon and mussels in a seafood broth with fresh tomato sauce, coconut milk, and cilantro. Served over linguine pasta

**Pacific Salmon** ....................................................................................... $33.95
Pacific salmon grilled with sweet and sour malagueta pepper sauce. Served with grilled melon and fresh vegetables

**Sword Fish** ............................................................................................. $34.95
Fresh sword fish filet brushed with olive oil and tri-colored peppercorns. Served with grilled melon and fresh vegetables

**Grilled Chicken Breast** ............................................................................ $29.95
Tender chicken breast seasoned with olive oil, fresh herbs and grilled garlic. Served with steamed rice and grilled vegetables

All entrees served with a choice of fresh salad bar or Caesar salad, and choice of french fries, or mashed potatoes
* Please note that a 20% gratuity will be applied to parties of six or more

Menu Sampler - Prices and menu subject to change.

---

3663 Las Vegas Blvd S Suite 610
(Located in the Miracle Mile Shops at the Planet Hollywood Hotel & Casino)
Las Vegas, NV
(702) 737-4748
www.pampasusa.com

| How was service? | ☐ Excellent | ☐ Good | ☐ Poor | |
|---|---|---|---|---|
| How was your food? | ☐ Excellent | ☐ Good | ☐ Poor | Birthday: _____ |
| How was the atmosphere? | ☐ Excellent | ☐ Good | ☐ Poor | |
| Was this your first visit? | ☐ Yes | ☐ No | | |
| Do you plan to return? | ☐ Yes | ☐ No | | Anniversary: _____ |

Name: _____

Email Address*: _____

*In the event we send news and information about upcoming events and products via email.

*Tipping should be 15% to 20% of the total bill before discount.*

elmescalmexicanrestaurantlasvegas.com

4460 S. Durango Dr.
Ste. H
(W. Flamingo &
S. Durango)
Las Vegas, NV

(702) 834-3702

*Come try our authentic homemade food and it will transport you to Mexico! Fresh seafood dishes along with some favorites like fajitas, tacos, and enchiladas.*

*We have lunch and dinner combinations or join us for breakfast. Happy Hour everyday. Full bar with delicious margaritas!*

*Open daily.*

## SPINACH QUESADILLA

Two flour tortilla stuffed with fresh spinach cooked with pico de gallo and mushrooms, topped with lettuce, tomatoes, guacamole and sour cream. 12.25

## BURRITO DE CARNE ASADA

Filled with slices of grilled over charcoal skirt steak. 15.25

## CHILE VERDE

Chunks of pork cooked in a tomatillo sauce. 15.25

## TACOS DE CAMARÓN

Sautéed shrimp. Served with lettuce, tomatoes and avocado slices. 16.99

## CECINAS A LA PLANCHA

Skirt steak grilled with onions and bell peppers. 15.99

## EL MESCAL ENCHILADAS

(3)Enchiladas one chicken covered with chipotle sauce,one chicken covered with mole sauce and one more filled with pork covered with green sauce. 13.75

## POLLO MORELIA

Chicken breast cooked with bell peppers & onions, pico de gallo and our special cheese creamy sauce. 15.50

## FAJITAS ACAPULCO

Carne asada delivered sizzling hot over a bed of sautéed onions, bell peppers and tomatoes. Topped with cheese dip. Served with sour cream and guacamole. 18.50

## MOJARRA

A traditional Mexican seafood dish created from an old fashioned Puerto Vallarta recipe. This is a complete fish! 16.50

---

Menu Sampler - Prices and menu subject to change.

---

4460 S. Durango Dr., Ste. H
(W. Flamingo & S. Durango)
Las Vegas, NV

(702) 834-3702
elmescalmexicanrestaurantlasvegas.com

| | | | | |
|---|---|---|---|---|
| How was service? | ☐ Excellent | ☐ Good | ☐ Poor | |
| How was your food? | ☐ Excellent | ☐ Good | ☐ Poor | Birthday: _____ |
| How was the atmosphere? | ☐ Excellent | ☐ Good | ☐ Poor | |
| Was this your first visit? | ☐ Yes | ☐ No | | |
| Do you plan to return? | ☐ Yes | ☐ No | | Anniversary: _____ |

Name: _____

Email Address*: _____

*In the event we send news and information about upcoming events and products via email.

*Tipping should be 15% to 20% of the total bill before discount.*

www.MezzoBistro.com
4275 N. Rancho Dr.
Ste. 130
Las Vegas, NV
(702) 944-8880

*We are a hidden gem in the Northwest area of Las Vegas. Serving an authentic Italian bistro menu with seafood and steak as well as a large collection of wine by the glass or bottle. We use only the freshest ingredients and cater to our customer's needs. Daily Happy Hour.*

**Fresh Grilled Veggie Platter**    **$14.00**
a wide assortment of fresh vegetables
grilled italian style

**Mezzo's Artesian Meat & Cheese
Platter**    **$9.00**
an assortment of imported meat,
cheeses and fruit

**Meatballs**    **$9.00**
two - 6oz homemade meatballs served
in our sunday sauce

**Calamari Fritte**    **$10.00**
lightly breaded baby squid served
with marinara and pepperoncini's

**The Mezzo**    **$14.00**
tomato sauce, house made goat
cheese sausage, mozzarella

**Eggplant Parmesan**    **$15.00**
old family recipe (non-breaded)
served with side of pasta

**Fettuccine**    **$17.00**
homemade served with vodka sauce
with pancetta or alfredo sauce

**Riggies**    **$18.00**
chicken tenders sauteed with prosciutto,
mushrooms, and hot & sweet peppers tossed
with marinara sauce & mozzarella

**Tuscan Tenderloin**    **$20.00**
seared then cooked in chianti served with
apples cooked in prosecco and asparagus

**Frutti Di Mare**    **$20.00**
clams, mussels, calamari, shrimp and fish
(fresh catch) cooked in a spicy sherry sauce
with fresh herbs tossed in linguini

**Filetto Gorgonzola 9 Oz.**    **$28.00**
grilled filet mignon with a gorgonzola cream
sauce topped with crispy pancetta. served
with mashed potatoes and grilled asparagus,
(no pasta)

Menu Sampler - Prices and menu subject to change.

---

4275 N. Rancho Dr.
Ste 130
Las Vegas, NV
(702) 944-8880

www.MezzoBistro.com

| | | | |
|---|---|---|---|
| How was service? | ☐ Excellent | ☐ Good | ☐ Poor |
| How was your food? | ☐ Excellent | ☐ Good | ☐ Poor |
| How was the atmosphere? | ☐ Excellent | ☐ Good | ☐ Poor |
| Was this your first visit? | ☐ Yes | ☐ No | |
| Do you plan to return? | ☐ Yes | ☐ No | |

Birthday: _____

Anniversary: _____

Name: _____

Email Address*: _____
*In the event we send news and information about upcoming events and products via email.

*Tipping should be 15% to 20% of the total bill before discount.*

www.cafemayakovsky.com
1775 E. Tropicana Ave.
Ste. 30
Las Vegas, NV
(702)848-1775

*Serving authentic traditional Russian dishes. We also extend our menu with American burgers, Italian pastas, pizzas and Spanish ceviche so our customer have a variety of food to select from. Full bar including some exclusive Russian Vodkas and beers. Check our schedule for entertainment. Open daily till late on the weekends.*

# Pelmeni
*Homemade meat ravioli served with sour cream*     $6.95

# Golubtsy
*Cabbage rolls stuffed with ground beef, ground pork and spices, served with sour cream*     $6.95

# Beef Stroganoff
*Beef tenderloin strips sautéed in onion sauce, mushrooms and sour cream*     $13.95

# Goulash
*Chopped pork loin slowly cooked with vegetables*     $11.95

# Chicken Kiev
*Breaded chicken breast filled with seasoned butter*     $12.95

# Spaghetti
*Cafe Mayakovsky's version of a classic Italian staple served with marinara sauce*     $10.95

Menu Sampler - Prices and menu subject to change.

---

1775 E. Tropicana Ave.
Ste. 30 Las Vegas, NV
(702) 848-1775

www.cafemayakovsky.com

| | | | | |
|---|---|---|---|---|
| How was service? | ☐ Excellent | ☐ Good | ☐ Poor | |
| How was your food? | ☐ Excellent | ☐ Good | ☐ Poor | Birthday: _____ |
| How was the atmosphere? | ☐ Excellent | ☐ Good | ☐ Poor | |
| Was this your first visit? | ☐ Yes | ☐ No | | |
| Do you plan to return? | ☐ Yes | ☐ No | | Anniversary: _____ |

Name: _____

Email Address*: _____

*In the event we send news and information about upcoming events and products via email.

*Tipping should be 15% to 20% of the total bill before discount.*

0000000PL5U

# BOMBAY *Bites*

## CHICKEN
**CHICKEN TIKKA** ◉ [GF] **$8.95** Chicken cubes marinated in yogurt, mustard oil, red chili and select herbs

**BOMBAY GRILLED CHICKEN SLIDERS $10.95** Ground chicken marinated in ginger, garlic, green chilies and herbs

## LAMB
**LAMB SHEEKH KEBAB** ◉ [GF] **$8.95** Ground lamb skewers, marinated in traditional Bombay spices, roasted in oven

**LAMB CUTLETS $8.95** Ground lamb patties with spiced potato mash crumb fried served with cilantro chutney

## SEAFOOD
**GUN POWER SHRIMPS** ◉ **$11.95** Grilled shrimps tossed with our special, hot spice mix

**CURRY LEAF SHRIMPS $11.95** Grilled shrimps tossed with South Indian spices and curry leaves

## VEGETARIAN ◉
**PANEER TIKKA** ◉ [GF] **$7.95** Tandoori sauce marinated cottage cheese cubes, oven grilled

**BHEL $4.95** [GF] Rice puffs tossed with finely chopped vegetables and tossed in tangy tamarind sauce

Menu Sampler - Prices and menu subject to change.

---

3900 Paradise Rd.
Ste. G Las Vegas, NV
(702) 826-3217

www.urbanturbanlv.com

| | | | | |
|---|---|---|---|---|
| How was service? | ☐ Excellent | ☐ Good | ☐ Poor | |
| How was your food? | ☐ Excellent | ☐ Good | ☐ Poor | Birthday: _____ |
| How was the atmosphere? | ☐ Excellent | ☐ Good | ☐ Poor | |
| Was this your first visit? | ☐ Yes | ☐ No | | |
| Do you plan to return? | ☐ Yes | ☐ No | | Anniversary: _____ |

Name: _____

Email Address*: _____

*In the event we send news and information about upcoming events and products via email.

*Tipping should be 15% to 20% of the total bill before discount.*

# Get Sauced!

### CHOOSE YOUR SAUCE:

**Marinara** - Our traditional red sauce.
**Pomodoro** - Homemade crushed tomato sauce with fresh garlic & basil.
**Bolognese** - A rich hearty sauce with Italian sausage, hamburger, prosciutto and bacon.
**Rose** - Our marinara with a touch of creamy alfredo sauce.
**Alfredo** - A roasted garlic cream sauce blended with parmesan & asiago cheese.
**Pesto Cream** - A combination of our fresh basil pesto and alfredo sauce.
**Basil Pesto** - Fresh garlic and basil mixed with extra virgin olive oil and walnuts.
**Lemon Butter** - Fresh garlic & basil, lemon, chicken stock and butter.

### CHOOSE YOUR PASTA:

Fettuccini
Spaghetti
Angel Hair
Penne
Cheese Tortellini - add $1
Wheat Penne - add $1
Cheese Ravioli - add $2
Gluten-Free Penne - add $2

### ADD TWO TOPPINGS:

Roasted Red Peppers
Broccoli
Sun-Dried Tomatoes
Diced Jalapenos
Wild Mushrooms
Roasted Galic
Artichoke Hearts
Black Olives
Sliced Tomatoes
Sauteed Spinach
Caramelized Onions
Red Onions
*Each additional topping - $1.50*

### MORE TOPPINGS:

**Grilled Chicken** - add $3
**Shrimp** - add $4
**Bacon** - add $2
**Portabella Mushrooms** - add $3
**Prosciutto** - add $3
**Pepperoni** - add $2
**Meatballs** - add $1.50 each
**Anchovy** - add $3

Menu Sampler - Prices and menu subject to change.

---

721 Mall Ring Cir
Henderson, NV
(702) 566-1686

www.saucelv.com

| | | | | |
|---|---|---|---|---|
| How was service? | ☐ Excellent | ☐ Good | ☐ Poor | |
| How was your food? | ☐ Excellent | ☐ Good | ☐ Poor | Birthday: _____ |
| How was the atmosphere? | ☐ Excellent | ☐ Good | ☐ Poor | |
| Was this your first visit? | ☐ Yes | ☐ No | | |
| Do you plan to return? | ☐ Yes | ☐ No | | Anniversary: _____ |

Name: _____

Email Address*: _____
*In the event we send news and information about upcoming events and products via email.

*Tipping should be 15% to 20% of the total bill before discount.*

www.anisetapas.com
3100 S. Durango Dr.
Las Vegas, NV
(702) 510-4664

*Transport all of your senses to the rustic Mediterranean Coast. We offer tapas, grill and entrée using the freshest ingredients. Come for lunch, dinner or late night. Live music & full bar. Catering available.*

---

UP TO $**17** VALUE

*Enjoy one FREE ENTREE when a second ENTREE of equal or greater value is purchased – maximum discount $17.*

Dine in only.

### Middle-Eastern Tapas

**Hummus Champignon** - Sauteed mushrooms with slow-cooked creamy garbanzo hummus. Served with pita.  V 9

**Shakshuka Poco** - Dense, flavorful matbucha with spicy paprika, peppers, onions, tomatoes, and garlic. Topped with an egg.  V 🌶 7

**Moroccan Frena Pan** - Traditional Moroccan bread served with, olive tapenade and tzatziki plus a roasted garlic bulb.  V 🌶 7

**Parglot Skewer** - Marinated grilled moist dark meat chicken . 10 ea

**Ground Beef Kebab - 3** Ground Angus beef patties with our special seasoning and herbs.  10 ea

**Shish Kebab Skewer** - Marinated minute steak.  11 ea

### Tapas de Vegetales V

**Pimientos Shiseido** - This mildly spicy Japanese pepper is flash fried and served w/ ponzu citrus sauce, toasted sesame, & fresh garlic. 🌶 6

**Espinaca Artichoke Fondue** - Rich dip full of roasted artichokes and fresh spinach and topped with panko bread crumbs. Served with tortilla chips. 8

**Patatas Bravas** - Fried potatoes with garlic aioli and harissa. 6

**Tomates Ajo Asado** - A medley of fire-roasted plump tomatoes, cloves of garlic, and fresh basil-infused olive oil, all placed on frena bread. 7

**Drunken Avocado Empanadillas** - Finely crisped egg rolls filled with seasoned avocados and fresh cilantro. Served with Patron jalapeno agave sauce. 9

### Tapas Pescado - de Pollo - de Carne

**Pasteles de Mar** - Fresh ground fish and imitation "crab" with herbs, jalapenos, red peppers, cilantro, and onions, formed into panko encrusted cakes. Served with saffron aioli 7

**Atun Tartare** - Petite tower of fresh ponzu-marinated tuna layered with avocado, firm egg yolk, pickled ginger, and black sesame. Served with wonton crisps and wasabi aioli. 9

**Shawarma Fajita** - Seasoned, marinated chicken thighs are grilled with peppers and onions. 🌶 8

**Wings Anise** - 7 Crispy chicken wings in sweet chili glaze. 🌶 8

**Paella Para Mi'** - Spanish rice with flame grilled tomatoes, onions, peppers, succulent marinated chicken, blackened saffron rice, and bits of spiced lamb sausage, topped by scallions. 🌶 9

---

Menu Sampler - Prices and menu subject to change.

---

3100 S. Durango Dr.
Las Vegas, NV
(702) 510-4664

www.anisetapas.com

| | | | |
|---|---|---|---|
| How was service? | ☐ Excellent | ☐ Good | ☐ Poor |
| How was your food? | ☐ Excellent | ☐ Good | ☐ Poor | Birthday: _____
| How was the atmosphere? | ☐ Excellent | ☐ Good | ☐ Poor |
| Was this your first visit? | ☐ Yes | ☐ No | |
| Do you plan to return? | ☐ Yes | ☐ No | Anniversary: _____ |

Name: _____

Email Address*: _____

*In the event we send news and information about upcoming events and products via email.

*Tipping should be 15% to 20% of the total bill before discount.*

# Sushi-Ko

### modern twist to traditional japanese cuisine

## CHEF'S RECOMMENDATION

| | |
|---|---|
| 1. Alaska King Crab Roll | 14.95 |
| 2. Special Tuna Tataki Roll | 11.95 |
| 3. Jalapeno Sauce Sashimi | (L) 16.00 |
| *(Yellowtail/White Tuna)* | (S) 11.95 |
| | |
| 4. Jalapeno Popper | 9.50 |
| 5. Oyster Shooter | 4.50 |
| 6. Screaming Orgasm | (L) 16.00 |
| | (S) 11.95 |
| 7. Honey Moon Lover | 13.95 |
| 8. Spicy Garlic Sashimi | (L) 16.00 |
| *(Tuna/Salmon/Albacore)* | (S) 11.95 |
| | |
| 9. Sushi – Ko Rice | 7.50 |
| 10. Tuna Carpaccio Sashimi | (S) 9.95 |
| | (L) 14.95 |
| 11. Avocado Lover | 9.95 |
| 12. Asparagus Torpedos | 6.50 |
| 13. Angry Bird | (L) 12.95 |
| | (S) 9.95 |
| 14. Zig Zag Hand Roll | 6.00 |
| 15. 101 Degree Special Roll | 9.95 |
| 16. Lion King | 13.95 |
| 17. Smoking ACE I *(Salmon)* | (L) 16.00 |
| | (S) 11.95 |
| 18. Smoking ACE II *(White Tuna)* | (L) 16.00 |
| | (S) 11.95 |

Menu Sampler - Prices and menu subject to change.

---

# Sushi-Ko

### modern twist to traditional japanese cuisine

7101 W. Craig Rd.
(Craig Marketplace)
Las Vegas, NV
(702) 655-5782

www.sushikolv.com

| | | | |
|---|---|---|---|
| How was service? | ☐ Excellent | ☐ Good | ☐ Poor |
| How was your food? | ☐ Excellent | ☐ Good | ☐ Poor |
| How was the atmosphere? | ☐ Excellent | ☐ Good | ☐ Poor |
| Was this your first visit? | ☐ Yes | ☐ No | |
| Do you plan to return? | ☐ Yes | ☐ No | |

Birthday: _____

Anniversary: _____

Name: _____

Email Address*: _____

*In the event we send news and information about upcoming events and products via email.

*Tipping should be 15% to 20% of the total bill before discount.*

# SIENA
### GOLF CLUB

# *Chef's Featured Entrees*
### *Available daily after 11:00am*
*All entrees include choice of house salad, caesar salad or soup du jour.*

### 8 oz. USDA Choice Flat Iron Steak - 17
*Chargrilled and served with seasoned french fries, sweet potato fries, onion rings, siena chips or stemed baby potatoes and vegetable medley.*

### Pan Seared Pacific Salmon with Fettuccini - 24
*Fresh fillet of salmon over fettuccini tossed in a creamy pesto sauce and served with garlic bread.*

### Dover Sole Milanese - 16
*8 oz. dover sole fillet lightly breaded and sauteed golden brown served with steamed baby potatoes, vegetable medley and lemon beurre blanc sauce.*

### Chicken Saltimbocca - 17
*Scaloppini chicken layered with prosciutto, sage and provolone on top of angel hair pasta with a white wine caper sauce served with garlic bread.*

Menu Sampler - Prices and menu subject to change.

---

10575 Siena Monte Ave.
(Near the 215 & Town Ctr. Dr.)
Las Vegas, NV
(702) 562-2653
www.sienagolfclub.com

| How was service? | ☐ Excellent | ☐ Good | ☐ Poor | |
| How was your food? | ☐ Excellent | ☐ Good | ☐ Poor | Birthday: _____ |
| How was the atmosphere? | ☐ Excellent | ☐ Good | ☐ Poor | |
| Was this your first visit? | ☐ Yes | ☐ No | | |
| Do you plan to return? | ☐ Yes | ☐ No | | Anniversary: _____ |

Name: _____

Email Address*: _____
*In the event we send news and information about upcoming events and products via email.

*Tipping should be 15% to 20% of the total bill before discount.*

## Origin India
### RESTAURANT & BAR

www.originindiarestaurant.com/
4480 Paradise Rd.
Ste. 1200
Las Vegas, NV
(702) 734-6342

*Origin India's dynamic menu features the city's only refined, modern Indian cuisine. The restaurant offers a full bar that includes a variety of signature cocktails. Lunch buffet Mon-Fri $11.95 and Sat and Sun $14.95. Catering available. We are open seven days a week from 11:30a.m. to 10:30p.m. and feature a weekday Happy Hour from 5p.m. to 7p.m. with everything priced under $6.*

**UP TO $18 VALUE**

Enjoy one **FREE DINNER ENTREE** when a second **DINNER ENTREE** of equal or greater value is purchased – maximum discount $18.

Dine in only.

# Origin India™
## RESTAURANT & BAR

## ENTREES

### Sumunder se (from the sea)

**SHRIMP MOLLY** 24.00
Shrimp with julienned bell peppers and onions
cooked in a tangy coconut based sauce (a specialty
of the south Indian state of Kerala)

**MACHALI TIKKA MASALA**
(Fish Tikka Masala) 21.00
Sautéed Swai tikka cooked in an tomato based sauce
and finished with a touch of cream

**JHINGA LASOONI** (Garlic Shrimp) 24.00
Shrimp cooked with chopped garlic, chives,
parsley and cilantro in a tangy sauce

**SOUTHERN GRILLED FISH** 22.00
Swai marinated with mustard, coconut, rice flour
and spices grilled on a tawa

**MACHLI DAHIWALA** (Fish with Yogurt) 21.00
Sautéed Swai in yogurt based sauce with mild spices
a house specialty

### CHEF'S TASTING MENU
Five Courses
$55 per person
*Additional $30 for wine pairing*

### Meats

**DUM KI NALLI** (Lamb Shank) 33.00
Lamb shank cooked in Kashmiri red rogan josh sauce
flavored with dry fennel and ginger powder

**LAMB VINDALOO** 22.00
Lamb marinated in garlic and vinegar, cooked in a
red chili based sweet and sour sauce

**LAMB NIHARI** 22.00
Pieces of lamb sautéed in a spicy ginger-garlic paste
in a ginger, garlic, fennel, cumin based sauce and
finished with fried onions

**PASHWARI BHUNA LAMB** 25.00
Lamb chops slowly simmered in a spicy mint and
tomato based sauce with touch of yogurt, served with
julienned ginger and green chilies

### Poultry

**KALI MIRCH KA MURGH**
(Chicken with Black Pepper) 16.00
Chicken cooked in a white creamy sauce and finished
with crushed black pepper

**DILWALA MURGH MUKHANI** (Chicken Mukhani)
16.00
Tandoori chicken tikka in a tomato and cream sauce
and finished with butter

---

Menu Sampler - Prices and menu subject to change.

---

# Origin India™
## RESTAURANT & BAR

4480 Paradise Rd.
Ste. 1200 Las Vegas, NV
(702) 734-6342

www.originindiarestaurant.com/

| | | | | |
|---|---|---|---|---|
| How was service? | ☐ Excellent | ☐ Good | ☐ Poor | |
| How was your food? | ☐ Excellent | ☐ Good | ☐ Poor | Birthday: _____ |
| How was the atmosphere? | ☐ Excellent | ☐ Good | ☐ Poor | |
| Was this your first visit? | ☐ Yes | ☐ No | | |
| Do you plan to return? | ☐ Yes | ☐ No | | Anniversary: _____ |

Name: _____

Email Address*: _____

*In the event we send news and information about upcoming events and products *via* email.

*Tipping should be 15% to 20% of the total bill before discount.*

www.lasvegas-sushi.com

10920 S. Eastern Ave.
Henderson, NV
(702) 616-3788

4205 W. Sahara Ave.
Las Vegas, NV
(702)876-4988

*Osaka was Las Vegas' first Japanese restaurant established in 1967. We offer 3 different Japanese dining experiences—Sushi Bar, Teppanyaki Grill and Traditional Tatami Rooms. We open everyday for lunch till late night dining. Catering for all occasions and private parties. No matter what type of Japanese food you're craving, you are sure to find it here.*

👑 entertainment

UP TO $**20** VALUE

*Enjoy $20 off any purchase of $80 or more.*

Dine in only. Excludes Holidays.

## Teppan Grill

**Dinner Includes:** House Soup & Salad, Teppan Appetizer, Vegetable, Steamed Rice.
**For Fried Rice Add $3.50 For Extra Plate Add $5.00 For Ice Cream Add $2.00**

Appetizer : **Five Spices Sausage** -flavorful Asian five spices sausage   6.95

### -Meat-

| | | |
|---|---|---|
| *Kobe Beef –certified beef from Japan | 8oz New York | 85.00 |
| | 8oz Filet | 125.00 |
| *Filet Mignon | 8oz | 28.95 |
| *New York | 10oz | 26.95 |
| | 16oz | 32.95 |
| * Rib Eye | 10oz | 26.95 |
| Chicken | | 17.95 |
| Ginger Pork | | 18.95 |

### -Seafood-

| | | |
|---|---|---|
| Tiger Shrimp | | 23.95 |
| Gigantic Shrimp | | 33.95 |
| South American Lobster Tail | 8oz | 42.95 |
| | 12oz | 52.95 |
| Jumbo Sea Scallop | | 28.95 |
| Chilean Sea Bass | 10oz | 28.95 |
| Alaskan King Salmon Steak | 10oz | 25.95 |
| Japanese Crab Cake-new fusion style crab cake | | 18.95 |
| | Appetizer (grilled or deep fried) | 8.50 |
| Calamari Steak | | 15.95 |
| | Appetizer | 7.95 |

## Nigiri Sushi (2pc per order)

| | |
|---|---|
| Inari-marinated tofu stuffed with rice | 4.00 |
| Hokkigai-Canadian surf clam | 4.25 |
| Kani-imitation crab | 4.25 |
| *Ika-squid | 4.25 |
| Masago-smelt eggs | 4.75 |
| Kaibashira-baby scallops | 4.75 |
| *Hirame-halibut | 5.75 |
| *San Diego Salmon-w/avocado and ponzu | 5.75 |
| Anago-sea water eel | 6.00 |
| *Hamachi-yellowtail | 6.50 |
| Unagi-fresh water eel | 6.50 |
| *Tai-red snapper | 6.75 |
| *Garlic Tuna-w/scallion & special sauce | 7.50 |
| *Ama Ebi-sweet shrimp | 8.25 |
| *Shima Aji-skipjack (seasonal) | 8.25 |
| *Uni-sea urchin | 9.25 |
| *Awabi (seasonal) - abalone | MKP |
| Tamago yaki- sweet egg omelet | 4.00 |
| Tako-octopus | 4.25 |
| *Saba-mackerel | 4.25 |
| Miki Special-crab, masago, mayo | 4.50 |
| Ebi-boiled shrimp | 4.75 |
| *Sake-salmon | 5.00 |
| Tobiko-flying fish eggs | 5.75 |

Menu Sampler - Prices and menu subject to change.

---

10920 S. Eastern Ave., Henderson, NV
(702) 616-3788
4205 W. Sahara Ave., Las Vegas, NV
(702) 876-4988
www.lasvegas-sushi.com

| | | | |
|---|---|---|---|
| How was service? | ☐ Excellent | ☐ Good | ☐ Poor |
| How was your food? | ☐ Excellent | ☐ Good | ☐ Poor |
| How was the atmosphere? | ☐ Excellent | ☐ Good | ☐ Poor |
| Was this your first visit? | ☐ Yes | ☐ No | |
| Do you plan to return? | ☐ Yes | ☐ No | |

Birthday: _____

Anniversary: _____

Name: _____

Email Address*: _____

*In the event we send news and information about upcoming events and products via email.

*Tipping should be 15% to 20% of the total bill before discount.*

# Casual & Family Dining Index

**CASUAL & FAMILY DINING INDEX**

## Get these offers, and thousands more, on the mobile app!

Search for "Entertainment® Coupons" in your app store to download.

# Casual & Family Dining Index

**CASUAL & FAMILY DINING INDEX**

# Pizza Hut

**ANY** PIZZA
**ANY** TOPPINGS
**ANY** SPECIALTY
**ANY** CRUST FLAVOR

$**6**^**99** EACH

**ANY DEAL**

**2 MEDIUM PIZZAS**

HAND TOSSED | PAN | THIN 'N CRISPY®

**THE DELIVERY CHARGE IS NOT A DRIVER TIP.**
LIMITED TIME OFFER. ADDITIONAL CHARGE FOR EXTRA CHEESE. Product availability, combinability of discounts and specials, prices, participation, delivery areas and charges, and minimum purchase requirements for delivery may vary. The Pizza Hut name, logos and related marks are trademarks of Pizza Hut, Inc. © 2016 Pizza Hut, Inc.

---

entertainment.
www.entertainment.com

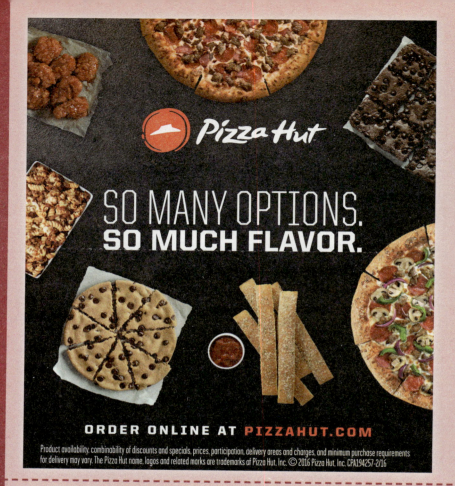

# SO MANY OPTIONS.
## SO MUCH FLAVOR.

**ORDER ONLINE AT PIZZAHUT.COM**

Product availability, combinability of discounts and specials, prices, participation, delivery areas and charges, and minimum purchase requirements for delivery may vary. The Pizza Hut name, logos and related marks are trademarks of Pizza Hut, Inc. © 2016 Pizza Hut, Inc. CPA194257-2/16

Valid at All Participating Pizza Hut® Locations.

Steak Fajitas

Borderita

Guacamole Live!

Border Brownie Sundae

ON THE BORDER
MEXICAN GRILL & CANTINA

---

**entertainment.**
www.entertainment.com

Shrimp and Chicken Fajitas

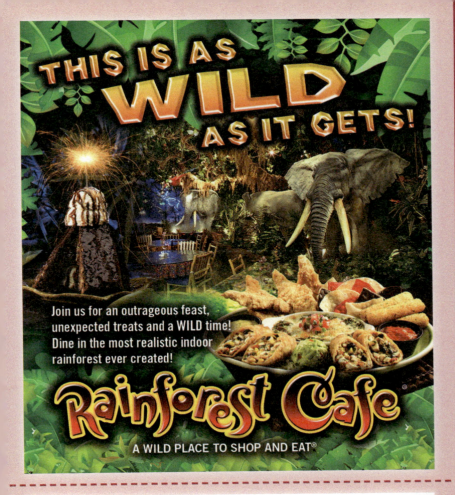

**BUY ONE GET ONE**

www.ihop.com

### Enjoy one FREE ENTREE when a second ENTREE of equal or greater value is purchased.

Dine in only. Tipping should be 15% to 20% of total bill before discount.

**Promotion valid now thru 12/30/2017**
See reverse side for additional conditions or restrictions.　　**B4**

---

 **UP TO $8 VALUE**

**EGG WORKS**

www.theeggworks.com

### Enjoy one FREE BREAKFAST or LUNCH ENTREE when a second BREAKFAST or LUNCH ENTREE of equal or greater value is purchased - maximum discount $8.

Dine in only.

**Promotion valid now thru 12/30/2017**
See reverse side for additional conditions or restrictions.　　**B5**

---

 **BUY ONE GET ONE**

www.ihop.com

### Enjoy one FREE ENTREE when a second ENTREE of equal or greater value is purchased.

Dine in only. Tipping should be 15% to 20% of total bill before discount.

**Promotion valid now thru 12/30/2017**
See reverse side for additional conditions or restrictions.　　**B6**

---

 **UP TO $8 VALUE**

www.eggandi.com

### Enjoy one complimentary BREAKFAST or LUNCH ENTREE when a second BREAKFAST or LUNCH ENTREE of equal or greater value is purchased - maximum discount $8.

Dine in only.

**Promotion valid now thru 12/30/2017**
See reverse side for additional conditions or restrictions.　　**B7**

---

 **BUY ONE GET ONE**

www.ihop.com

### Enjoy one FREE ENTREE when a second ENTREE of equal or greater value is purchased.

Dine in only. Tipping should be 15% to 20% of total bill before discount.

**Promotion valid now thru 12/30/2017**
See reverse side for additional conditions or restrictions.　　**B8**

---

 **UP TO $8 VALUE**

*Fanny's*
Bistro & Deli

www.fannysbistro.com

### Enjoy one FREE ENTREE when a second ENTREE of equal or greater value is purchased - maximum discount $8.

**Promotion valid now thru 12/30/2017**
See reverse side for additional conditions or restrictions.　　**B9**

# Egg Works

| | | |
|---|---|---|
| 10839 S Eastern Ave (Eastern & Horizon Ridge) Henderson, NV (702)485-5585 | 2490 E Sunset Rd (E Sunset @ Eastern) Las Vegas, NV (702)873-3447 | 9355 W Flamingo Rd (W Flamingo @ Fort Apache) Las Vegas, NV (702)368-3447 |
| 2025 Village Center Cir Las Vegas, NV (702)445-7330 | 6960 S Rainbow Blvd (Rainbow & off the 215) Las Vegas, NV (702)361-3447 | |

# Egg & I

- Enjoy our outdoor patio
- Lunch is also a specialty here
- Open 6am-3pm
- The best breakfast in town!
- Fresh is the name of the game at the Egg & I
- Egg & I is the spot for breakfast in Las Vegas
- Free Wi-Fi

4533 W Sahara Ave
Las Vegas, NV
(702)364-9686

# Fanny's Bistro & Deli

- Catering available
- Hot & cold sandwiches, soups & salads
- Dine In, Carry Out, or Delivery
- Open Monday-Friday, 10am-5pm
- A hidden gem in Green Valley!

80 N PECOS RD STE F
HENDERSON, NV
(702)269-1699

# IHOP Restaurant

- Lunch & dinner menu items include: sandwiches, burgers, melts, chicken, steaks & more
- Come Hungry, Leave Happy
- Soups, salads, appetizers, senior specials, Just for Kid's menu & desserts
- Famous pancakes, omelettes, signature breakfasts, classic combinations, French toasts, waffles & crepes

9651 Trailwood Dr
(at Village Center Circle in Summerlin)
Las Vegas, NV
(702)243-2587

# IHOP Restaurant

- Lunch & dinner menu items include: sandwiches, burgers, melts, chicken, steaks & more
- Come Hungry, Leave Happy
- Soups, salads, appetizers, senior specials, Just for Kid's menu & desserts
- Famous pancakes, omelettes, signature breakfasts, classic combinations, French toasts, waffles & crepes

9651 Trailwood Dr
(at Village Center Circle in Summerlin)
Las Vegas, NV
(702)243-2587

# IHOP Restaurant

- Lunch & dinner menu items include: sandwiches, burgers, melts, chicken, steaks & more
- Come Hungry, Leave Happy
- Soups, salads, appetizers, senior specials, Just for Kid's menu & desserts
- Famous pancakes, omelettes, signature breakfasts, classic combinations, French toasts, waffles & crepes

9651 Trailwood Dr
(at Village Center Circle in Summerlin)
Las Vegas, NV
(702)243-2587

## 15% OFF

www.roundtablepizza.com

**Enjoy 15% off your ORDER.**

Discount applies to regular menu prices only. Offer excludes alcohol, lunch combos, buffet, manager's specials, kid's meals, value & promotional products. Limited delivery area & hours. Additional tax, delivery fee, delivery minimum & other terms may apply. One coupon per order. Dine In - Carry Out - Delivery.

**Coupon Code: #515**

**Promotion valid now thru 12/30/2017**
See reverse side for additional conditions or restrictions.    **B10**

---

## UP TO $12 VALUE

www.sammyspizza.com

**Enjoy one FREE MENU ITEM when a second MENU ITEM of equal or greater value is purchased - maximum discount $12.**

Not valid with catering or takeout orders. Not valid at airport locations. Limit one coupon per party of four or fewer.
**Code: EB104**

**Promotion valid now thru 12/30/2017**
See reverse side for additional conditions or restrictions.    **B11**

---

## UP TO $4 OFF

www.roundtablepizza.com

**Enjoy $4 off X-LARGE or $3 off LARGE or $2 off MEDIUM PIZZA.**

Discount applies to regular menu prices only. Not valid with other discounts, value pizzas or promotional pizzas. Limited delivery area & hours. Additional tax, delivery fee, delivery minimum & other terms may apply. One coupon per order. Dine In - Carry Out - Delivery.

**Coupon Codes: XL#135; LG#136; MED#137**

**Promotion valid now thru 12/30/2017**
See reverse side for additional conditions or restrictions.    **B12**

---

## UP TO $12 VALUE

www.sammyspizza.com

**Enjoy one FREE MENU ITEM when a second MENU ITEM of equal or greater value is purchased - maximum discount $12.**

Not valid with catering or takeout orders. Not valid at airport locations. Limit one coupon per party of four or fewer.
**Code: EB104**

**Promotion valid now thru 12/30/2017**
See reverse side for additional conditions or restrictions.    **B13**

---

## $5 OFF

www.roundtablepizza.com

**Enjoy $5 off any LARGE or X-LARGE SPECIALTY PIZZA.**

Discount applies to regular menu prices only. Not valid with other discounts, value pizzas or promotional pizzas. Limited delivery area & hours. Additional tax, delivery fee, delivery minimum & other terms may apply. One coupon per order. Dine In - Carry Out - Delivery.

**Coupon Code: #704**

**Promotion valid now thru 12/30/2017**
See reverse side for additional conditions or restrictions.    **B14**

---

## UP TO $12 VALUE

www.sammyspizza.com

**Enjoy one FREE MENU ITEM when a second MENU ITEM of equal or greater value is purchased - maximum discount $12.**

Not valid with catering or takeout orders. Not valid at airport locations. Limit one coupon per party of four or fewer.
**Code: EB104**

**Promotion valid now thru 12/30/2017**
See reverse side for additional conditions or restrictions.    **B15**

## Sammy's Woodfired Pizza & Grill

• Sammy's Woodfired Pizza & Grill is known for its award-winning gourmet wood fired pizzas, tapas, salads, pastas and signature Messy Sundae®
• Sammy's is committed to bringing healthy lifestyles to the table by offering a wide selection of gluten free and vegan menu items
• Sammy's strives to use locally sourced, organice and sustainable items wherever possible
• Globally inspired. Locally produced.

Valid at all participating locations.

This promotional offer is not valid on any other discount/promotion or on defined holidays. See Rules of Use for more details. Offer valid at all participating locations. Excludes tax, tip, alcohol, and some sale items.     00000001R4Z

## Round Table Pizza

Valid at participating locations only. Not valid in Fresno, Portland, Reno & Spokane areas.

This promotional offer is not valid on any other discount/promotion or on defined holidays. See Rules of Use for more details. Offer valid at all participating locations. Excludes tax, tip, alcohol, and some sale items.     000000003YC

---

## Sammy's Woodfired Pizza & Grill

• Sammy's Woodfired Pizza & Grill is known for its award-winning gourmet wood fired pizzas, tapas, salads, pastas and signature Messy Sundae®
• Sammy's is committed to bringing healthy lifestyles to the table by offering a wide selection of gluten free and vegan menu items
• Sammy's strives to use locally sourced, organice and sustainable items wherever possible
• Globally inspired. Locally produced.

Valid at all participating locations.

This promotional offer is not valid on any other discount/promotion or on defined holidays. See Rules of Use for more details. Offer valid at all participating locations. Excludes tax, tip, alcohol, and some sale items.     00000001R4Z

## Round Table Pizza

Valid at participating locations only. Not valid in Fresno, Portland, Reno & Spokane areas.

This promotional offer is not valid on any other discount/promotion or on defined holidays. See Rules of Use for more details. Offer valid at all participating locations. Excludes tax, tip, alcohol, and some sale items.     000000003YS

---

## Sammy's Woodfired Pizza & Grill

• Sammy's Woodfired Pizza & Grill is known for its award-winning gourmet wood fired pizzas, tapas, salads, pastas and signature Messy Sundae®
• Sammy's is committed to bringing healthy lifestyles to the table by offering a wide selection of gluten free and vegan menu items
• Sammy's strives to use locally sourced, organice and sustainable items wherever possible
• Globally inspired. Locally produced.

Valid at all participating locations.

This promotional offer is not valid on any other discount/promotion or on defined holidays. See Rules of Use for more details. Offer valid at all participating locations. Excludes tax, tip, alcohol, and some sale items.     00000001R4Z

## Round Table Pizza

Valid at participating locations only. Not valid in Fresno, Portland, Reno & Spokane areas.

This promotional offer is not valid on any other discount/promotion or on defined holidays. See Rules of Use for more details. Offer valid at all participating locations. Excludes tax, tip, alcohol, and some sale items.     000000003X4

## SAVE

www.crabcornerlv.com

**Enjoy one complimentary ENTREE
when a second ENTREE of equal or
greater value and 2 beverages are
purchased - maximum discount $9.**

Dine in only.

**Promotion valid now thru 12/30/2017**
See reverse side for additional conditions or restrictions.      **B16**

---

UP TO **$25** VALUE

www.bigdogsbrews.com

**Enjoy 25% off the TOTAL BILL -
maximum discount $25.**
Dine in only.

**Tracking Code: #783**

**Promotion valid now thru 12/30/2017**
See reverse side for additional conditions or restrictions.      **B17**

---

## SAVE

www.stakeoutlv.com

**Enjoy FREE ENTREE when a second
ENTREE of equal or greater value
and 2 BEVERAGES are purchased -
maximum discount $8.**

Dine in only. Ages 21 & Up.

**Promotion valid now thru 12/30/2017**
See reverse side for additional conditions or restrictions.      **B18**

---

UP TO **$25** VALUE

www.bigdogsbrews.com

**Enjoy 25% off the TOTAL BILL -
maximum discount $25.**
Dine in only.

**Tracking Code: #783**

**Promotion valid now thru 12/30/2017**
See reverse side for additional conditions or restrictions.      **B19**

---

UP TO **$15** VALUE

www.rusticapizzeria.com

**Enjoy one FREE PIZZA when a
second PIZZA of equal or greater
value is purchased - maximum
discount $15.**

Specials Excluded. Delivery Excluded.

**Promotion valid now thru 12/30/2017**
See reverse side for additional conditions or restrictions.      **B20**

---

UP TO **$25** VALUE

www.bigdogsbrews.com

**Enjoy 25% off the TOTAL BILL -
maximum discount $25.**
Dine in only.

**Tracking Code: #783**

**Promotion valid now thru 12/30/2017**
See reverse side for additional conditions or restrictions.      **B21**

# Big Dog's Draft House

- Award-winning Brews
- Home of Big Dog's Brewing Co
- Las Vegas' Original Brewery
- Great Food
- Midwestern Favorites

4543 N Rancho Dr
(N. Rancho at Craig)
Las Vegas, NV
(702)645-1404

# Crab Corner

- Authentic Maryland Style Crab House
- Open daily
- Steamed blue crabs, crab cakes, seafood entrees, sandwiches, sides & desserts
- Casual atmosphere
- Weekly specials & kids menu
- We are also the premier distributor of live blue crabs, live crawfish & gulf shrimp in Vegas!

4161 S Eastern Ave Ste A1
(Eastern & Flamingo)
Las Vegas, NV
(702)489-4646

# Big Dog's Draft House

- Award-winning Brews
- Home of Big Dog's Brewing Co
- Las Vegas' Original Brewery
- Great Food
- Midwestern Favorites

4543 N Rancho Dr
(N. Rancho at Craig)
Las Vegas, NV
(702)645-1404

# Stake Out Bar & Grill

- Sizzling Video Poker Machines
- Great Food!
- Private Banquet Facilities & Meeting Rooms Available
- Check Our Menu for Other Great Selections & Daily Specials
- Fabulous Philly Cheese Steaks
- Guaranteed the "Best Baby Back Ribs in Las Vegas"
- Super Salads

4800 S Maryland Pkwy
(Tropicana & Maryland Pkwy, behind Starbucks)
Las Vegas, NV
(702)798-8383

# Big Dog's Draft House

- Award-winning Brews
- Home of Big Dog's Brewing Co
- Las Vegas' Original Brewery
- Great Food
- Midwestern Favorites

4543 N Rancho Dr
(N. Rancho at Craig)
Las Vegas, NV
(702)645-1404

# Rustica Pizzeria

- Catering Available
- Delicious Pasta, Pizza, Strombolis, Calzones, Salads and much more!
- Everyday Lunch Specials
- Open Daily
- We Deliver All Day

9730 W Tropicana Ave Ste 140
Las Vegas, NV
(702)778-4444

## UP TO $11 VALUE

dickeys.com

**Enjoy one FREE ENTREE when a second ENTREE of equal or greater value is purchased - maximum discount $11.**

**Promotion valid now thru 12/30/2017**
See reverse side for additional conditions or restrictions.     **B22**

---

## UP TO $14 VALUE

THE FAMILY PIZZERIA SINCE 1959

www.aureliospizza.com

**Enjoy one FREE PIZZA when a second PIZZA of equal or greater value is purchased - maximum discount $14.**

Delivery excluded. Specials excluded.

**Promotion valid now thru 12/30/2017**
See reverse side for additional conditions or restrictions.     **B23**

---

## UP TO $10 VALUE

www.dickeys.com

**Enjoy one FREE LUNCH OR DINNER ENTREE when a second LUNCH OR DINNER ENTREE of equal or greater value is purchased - maximum discount $10.**

**Promotion valid now thru 12/30/2017**
See reverse side for additional conditions or restrictions.     **B24**

---

## UP TO $9 VALUE

THE FAMILY PIZZERIA SINCE 1959

www.aureliospizza.com

**Enjoy one FREE SANDWICH when a second SANDWICH of equal or greater value is purchased - maximum discount $9.**

Delivery excluded. Specials excluded.

**Promotion valid now thru 12/30/2017**
See reverse side for additional conditions or restrictions.     **B25**

---

## UP TO $10 VALUE

www.dotssouthernkitchen2.com

**Enjoy one FREE ENTREE when a second ENTREE of equal or greater value is purchased - maximum discount $10.**

Dine in only.

**Promotion valid now thru 12/30/2017**
See reverse side for additional conditions or restrictions.     **B26**

---

## UP TO $5 VALUE

THE FAMILY PIZZERIA SINCE 1959

www.aureliospizza.com

**Enjoy $5 off minimum purchase of $20.**

**Promotion valid now thru 12/30/2017**
See reverse side for additional conditions or restrictions.     **B27**

# Aurelio's Is Pizza

- The Family Pizzeria since 1959
- Pizzas, Pastas, Sandwiches, and Salads
- Catering Available.
- Beer & Wine

445 West Craig Road, Suite 105
Las Vegas, NV
(702)399-3131

# DICKEY'S BARBECUE PIT

6584 N Decatur Blvd Ste 100
Las Vegas, NV
(702)655-0027

5597 S Rainbow Blvd Ste 110
Las Vegas, NV
(702)776-4200

# Aurelio's Is Pizza

- The Family Pizzeria since 1959
- Pizzas, Pastas, Sandwiches, and Salads
- Catering Available.
- Beer & Wine

445 West Craig Road, Suite 105
Las Vegas, NV
(702)399-3131

# DICKEY'S BARBECUE PIT

- Hickory smoked meats: Beef brisket, Southern pulled pork, Sweet pork ribs, Spicy hot links, Polish sausage, Chicken & turkey breasts, & Virginia style ham
- Homestyle sides, Sandwiches, Salads, Kid's menu & more
- Catering available

7430 Las Vegas Blvd S
(In front of the Las Vegas Outlet Ctr.)
Las Vegas, NV
(702)220-4227

# Aurelio's Is Pizza

- The Family Pizzeria since 1959
- Pizzas, Pastas, Sandwiches, and Salads
- Catering Available.
- Beer & Wine

445 West Craig Road, Suite 105
Las Vegas, NV
(702)399-3131

# Dot's Southern Kitchen

- A Touch of the South.
- Seafood & Burgers.
- Family & Lunch Specials.
- Open 11am - 10pm Daily.
- Catering.
- Down Home BBQ & Dinners.
- Homemade Sides.

3055 E Flamingo Rd
Las Vegas, NV
(702)643-1170

**UP TO $7 VALUE**

www.omelethouse.net

**Enjoy one complimentary BREAKFAST or LUNCH ENTREE when a second BREAKFAST or LUNCH ENTREE of equal or greater value is purchased - maximum discount $7.**

Present coupon/card before ordering. Dine in only.

**Promotion valid now thru 12/30/2017**
See reverse side for additional conditions or restrictions.
**B28**

---

**UP TO 50% OFF**

**Enjoy one ENTREE at 50% off when a second ENTREE of equal or greater value and 2 BEVERAGES are purchased.**

Exclude weekends & holidays. Limit one coupon per table. Not valid with any other discount offer. Valid Monday - Friday Only. Dine in only.

**Promotion valid now thru 12/30/2017**
See reverse side for additional conditions or restrictions.
**B29**

---

**UP TO $7 VALUE**

www.omelethouse.net

**Enjoy one complimentary BREAKFAST OR LUNCH ENTREE when a second BREAKFAST OR LUNCH ENTREE of equal or greater value is purchased - maximum discount $7.**

Specials Excluded. Dine in only.

**Promotion valid now thru 12/30/2017**
See reverse side for additional conditions or restrictions.
**B30**

---

**UP TO 50% OFF**

**Enjoy one ENTREE at 50% off when a second ENTREE of equal or greater value and 2 BEVERAGES are purchased.**

Exclude weekends & holidays. Limit one coupon per table. Not valid with any other discount offer. Valid Monday - Friday Only. Dine in only.

**Promotion valid now thru 12/30/2017**
See reverse side for additional conditions or restrictions.
**B31**

---

**UP TO $7 VALUE**

www.omelethouse.net

**Enjoy one complimentary BREAKFAST or LUNCH ENTREE when a second BREAKFAST or LUNCH ENTREE of equal or greater value is purchased - maximum discount $7.**

Present coupon/card before ordering. Dine in only.

**Promotion valid now thru 12/30/2017**
See reverse side for additional conditions or restrictions.
**B32**

---

**UP TO 50% OFF**

**Enjoy one ENTREE at 50% off when a second ENTREE of equal or greater value and 2 BEVERAGES are purchased.**

Excludes holidays. Limit one coupon per table. Not valid with any other discount offer. Valid Saturday and Sunday only from 7am-9am. Dine in only.

**Promotion valid now thru 12/30/2017**
See reverse side for additional conditions or restrictions.
**B33**

# Sunrise Cafe

- Sandwiches & specialty benedicts
- Serving breakfast & lunch ALL DAY everyday 7am-3pm
- Kids menu, outdoor patio seating & private parties available
- Specialty & create your own omelettes, salads, wraps and burgers

8975 S Eastern Ave
(Off of 215 & Eastern)
Las Vegas, NV
(702)257-8877

# Omelet House

- Menu selection includes: hamburgers, sandwiches, homemade soups, chili, salads, breakfast specials and omelets, of course
- Open 7am - 3pm
- Voted best breakfast house in Las Vegas year after year
- Open Fri-Sat 7pm-8pm for dinner at 6520 Boulder Hwy location

316 N Boulder Hwy
(at Lake Mead)
Henderson, NV
(702)566-7896

2227 N Rampart Blvd
(at Lake Mead)
Las Vegas, NV
(702)315-2828

2160 W Charleston Blvd
(at Rancho)
Las Vegas, NV
(702)384-6868

6520 Boulder Hwy
(at Russell)
Las Vegas, NV
(702)307-5777

---

# Sunrise Cafe

- Sandwiches & specialty benedicts
- Serving breakfast & lunch ALL DAY everyday 7am-3pm
- Kids menu, outdoor patio seating & private parties available
- Specialty & create your own omelettes, salads, wraps and burgers

8975 S Eastern Ave
(Off of 215 & Eastern)
Las Vegas, NV
(702)257-8877

# Omelet House

- Menu selection includes: hamburgers, sandwiches, homemade soups, chili, salads, breakfast specials and omelets, of course
- Open 7am - 3pm
- Voted best breakfast house in Las Vegas year after year
- Open Fri-Sat 7pm-8pm for dinner at 6520 Boulder Hwy location

316 N Boulder Hwy
(at Lake Mead)
Henderson, NV
(702)566-7896

2227 N Rampart Blvd
(at Lake Mead)
Las Vegas, NV
(702)315-2828

2160 W Charleston Blvd
(at Rancho)
Las Vegas, NV
(702)384-6868

6520 Boulder Hwy
(at Russell)
Las Vegas, NV
(702)307-5777

---

# Sunrise Cafe

- Sandwiches & specialty benedicts
- Serving breakfast & lunch ALL DAY everyday 7am-3pm
- Kids menu, outdoor patio seating & private parties available
- Specialty & create your own omelettes, salads, wraps and burgers

8975 S Eastern Ave
(Off of 215 & Eastern)
Las Vegas, NV
(702)257-8877

# Omelet House

- Menu selection includes: hamburgers, sandwiches, homemade soups, chili, salads, breakfast specials and omelets, of course
- Open 7am - 3pm
- Voted best breakfast house in Las Vegas year after year
- Open Fri-Sat 7pm-8pm for dinner at 6520 Boulder Hwy location

316 N Boulder Hwy
(at Lake Mead)
Henderson, NV
(702)566-7896

2227 N Rampart Blvd
(at Lake Mead)
Las Vegas, NV
(702)315-2828

2160 W Charleston Blvd
(at Rancho)
Las Vegas, NV
(702)384-6868

6520 Boulder Hwy
(at Russell)
Las Vegas, NV
(702)307-5777

**UP TO $8 VALUE**

*Authentic Trattoria*
www.sienaitalian.com

**Enjoy 50% off one ENTREE when a second ENTREE of equal or greater value is purchased - maximum discount $8.**

Dine in only. Not valid for happy hour. Not valid on holidays. Limit one coupon per table. No split check.

**Promotion valid now thru 12/30/2017**
See reverse side for additional conditions or restrictions. **B34**

---

**50% OFF**

*Authentic Trattoria*
www.sienaitalian.com

**Enjoy 50% off one BRUNCH when a second BRUNCH of equal or greater value is purchased.**

Dine in only. Valid Saturday & Sunday only. Limit one coupon per table. No split check.

**Promotion valid now thru 12/30/2017**
See reverse side for additional conditions or restrictions. **B35**

---

**UP TO $9 VALUE**

www.enzosgvpizza.com

**Enjoy any one complimentary PIZZA when a second PIZZA of equal or greater value is purchased - maximum discount $9.**

Delivery excluded. Dine In or Pick Up Only.

**Promotion valid now thru 12/30/2017**
See reverse side for additional conditions or restrictions. **B36**

---

**UP TO $9 VALUE**

www.enzosgvpizza.com

**Enjoy one complimentary PASTA when a second PASTA of equal or greater value is purchased - maximum discount $9.**

Delivery excluded. Dine In Only.

**Promotion valid now thru 12/30/2017**
See reverse side for additional conditions or restrictions. **B37**

---

**UP TO $10 VALUE**

www.joesnypizza.com

**Enjoy one complimentary MENU ITEM when a second MENU ITEM of equal or greater value is purchased - maximum discount $10.**

**Promotion valid now thru 12/30/2017**
See reverse side for additional conditions or restrictions. **B38**

---

**UP TO $18 VALUE**

www.joesnypizza.com

**Enjoy any one complimentary PIZZA when a second PIZZA of equal or greater value is purchased - maximum discount $18.**

**Promotion valid now thru 12/30/2017**
See reverse side for additional conditions or restrictions. **B39**

# Siena Italian Trattoria

- Celebrating over 25 years as a Las Vegas tradition.
- Daily happy hour.
- Authentic Trattoria.
- Specialty market.
- Deli.
- Bakery.

9500 W Sahara Ave
(Between Fort Apache & Hualapai)
Las Vegas, NV
(702)360-3358

This promotional offer is not valid on any other discount/promotion or on defined holidays. See Rules of Use for more details. Offer valid at all participating locations. Excludes tax, tip, alcohol, and some sale items.    00000000PSV

# Siena Italian Trattoria

- Celebrating over 25 years as a Las Vegas tradition.
- Daily happy hour.
- Authentic Trattoria.
- Specialty market.
- Deli.
- Bakery.

9500 W Sahara Ave
(Between Fort Apache & Hualapai)
Las Vegas, NV
(702)360-3358

This promotional offer is not valid on any other discount/promotion or on defined holidays. See Rules of Use for more details. Offer valid at all participating locations. Excludes tax, tip, alcohol, and some sale items.    00000000PSR

# Enzo's

- Catering available
- Dine In, Pick Up or Delivery
- Daily lunch specials
- Now serving gelato
- Pizza, Pasta, Chicken, Hot & Cold Subs, Salads and Desserts
- Private party room
- Mon - Sat 11am - 9pm
- Over 20 years of service at this location!
- Sun 1pm - 9pm

2724 N Green Valley Pkwy
(At Sunset)
Henderson, NV
(702)458-2166

This promotional offer is not valid on any other discount/promotion or on defined holidays. See Rules of Use for more details. Offer valid at all participating locations. Excludes tax, tip, alcohol, and some sale items.    136454

# Enzo's

- Catering available
- Dine In, Pick Up or Delivery
- Daily lunch specials
- Now serving gelato
- Pizza, Pasta, Chicken, Hot & Cold Subs, Salads and Desserts
- Private party room
- Mon - Sat 11am - 9pm
- Over 20 years of service at this location!
- Sun 1pm - 9pm

2724 N Green Valley Pkwy
(At Sunset)
Henderson, NV
(702)458-2166

This promotional offer is not valid on any other discount/promotion or on defined holidays. See Rules of Use for more details. Offer valid at all participating locations. Excludes tax, tip, alcohol, and some sale items.    35479

# Joe's New York Pizza

- Catering Available
- Bigger & Better Pizza!
- Specialty & Build Your Own Pizzas
- Dine In, Carry out and Delivery
- Appetizers, Salads, Calzones, Subs and Desserts
- Pizza by the slice
- Daily Specials

4480 Paradise Rd
(located across from the Hard Rock)
Las Vegas, NV
(702)792-9001

7580 Las Vegas Blvd S
(located Front of the Outlet Mall)
Las Vegas, NV
(702)897-1717

This promotional offer is not valid on any other discount/promotion or on defined holidays. See Rules of Use for more details. Offer valid at all participating locations. Excludes tax, tip, alcohol, and some sale items.    35405

# Joe's New York Pizza

- Catering Available
- Bigger & Better Pizza!
- Specialty & Build Your Own Pizzas
- Dine In, Carry out and Delivery
- Appetizers, Salads, Calzones, Subs and Desserts
- Pizza by the slice
- Daily Specials

4480 Paradise Rd
(located across from the Hard Rock)
Las Vegas, NV
(702)792-9001

7580 Las Vegas Blvd S
(located Front of the Outlet Mall)
Las Vegas, NV
(702)897-1717

This promotional offer is not valid on any other discount/promotion or on defined holidays. See Rules of Use for more details. Offer valid at all participating locations. Excludes tax, tip, alcohol, and some sale items.    35406

**UP TO $10 VALUE**

**Maria's**
**Mexican Restaurant**

**Enjoy one FREE ENTREE when a second ENTREE of equal or greater value is purchased - maximum discount $10.**

Fridays Excluded. Dine in only. Specials Excluded.

**Promotion valid now thru 12/30/2017**
See reverse side for additional conditions or restrictions.　**B40**

**UP TO $9 VALUE**

www.LeticiasLV.com

**Enjoy one FREE LUNCH ENTREE when a second LUNCH ENTREE of equal or greater value is purchased - maximum discount $9.**

Dine in only.

**Promotion valid now thru 12/30/2017**
See reverse side for additional conditions or restrictions.　**B41**

**UP TO $20 VALUE**

**DeLucias**
www.deluciaspizzeria.com

**Enjoy any one complimentary PIZZA when a second PIZZA of equal or greater value is purchased - maximum discount $20.**

Delivery excluded.

**Promotion valid now thru 12/30/2017**
See reverse side for additional conditions or restrictions.　**B42**

**UP TO $20 VALUE**

**DeLucias**
www.deluciaspizzeria.com

**Enjoy any one complimentary PIZZA when a second PIZZA of equal or greater value is purchased - maximum discount $20.**

Delivery excluded.

**Promotion valid now thru 12/30/2017**
See reverse side for additional conditions or restrictions.　**B43**

**UP TO 10% OFF**

**Maestro's**
*Pizza Calzones Sandwiches and More*

**Enjoy 10% off the TOTAL BILL.**

Delivery Excluded.

**Promotion valid now thru 12/30/2017**
See reverse side for additional conditions or restrictions.　**B44**

**UP TO $10 VALUE**

**Maestro's**
*Pizza Calzones Sandwiches and More*

**Enjoy one FREE PIZZA when a second PIZZA of equal or greater value is purchased - maximum discount $10.**

Delivery Excluded.

**Promotion valid now thru 12/30/2017**
See reverse side for additional conditions or restrictions.　**B45**

## Leticia's Mexican Cocina

- John Curtas says it's "The Best Mexican Restaurant in Las Vegas!"
- Mon - Sat 11am - 12am & Sun 10am - 10pm
- The real taste of Mexico.
- Happy Hour.
- Saturday night karaoke.
- Catering & banquet room.
- Cocktails, music & gaming.

7585 Norman Rockwell Ln Bldg 1
Las Vegas, NV
(702)445-7722

## Mama Maria's Mexican Restaurant

- Authentic Mexican Cuisine & Pastries.
- Bakery.
- Open 7 days.
- Catering Available.

6055 E LAKE MEAD BLVD
Las Vegas, NV
(702)453-3111

## DeLucias Pizzeria

- Dine In, Carry Out and Delivery
- New York style hand tossed pizzas and great pasta dishes
- Serving beer & wine
- We use Grande Cheese and Stanislaus products
- Everything made In-house
- Sun-Thurs 11am-9pm
- Fri & Sat 11am-10pm

2345 E Centennial Pkwy
(In the Smith Food King Shopping Center)
North Las Vegas, NV
(702)658-7111

## DeLucias Pizzeria

- Dine In, Carry Out and Delivery
- New York style hand tossed pizzas and great pasta dishes
- Serving beer & wine
- We use Grande Cheese and Stanislaus products
- Everything made In-house
- Sun-Thurs 11am-9pm
- Fri & Sat 11am-10pm

2345 E Centennial Pkwy
(In the Smith Food King Shopping Center)
North Las Vegas, NV
(702)658-7111

## Maestro's Pizzeria

- Catering available.
- Italian, Greek & Continental Food.
- Dine in, Pick up and Delivery.
- Everyday lunch specials.

3230 E Flamingo Rd
Las Vegas, NV
(702)434-5770

## Maestro's Pizzeria

- Catering available.
- Italian, Greek & Continental Food.
- Dine in, Pick up and Delivery.
- Everyday lunch specials.

3230 E Flamingo Rd
Las Vegas, NV
(702)434-5770

**UP TO $9 VALUE**

# BRONZE CAFÉ

**Enjoy one FREE ENTREE when a second ENTREE of equal or greater value is purchased - maximum discount $9.**

Dine in only.

**Promotion valid now thru 12/30/2017**
See reverse side for additional conditions or restrictions. **B46**

---

**UP TO $11 VALUE**

www.violettesvegan.com

**Enjoy one FREE ENTREE when a second ENTREE of equal or greater value is purchased - maximum discount $11.**

Dine In only. Please present coupon when ordering.

**Promotion valid now thru 12/30/2017**
See reverse side for additional conditions or restrictions. **B47**

---

**UP TO $9 VALUE**

# BRONZE CAFÉ

**Enjoy one FREE ENTREE when a second ENTREE of equal or greater value is purchased - maximum discount $9.**

Dine in only.

**Promotion valid now thru 12/30/2017**
See reverse side for additional conditions or restrictions. **B48**

---

**UP TO $25 VALUE**

www.The052.com

**Enjoy 20% off the total bill (tax, tip & alcoholic beverages excluded) - maximum discount $25.**

**Promotion valid now thru 12/30/2017**
See reverse side for additional conditions or restrictions. **B49**

---

**UP TO $9 VALUE**

# BRONZE CAFÉ

**Enjoy one FREE ENTREE when a second ENTREE of equal or greater value is purchased - maximum discount $9.**

Dine in only.

**Promotion valid now thru 12/30/2017**
See reverse side for additional conditions or restrictions. **B50**

---

**UP TO $10 VALUE**

www.The052.com

**Enjoy one complimentary ENTREE when a second ENTREE of equal or greater value is purchased - maximum discount $10.**

**Promotion valid now thru 12/30/2017**
See reverse side for additional conditions or restrictions. **B51**

# Violette's Vegan

- Fresh Healthy Salads, Tasty Sides & Starters, Delicious Entrees & Organic Smoothies
- Live Entertainment on Selected Evenings
- Using Only the Freshest & Organic Ingredients!
- We Deliver

8560 W Desert Inn Rd Ste D5
Las Vegas, NV
(702)685-0466

# Bronze Cafe

- Gluten-Free Options Available
- Catering Available
- Sandwiches, Salads, Smoothies, Coffee & Espresso, Fresh Baked Pastries
- Vegan Options Available

401 S Maryland Pkwy
Las Vegas, NV
(702)202-3100

# The 052

- Come try our $8.99 Nightly Dinner Specials!
- Burgers, sandwiches, & pizza
- Come watch your favorite sports programs with us!

11261 S Eastern Ave
Henderson, NV
(702)485-5609

# Bronze Cafe

- Gluten-Free Options Available
- Catering Available
- Sandwiches, Salads, Smoothies, Coffee & Espresso, Fresh Baked Pastries
- Vegan Options Available

401 S Maryland Pkwy
Las Vegas, NV
(702)202-3100

# The 052

- Come try our $8.99 Nightly Dinner Specials!
- Burgers, sandwiches, & pizza
- Come watch your favorite sports programs with us!

11261 S Eastern Ave
Henderson, NV
(702)485-5609

# Bronze Cafe

- Gluten-Free Options Available
- Catering Available
- Sandwiches, Salads, Smoothies, Coffee & Espresso, Fresh Baked Pastries
- Vegan Options Available

401 S Maryland Pkwy
Las Vegas, NV
(702)202-3100

# Double Helix Wine & Whiskey Lounge

• Charcuterie and cheese boards, flatbreads, gourmet comfort food dishes, a variety of sliders and seared yellowfin tuna
• Over 40 unique wines by the glass, 100 whiskey labels, sampler flights and Double Helix's signature cocktails
• Patio seating available

6599 Las Vegas Blvd S Ste 150b
Las Vegas, NV
(702)473-5415

# Izakaya Go

• Open Daily 5pm - 2am
• Authentic & Fusion Dishes
• Sushi & Tapas.
• Full Bar
• Variety of Sake

3775 Spring Mountain Rd Ste 301
Las Vegas, NV
(702)247-1183

# Jasmine Express

• Chinese & Vietnamese cuisine.
• Open 7 days.
• Smoothies & specialty drinks.
• Dine in, take out & delivery.

5546 Camino Al Norte Ste 1-5
N Las Vegas, NV
(702)399-8525

# Jasmine Express

• Chinese & Vietnamese cuisine.
• Open 7 days.
• Smoothies & specialty drinks.
• Dine in, take out & delivery.

5546 Camino Al Norte Ste 1-5
N Las Vegas, NV
(702)399-8525

# Stir Krazy Mongolian Grill

• Different types of homemade sauces to choose from
• All you can eat dinner
• Large selection of meat, vegetables and noodles
• Fresh, delicious and healthy!
• Open daily

3345 E Patrick Ln Ste 100
Las Vegas, NV
(702)538-8787

# Jolly Bar Ethiopian Restaurant

• Catering and Banquet room available
• Traditional family recipes
• Authentic Ethiopian food
• Entertainment weekly
• Full bar

6182 W Flamingo Rd
Las Vegas, NV
(702)476-3587

## BUY ONE GET ONE

# SALVADOREÑO

**Enjoy one complimentary LUNCH OR DINNER ENTREE** when a second **LUNCH OR DINNER ENTREE** of equal or greater value is purchased.

Dine in only.

**Promotion valid now thru 12/30/2017**
See reverse side for additional conditions or restrictions.　　**B58**

---

## UP TO $25 VALUE

# SALVADOREÑO

**Enjoy an ongoing 20% off the total bill** (tax, tip & alcoholic beverages excluded) - maximum discount $25.

Dine in only.

**Promotion valid now thru 12/30/2017**
See reverse side for additional conditions or restrictions.　　**B59**

---

## BUY ONE GET ONE

# SALVADOREÑO

**Enjoy one complimentary LUNCH OR DINNER ENTREE** when a second **LUNCH OR DINNER ENTREE** of equal or greater value is purchased.

Dine in only.

**Promotion valid now thru 12/30/2017**
See reverse side for additional conditions or restrictions.　　**B60**

---

## BUY ONE GET ONE

# SALVADOREÑO

**Enjoy one complimentary LUNCH OR DINNER ENTREE** when a second **LUNCH OR DINNER ENTREE** of equal or greater value is purchased.

Dine in only.

**Promotion valid now thru 12/30/2017**
See reverse side for additional conditions or restrictions.　　**B61**

---

## UP TO $9 VALUE

### Lazeez
Indian Mediterranean Grill
www.lazeezgrill.org

**Enjoy one FREE ENTREE** when a second **ENTREE** of equal or greater value is purchased - maximum discount $9.

Specials Excluded. Dine in only.

**Promotion valid now thru 12/30/2017**
See reverse side for additional conditions or restrictions.　　**B62**

---

## SPECIAL PRICE

www.lvmgp.com

**Enjoy a 16" LARGE 1-TOPPING PIZZA for $6.99.**
Valid Monday - Thursday. One coupon per person per day.

**Promotion valid now thru 12/30/2017**
See reverse side for additional conditions or restrictions.　　**B63**

# Salvadoreno Restaurant

- Breakfast served as well
- Mild, fresh, delicious Salvadoran specialties since 1987
- Pork, beef, chicken & all the typical foods
- Even shrimp, ocean perch, burgers, flautas, tostadas & more

720 N Main St
Las Vegas, NV
(702)385-3600

This promotional offer is not valid on any other discount/promotion or on defined holidays. See Rules of Use for more details. Offer valid at all participating locations. Excludes tax, tip, alcohol, and some sale items.     135627

# Salvadoreno Restaurant

- Breakfast served as well
- Mild, fresh, delicious Salvadoran specialties since 1987
- Pork, beef, chicken & all the typical foods
- Even shrimp, ocean perch, burgers, flautas, tostadas & more

720 N Main St
Las Vegas, NV
(702)385-3600

This promotional offer is not valid on any other discount/promotion or on defined holidays. See Rules of Use for more details. Offer valid at all participating locations. Excludes tax, tip, alcohol, and some sale items.     35211

# Salvadoreno Restaurant

- Breakfast served as well
- Mild, fresh, delicious Salvadoran specialties since 1987
- Pork, beef, chicken & all the typical foods
- Even shrimp, ocean perch, burgers, flautas, tostadas & more

720 N Main St
Las Vegas, NV
(702)385-3600

This promotional offer is not valid on any other discount/promotion or on defined holidays. See Rules of Use for more details. Offer valid at all participating locations. Excludes tax, tip, alcohol, and some sale items.     35211

# Salvadoreno Restaurant

- Breakfast served as well
- Mild, fresh, delicious Salvadoran specialties since 1987
- Pork, beef, chicken & all the typical foods
- Even shrimp, ocean perch, burgers, flautas, tostadas & more

720 N Main St
Las Vegas, NV
(702)385-3600

This promotional offer is not valid on any other discount/promotion or on defined holidays. See Rules of Use for more details. Offer valid at all participating locations. Excludes tax, tip, alcohol, and some sale items.     35211

# Las Vegas Mini Gran Prix

- Open Year Round--7 Days a Week.
- Adult Gran Prix Cars.
- Sprint Kart Speedway & Kiddie Karts.
- Dragon Roller Coaster & Tornado Twister.
- Super Fun Slide.
- Arcade Games.
- Restaurant & Party Room.
- Parties & Group Events.

1401 N Rainbow Blvd
(at Vegas Drive)
Las Vegas, NV
(702)259-7000

This promotional offer is not valid on any other discount/promotion or on defined holidays. See Rules of Use for more details. Offer valid at all participating locations. Excludes tax, tip, alcohol, and some sale items.     49781879

# Lazeez Indian Mediterranean Grill

- Healthy & tasty
- Open daily
- Fresh & authentic Indian Mediterranean cuisine
- Vegetarian & Vegan options
- Halal
- Weekend specials

8560 W Desert Inn Rd Ste D3
Las Vegas, NV
(702)778-1613

This promotional offer is not valid on any other discount/promotion or on defined holidays. See Rules of Use for more details. Offer valid at all participating locations. Excludes tax, tip, alcohol, and some sale items.     0000000PL5R

UP TO **$15** VALUE

**Enjoy one complimentary ENTREE when a second ENTREE of equal or greater value is purchased - maximum discount $15.**

Dine in only.

**Promotion valid now thru 12/30/2017**
See reverse side for additional conditions or restrictions. **B64**

UP TO **$9** VALUE

## TC's World Famous BBQ RIB CRIB

www.tcsribcrib.com

**Enjoy one FREE BREAKFAST OR LUNCH ENTREE when a second BREAKFAST OR LUNCH ENTREE of equal or greater value is purchased - maximum discount $9.**
One discount per table per visit.

**Promotion valid now thru 12/30/2017**
See reverse side for additional conditions or restrictions. **B65**

UP TO **$15** VALUE

**Enjoy one complimentary ENTREE when a second ENTREE of equal or greater value is purchased - maximum discount $15.**

Dine in only.

**Promotion valid now thru 12/30/2017**
See reverse side for additional conditions or restrictions. **B66**

UP TO **$13** VALUE

## EL HERRADERO RESTAURANT

**Enjoy one FREE ENTREE when a second ENTREE of equal or greater value is purchased - maximum discount $13.**

Dine in only.

**Promotion valid now thru 12/30/2017**
See reverse side for additional conditions or restrictions. **B67**

UP TO **$15** VALUE

**Enjoy one complimentary ENTREE when a second ENTREE of equal or greater value is purchased - maximum discount $15.**

Dine in only.

**Promotion valid now thru 12/30/2017**
See reverse side for additional conditions or restrictions. **B68**

UP TO **$6** VALUE

GREAT LINKS
HOT DOGS & GRILL

**Enjoy one complimentary ENTREE when a second ENTREE of equal or greater value is purchased - maximum discount $6.**

**Promotion valid now thru 12/30/2017**
See reverse side for additional conditions or restrictions. **B69**

# TC's Rib Crib

- Best of Las Vegas 2007 & 2010
- Open 7 days
- Daily lunch & dinner specials
- Catering for all occasions
- Come try our world famous BBQ!
- Homemade sides

3655 S Durango Dr
(Durango & Spring Mountain)
Las Vegas, NV
(702)451-7427

# M & M's Soul Food Cafe

- Homemade desserts
- Your favorite soul food entrees include smothered chicken, pork chops, gumbo, fried chicken, meat loaf, oxtails, catfish, short ribs & much more!
- Breakfast entrees & omelets
- Voted "Best of Las Vegas" by The Review Journal in 2003 & 2004!

3923 W Charleston Blvd
(S.E. corner of Valley View)
Las Vegas, NV
(702)453-7685

# El Herradero Restaurant

- Closed Sunday.
- Breakfast, lunch & dinner.
- Serving authentic mexican food since 2004.
- Serving authentic Mexican food since 2004.

1725 E Warm Springs Rd
Las Vegas, NV
(702)270-3444

# M & M's Soul Food Cafe

- Homemade desserts
- Your favorite soul food entrees include smothered chicken, pork chops, gumbo, fried chicken, meat loaf, oxtails, catfish, short ribs & much more!
- Breakfast entrees & omelets
- Voted "Best of Las Vegas" by The Review Journal in 2003 & 2004!

3923 W Charleston Blvd
(S.E. corner of Valley View)
Las Vegas, NV
(702)453-7685

# Great Links Hot Dogs & Grill

- Open daily from 10am
- World's finest real draft root beer and ice cold draft & bottled beer
- Our 100% Beef Hot Dogs are custom made in New York City by Boar's Head
- Gourmet sausages and grilled sandwiches
- Kid's meals
- Vegetarian selections

6010 W Craig Rd
(NW. Corner Craig & Jones in Lowes Plaza)
Las Vegas, NV
(702)877-3647

# M & M's Soul Food Cafe

- Homemade desserts
- Your favorite soul food entrees include smothered chicken, pork chops, gumbo, fried chicken, meat loaf, oxtails, catfish, short ribs & much more!
- Breakfast entrees & omelets
- Voted "Best of Las Vegas" by The Review Journal in 2003 & 2004!

3923 W Charleston Blvd
(S.E. corner of Valley View)
Las Vegas, NV
(702)453-7685

**UP TO $26 VALUE**

www.RumorVegas.com

**Enjoy one FREE ENTREE when a second ENTREE of equal or greater value is purchased - maximum discount $26.**

Dine in only.

**Promotion valid now thru 12/30/2017**
See reverse side for additional conditions or restrictions.          **B70**

**UP TO $30 VALUE**

www.MtCharlestonResort.com

**Enjoy one FREE ENTREE when a second ENTREE of equal or greater value is purchased - maximum discount $30.**

Dine in only.

**Promotion valid now thru 12/30/2017**
See reverse side for additional conditions or restrictions.          **B71**

**FREE WITH PURCHASE**

www.jessieraesbbq.com

**Enjoy FREE SIDE & DRINK with Purchase of an ENTREE.**

**Promotion valid now thru 12/30/2017**
See reverse side for additional conditions or restrictions.          **B72**

**UP TO $8 VALUE**

JESSIE RAE'S BBQ
LAS VEGAS STYLE BBQ

www.jessieraesbbq.com

**Enjoy one FREE ENTREE when a second ENTREE of equal or greater value is purchased - maximum discount $8.**

**Promotion valid now thru 12/30/2017**
See reverse side for additional conditions or restrictions.          **B73**

**UP TO $15 VALUE**

www.palermoslv.com

**Enjoy one FREE PIZZA when a second PIZZA of equal or greater value is purchased - maximum discount $15.**

Delivery Excluded. Specials Excluded.

**Promotion valid now thru 12/30/2017**
See reverse side for additional conditions or restrictions.          **B74**

**UP TO $11 VALUE**

www.mrmamaslv.com

**Enjoy one FREE ENTREE when a second ENTREE of equal or greater value is purchased - maximum discount $11.**

Dine in only.

**Promotion valid now thru 12/30/2017**
See reverse side for additional conditions or restrictions.          **B75**

## A Cut Above at The Resort on Mt. Charleston

• Our chef is always cooking up something new and interesting to enhance our restaurant's menu of steaks, chicken, and delicious appetizers.
• One of the best things about a visit to The Resort on Mount Charleston is the dining.

2275 Kyle Canyon Rd
Las Vegas, NV
(702)872-5500

## Addiction Restaurant at RUMOR

• This sleek modern venue serves classic dishes with a twist for breakfast, lunch, and dinner.
• A truly unique Las Vegas restaurant.

455 E Harmon Ave
(Inside Rumor Hotel)
Las Vegas, NV
(702)369-5400

## Jessie Rae's BBQ

• Catering
• Join us at both our restaurant locations and our weekly outdoor Farmer's Market events!
• Award Winning Las Vegas Style BBQ!

5611 S Valley View Blvd
Las Vegas, NV
(702)541-5546

## Jessie Rae's BBQ

• Catering
• Join us at both our restaurant locations and our weekly outdoor Farmer's Market events!
• Award Winning Las Vegas Style BBQ!

5611 S Valley View Blvd
Las Vegas, NV
(702)541-5546

## Mr. Mamas Breakfast & Lunch

• Mon-Fri 6am-3pm, Sat & Sun 7am-2pm
• Our place will put a smile on your face!
• Delicious breakfast menu
• Burgers, salads and sandwiches

5693 S Jones Blvd Ste 106
Las Vegas, NV
(702)220-9224

## Palermo's Pizza LLC

• Dine In & Carry Out
• Free Delivery!
• Catering
• Daily Specials
• Free WiFi

1370 E Flamingo Rd
Las Vegas, NV
(702)866-0011

## UP TO $15 VALUE

### 24 Hour Pizzeria

www.24hrpizzeria.com

**Enjoy one FREE PIZZA when a second PIZZA of equal or greater value is purchased - maximum discount $15.**

Delivery Excluded.

**Promotion valid now thru 12/30/2017**
See reverse side for additional conditions or restrictions. **B76**

## UP TO $12 VALUE

**PH** PROTEINHOUSE

www.protein-house.com

**Enjoy one FREE ENTREE when a second ENTREE of equal or greater value is purchased - maximum discount $12.**

**Promotion valid now thru 12/30/2017**
See reverse side for additional conditions or restrictions. **B77**

## UP TO $17 VALUE

### Promenade CAFE

www.rampartcasino.com

**Enjoy one complimentary ENTREE when a second ENTREE of equal or greater value is purchased - maximum discount $17.**

Not Valid with any other discounts or promotions. Dine in only.

**Promotion valid now thru 12/30/2017**
See reverse side for additional conditions or restrictions. **B78**

## UP TO $10 VALUE

EST. 1995
**MUSCLE MAKER GRILL**
"Great Food with Your Health in Mind"

www.musclemakergrill.com

**Enjoy one FREE ENTREE when a second ENTREE of equal or greater value is purchased - maximum discount $10.**

Dine in only.

**Promotion valid now thru 12/30/2017**
See reverse side for additional conditions or restrictions. **B79**

## UP TO $10 VALUE

### JUKE JOINT Bar & Grill

**Enjoy one complimentary ENTREE when a second ENTREE of equal or greater value is purchased - maximum discount $10.**

Dine in only. Specials excluded.

**Promotion valid now thru 12/30/2017**
See reverse side for additional conditions or restrictions. **B80**

## UP TO $9 VALUE

### Oiga, mire, vea. COLOMBIAN·CUISINE

**Enjoy one complimentary ENTREE when a second ENTREE of equal or greater value is purchased - maximum discount $9.**

Dine in only.

**Promotion valid now thru 12/30/2017**
See reverse side for additional conditions or restrictions. **B81**

# Protein House

- Open daily 9am-10pm
- Breakfast available
- A place where you want to go to eat both healthy & tasty!
- Burgers, salads, bowls, wraps, pancakes & much more!
- Coffee, juice, tea & smoothies

9555 S Eastern Ave Ste 125
(S Eastern & Richmar)
Las Vegas, NV
(702)816-3443

# 24 HR Pizzeria

- Dine in, take out or fast delivery
- Gourmet or Build Your Own Pizza
- Lunch and Anytime Specials
- Burgers, subs, salads, pasta & Chef Specials
- Open daily

4850 W Flamingo Rd Ste 6
Las Vegas, NV
(702)410-9001

# Muscle Maker Grill

- Great food with your health in mind!
- Dine in, take out & delivery
- Pasta, appetizers, guiltless entrees, sandwiches & salads
- Vegetarian dishes
- Smoothies & shakes
- Catering
- Open daily
- Pasta, appetizers, guiltless entrees, sandwiches & salads, Vegetarian dishes; Smoothies & shakes
- Open daily; dine in, take out & delivery

5765 Centennial Center Blvd Ste 180
Las Vegas, NV
(702)778-8819

# Promenade Cafe

- Open 24 hours a day, 7 days a week, serving breakfast, lunch, dinner & late night menu
- Located within the Rampart Casino at The Resort at Summerlin
- Specialties include NY sirloin & porterhouse steaks, specialty salads, gourmet burgers, pasta dishes, filet mignon, crab cakes, extensive desserts & much more!
- Offering dishes from around the world

221 N Rampart Blvd
(inside the Rampart Casino)
Las Vegas, NV
(702)507-5966

# Oiga, Mire, Oiga, Mire, Vea Colombian Cuisine

- All our food is made to order
- Try an authentic taste of our country!
- Fresh Colombian food
- Open daily
- Try our specialties like Morcilla and Bandeja Paisa

2580 S Decatur Blvd
(S Decatur & Sahara)
Las Vegas, NV
(702)221-4359

# Juke Joint Bar & Grill

- Play your favorite song in our Jukebox!
- Full Bar
- Pool Tables, Dart Machines and Video Poker
- Karaoke Thursday Nights and DJs Friday Nights
- Come for our Breakfast, Lunch and Dinner Specials

4230 E Craig Rd
(Craig & Lamb)
North Las Vegas, NV
(702)307-2082

## UP TO $15 VALUE

# Bistro Pizza

**Enjoy any one complimentary
PIZZA when a second PIZZA of
equal or greater value is purchased
- maximum discount $15.**
Delivery Excluded.

**Promotion valid now thru 12/30/2017**
See reverse side for additional conditions or restrictions.          **B82**

---

## UP TO $5 VALUE

www.rollinsmokebarbeque.com

**Enjoy $5 off any purchase of $15 or
more.**

**Promotion valid now thru 12/30/2017**
See reverse side for additional conditions or restrictions.          **B83**

---

## UP TO $9 VALUE

**Enjoy one FREE ENTREE when a
second ENTREE of equal or greater
value is purchased  - maximum
discount $9.**
Dine in only.

**Promotion valid now thru 12/30/2017**
See reverse side for additional conditions or restrictions.          **B84**

---

## UP TO $8 VALUE

www.thaistreetcafevegas.com

**Enjoy one FREE ENTREE when a
second ENTREE of equal or greater
value is purchased  - maximum
discount $8.**
Excludes quick lunch set. Dine in only.

**Promotion valid now thru 12/30/2017**
See reverse side for additional conditions or restrictions.          **B85**

---

## UP TO $11 VALUE

# Klub Deens African Cuisine

**Enjoy one FREE ENTREE when a
second ENTREE of equal or greater
value is purchased  - maximum
discount $11.**
Dine in only.

**Promotion valid now thru 12/30/2017**
See reverse side for additional conditions or restrictions.          **B86**

---

## UP TO $19 VALUE

YOUR 24-HOUR NEIGHBORHOOD IRISH PUB

**Enjoy one complimentary ENTREE
when a second ENTREE of equal or
greater value is purchased  -
maximum discount $19.**
Dine in only. May subject to 18% gratuity.

**Promotion valid now thru 12/30/2017**
See reverse side for additional conditions or restrictions.          **B87**

# Rollin Smoke Barbeque

- Smokin Sides.
- Open 7 days.
- Southern Style Barbeque.
- Seafood Platter.
- Spare Ribs, Brisket, Pork, Chicken and Hot Links.
- Party Packs and Catering Available.

3185 S Highland Dr
Las Vegas, NV
(702)836-3621

# Bistro Pizza

- Every item cooked to order!
- Stromboli, calzones & pizza
- Dine in, Take out or Delivery
- Appetizers, salads, entrees, sandwiches

55 S Gibson Rd Ste 112
Henderson, NV
(702)558-7330

# Thai St. Cafe

- Authentic Thai Food
- No MSG
- Dine In, Take Out & Delivery
- Lunch Specials
- No MSG.
- Authentic Thai Food.

3137 Industrial Rd
Las Vegas, NV
(702)462-9944

# SNS Diner

- Everything fresh & homemade!
- Breakfast & Lunch.
- Smoked meat so delicious…you don't need bbq sauce!
- Saturdays 10am - 2pm.
- Omelets, Pancakes, Burgers, Ribs, Briskets, Pulled Pork, Chicken and Homemade Desserts.
- Mon - Fri 10am - 4pm.

1100 E Colton Ave
North Las Vegas, NV
(702)269-9696

# Three Angry Wives Pub

- Open daily for breakfast, lunch & dinner
- Burgers, chicken & sandwiches
- Omelettes, french toast, steak & eggs
- Soups, salads & starters
- Dinner specialties include BBQ pork ribs, corned beef & cabbage, fish & chips, New York steaks, shepard's pie & much more!
- Video gaming & fun all the time!

8820 W Charleston Blvd
(@ Rampart in the Boca Park Plaza)
Las Vegas, NV
(702)944-4411

# Klub Deens African Cuisine

- Catering
- Authentic African & Caribbean Food
- Happy Hour Sunday
- DJ Friday & Saturday Nights

953 E Sahara Ave Ste E22
Las Vegas, NV
(702)927-1116

## UP TO $13 VALUE

www.greendachalv.com

**Enjoy one FREE ENTREE when a second ENTREE of equal or greater value is purchased - maximum discount $13.**

Dine in only.

**Promotion valid now thru 12/30/2017**
See reverse side for additional conditions or restrictions.    **B88**

## UP TO $14 VALUE

Lefty's Pizza South

www.leftyslv.com

**Enjoy one FREE PIZZA when a second PIZZA of equal or greater value is purchased - maximum discount $14.**

**Promotion valid now thru 12/30/2017**
See reverse side for additional conditions or restrictions.    **B89**

## UP TO $14 VALUE

www.northstarbarandgrill.com

**Enjoy one complimentary ENTREE when a second ENTREE of equal or greater value is purchased - maximum discount $14.**

Dine in only.

**Promotion valid now thru 12/30/2017**
See reverse side for additional conditions or restrictions.    **B90**

## UP TO $9 VALUE

**Enjoy one FREE ENTREE when a second ENTREE of equal or greater value is purchased - maximum discount $9.**

Dine in only.

**Promotion valid now thru 12/30/2017**
See reverse side for additional conditions or restrictions.    **B91**

## UP TO $5 VALUE

# Thai Kitchen @ Red Label

**Enjoy one FREE ENTREE when a second ENTREE of equal or greater value is purchased - maximum discount $5.**

Specials Excluded. Dine in only.

**Promotion valid now thru 12/30/2017**
See reverse side for additional conditions or restrictions.    **B92**

## UP TO $8 VALUE

www.curryzen.com

**Enjoy one FREE ENTREE when a second ENTREE of equal or greater value is purchased - maximum discount $8.**

Dine in only.

**Promotion valid now thru 12/30/2017**
See reverse side for additional conditions or restrictions.    **B93**

# Lefty's Pizza South

- New York & Chicago Style Food
- Dine In, Carryout or Delivery
- Specialty Pizzas, Calzone, Stromboli, Pasta Dinners
- Hot & Cold Sandwiches, Rib Dinners, Salads
- Catering available

780 E Pyle Ave
(At Pollock)
Las Vegas, NV
(702)614-8575

# Green Dacha Grill & Hookah

- Seafood, kebabs, soups, meat platters and Russian style beef stew
- Private events and birthday parties available
- Open daily
- Serving breakfast, lunch & dinner
- Great Russian, Mediterranean, Ukrainian Cuisine

5795 W Tropicana Ave
Las Vegas, NV
(702)485-4945

# Off The Hook Fish N' Chips

- Deep fried desserts
- Calamari, Prawns, and Scallops
- Best Fish N Chips in town!
- Open daily
- Made with quality and fresh ingredients

4155 S Buffalo Dr
Las Vegas, NV
(702)222-3474

# North Star Bar & Grill

- Open 24 hours, 7 days a week
- Sandwiches, burgers, pizza & breakfast
- Pool tables, 60" high def tv screens
- We are your local tavern!

5150 Camino Al Norte
N Las Vegas, NV
(702)642-4690

# Zen Curry House Express

- Appetizers & Desserts
- Beer, Wine & Sake
- Japanese Curry Dishes.

7835 S Rainbow Blvd Ste 9
Las Vegas, NV
(702)912-4404

# Thai Kitchen @ Red Label

- Catering
- Open Late
- Authentic Thai Cuisine

332 W Sahara Ave
Las Vegas, NV
(702)818-3008

# Northside Nathan's Detroit Pizza

- Family Friendly Restaurant
- Dine In, Take Out or Delivery
- Old Fashioned Detroit Deep Dish Pizza
- Appetizers, Salads, Pastas, and Subs.
- Kid's Menu
- Open Daily

7531 West Lake Mead Blvd., Suite 120
Las Vegas, NV
(702)255-8822

# Huntridge Pharmacy & Soda Fountain

- Burgers, wraps, sandwiches, salads, pizza, pasta, shakes and much more
- A vegetarian restaurant with a 50s twist!
- Breakfast served all day
- Catering available
- Closed Saturdays
- Featuring Thrifty ice cream

1144 E Charleston Blvd
(E Charleston & Maryland)
Las Vegas, NV
(702)382-7373

# Truffles N Bacon Cafe

- Just great food and great service!
- Catering available
- Homemade salads, soups, appetizers, sandwiches, and entrees
- Open daily
- A unique and delicious restaurant
- Freshly baked scones

8872 S Eastern Ave Ste 100
Las Vegas, NV
(702)503-1102

# Verona Pizza

- Pizzas, Strombolis & Pastas
- Family Specials
- Great Food, Good Deals
- Sun.-Wed. 11 a.m.-11 p.m.
- Burgers, Sandwiches, Fish & Chips, Appetizers & much more
- We Deliver
- Fri.-Sat. 11 a.m.-2 a.m.
- Thurs. 11 a.m.-12 p.m.

710 E Flamingo Rd
Las Vegas, NV
(702)796-7333

# Ohjah Japanese Steakhouse

- Full bar
- Open daily 3 p.m.-11 p.m.
- Fresh sushi, Habachi grills, and Teppanyaki tables
- Chef's specialties

| 10144 W Flamingo Rd Suite C3 Las Vegas, NV (702)868-2888 | 2051 N Rainbow Blvd Ste 102 Las Vegas, NV (702)361-8888 | 8595 S Decatur Blvd Ste 102 Las Vegas, NV (702)868-9888 |

# Jerusalem Grill

- Voted Las Vegas' #1 Mediterranean Grill 2 years in a row
- 5 minutes from Las Vegas Strip
- Catering & Shabbath Meals Available
- Family owned restaurant serving home-style Israeli cuisine
- In House Pita & Laffa Bread Bakery
- Sun-Thur 11am-10pm
- Friday 10am-Sun Down

4825 W Flamingo Rd Suite 67
Las Vegas, NV
(702)341-5555

## UP TO $8 VALUE

**Enjoy one FREE ENTREE when a second ENTREE of equal or greater value is purchased - maximum discount $8.**

Dine in only.

**Promotion valid now thru 12/30/2017**
See reverse side for additional conditions or restrictions. **B100**

---

## UP TO $10 VALUE

www.cubacafelv.com

**Enjoy one complimentary MENU ITEM when a second MENU ITEM of equal or greater value is purchased - maximum discount $10.**

Tipping should be 15 - 20% of the total bill before discount. Dine in only.

**Promotion valid now thru 12/30/2017**
See reverse side for additional conditions or restrictions. **B101**

---

## UP TO $12 VALUE

# Cazino Cafe, Lounge & Gallery

**Enjoy one FREE DINNER ENTREE when a second DINNER ENTREE of equal or greater value is purchased - maximum discount $12.**

Dine in only.

**Promotion valid now thru 12/30/2017**
See reverse side for additional conditions or restrictions. **B102**

---

## UP TO $14 VALUE

**grinders** PIZZA LOUNGE

www.GrindersPizzaLounge.com

**Enjoy one FREE PIZZA when a second PIZZA of equal or greater value is purchased - maximum discount $14.**

Dine in only.

**Promotion valid now thru 12/30/2017**
See reverse side for additional conditions or restrictions. **B103**

---

## UP TO $10 VALUE

**Enjoy one FREE PIZZA when a second PIZZA of equal or greater value is purchased - maximum discount $10.**

Delivery excluded.

**Promotion valid now thru 12/30/2017**
See reverse side for additional conditions or restrictions. **B104**

---

## $5 OFF

www.tgifridays.com

**$5 OFF your Food Purchase of $15 or more.**

Must present coupon at time of ordering. Coupon is non-transferable. Not replaceable if lost or stolen. One time use only. Valid on regular priced items only. One coupon per table, per visit. Not valid in conjunction with any other coupon, promotion, or discount, including Value menu offers, Bar & Late Night specials, and endless offers. Limited time only. No substitutions. No cash value. No photocopies accepted. Unless required by law, coupon cannot be redeemed for cash. Alcohol, tax and gratuity not included.

**CODE: ENT $5OFF$15**

**Promotion valid now thru 12/30/2017**
See reverse side for additional conditions or restrictions. **B105**

# Cuba Cafe

- Specialty sandwiches
- Private parties up to 30 people
- Outdoor seating
- Beer & wine
- Delicious shakes & coffees
- Popular Cuban dishes
- Catering up to 80 people
- Lunch & dinner
- Take out available

2055 E Tropicana Ave
(Between Eastern & Spencer)
Las Vegas, NV
(702)795-7070

# Andale Fresh Food

- Daily specials
- Authentic Mexican & Salvadoran Food
- Breakfast, lunch & dinner
- Open 7 days
- Homemade Menudo

2185 E Windmill Ln Ste 200
Las Vegas, NV
(702)260-0585

# Grinders Pizza Lounge

- Dough made fresh daily--No such thing as day old bread!
- Catering.
- Dine In, Take Out and Delivery.
- Pizza by the Slice.
- Pizza, Sandwiches and Salads.

5625 S Rainbow Blvd Ste E
Las Vegas, NV
(702)293-5800

# Cazino Cafe, Lounge & Gallery

- Amazing Ethiopian Fusion Food.
- Open Nightly from 5pm.
- Vegan & Vegetarian Dishes.
- Good Music & Art

5150 Spring Mountain Rd
Las Vegas, NV
(702)381-2106

Offer valid in U.S. only participating locations in CA, AZ, NV, CT: Manchester, Newington, Orange, Hamden; NJ: Linden, Clifton, Flemington, East Windsor, East Hanover, Hazlet, Old Bridge, Wood-Ridge, Morganville, North Brunswick, Freehold, West Orange, Springfield, Piscataway, Hamilton, Bayonne; NY: Bronx, Staten Island, Yonkers.

© 2016 TGIFridays, Inc.

# Italiano's 2 for 1 Pizza

- Italian & Mediterranean Food
- Try Our Family Trays!
- Catering
- Dine In, Carry Out & Delivery

750 E Pyle Ave
Las Vegas, NV
(702)260-1042

**UP TO $15 VALUE**

# La Bocce Pizzeria

www.LaBoccePizza.com

**Enjoy one FREE PIZZA when a second PIZZA of equal or greater value is purchased - maximum discount $15.**

Specials Excluded. Delivery Excluded.

**Promotion valid now thru 12/30/2017**
See reverse side for additional conditions or restrictions.  **B106**

---

**UP TO $7 VALUE**

**Shawarma Plus**
Mediterranean Cuisine

www.shawarmaplusnv.com

**Enjoy one FREE ENTREE when a second ENTREE of equal or greater value is purchased - maximum discount $7.**

**Promotion valid now thru 12/30/2017**
See reverse side for additional conditions or restrictions.  **B107**

---

**UP TO $10 VALUE**

**THE HAMMER**
PUB · GRUB · PLAY

www.thehammerbar.com

**Enjoy one complimentary ENTREE when a second ENTREE of equal or greater value is purchased - maximum discount $10.**

Dine in only.

**Promotion valid now thru 12/30/2017**
See reverse side for additional conditions or restrictions.  **B108**

---

**UP TO $8 VALUE**

NEVADA CHICKEN CAFE

**Enjoy one complimentary MENU ITEM when a second MENU ITEM of equal or greater value is purchased - maximum discount $8.**

Delivery excluded.

**Promotion valid now thru 12/30/2017**
See reverse side for additional conditions or restrictions.  **B109**

---

**UP TO $8 VALUE**

COTTAGE CAFE

**Enjoy one complimentary LUNCH OR DINNER ENTREE when a second LUNCH OR DINNER ENTREE of equal or greater value is purchased - maximum discount $8.**

Dine in only.

**Promotion valid now thru 12/30/2017**
See reverse side for additional conditions or restrictions.  **B110**

---

**UP TO $7 VALUE**

50'S Diner

**Omelet House**

**Enjoy one complimentary BREAKFAST or LUNCH ENTREE when a second BREAKFAST or LUNCH ENTREE of equal or greater value is purchased - maximum discount $7.**

Specials excluded. Dine in only.

**Promotion valid now thru 12/30/2017**
See reverse side for additional conditions or restrictions.  **B111**

# Shawarma Plus

- Catering Available
- Vegetarian & Vegan Food
- Gyro, Sandwiches and Entrée Combos
- Quality Food with Fresh Ingredients
- Authentic Mediterranean Cuisine
- Open Daily

6530 S Decatur Blvd
Las Vegas, NV
(702)220-5499

# La Bocce Pizzeria

- Buffalo Classic Beef on Weck
- Delivery & Catering Available
- Halal
- Italian - American - Greek Cuisine
- Fresh Made Subs & Gyros
- Buffalo & NYC Style Pizza & Calzones
- Mon-Sun 9:30am-1am

310 E Warm Springs Rd Ste B
Las Vegas, NV
(702)262-7222

# Nevada Chicken Cafe

- Rotisserie & mesquite grilled chicken
- Family style meals
- Gourmet sandwiches, wraps, burgers, baby back ribs
- Let us cater your next event
- Side orders, soups, desserts and more
- Mon-Sat 10:30am - 9pm
- Eat good, eat fresh, eat healthy
- Sun 11am - 7pm
- Freshed tossed salads
- Fresh tossed salads

6155 W Sahara Ave
(SW Corner of Jones)
Las Vegas, NV
(702)889-4800

# The Hammer Bar & Grill

- Video Poker
- Full Bar
- HD TVs to watch your favorite sports
- Come try some of our American classics including burgers, sandwiches and salads

3990 W Russell Rd
(Russell & Valley View)
Las Vegas, NV
(702)597-1550

# 50's Diner Omelet House

- Omelets, French Toasts and Pancakes
- Burgers, Sandwiches, Soups and Salads
- Breakfast & Lunch
- Open 7 days

3050 E Desert Inn Rd
Las Vegas, NV
(702)737-0377

# Cottage Cafe

- Beef, chicken, lamb, trout & vegetarian dishes
- All entrees are offered at the heat level of your choice
- Authentic Ethiopian cuisine
- We offer a wide variety of refreshments including honey wine, domestic beer, espresso, coffee, tea & more
- Open daily

4647 Paradise Rd
(Between Harmon & Tropicana)
Las Vegas, NV
(702)650-3395

## FREE WITH PURCHASE

www.elmescalrestaurant.com

### Enjoy one FREE APPETIZER with purchase of an ENTREE.
Dine in only.

**Promotion valid now thru 12/30/2017**
See reverse side for additional conditions or restrictions.    **B112**

---

## UP TO $17 VALUE

www.BuonGustoLV.com

### Enjoy one FREE ENTREE when a second ENTREE of equal or greater value is purchased - maximum discount $17.
Specials Excluded. Dine in only.

**Promotion valid now thru 12/30/2017**
See reverse side for additional conditions or restrictions.    **B113**

---

## UP TO $8 VALUE

### Enjoy one complimentary MENU ITEM when a second MENU ITEM of equal or greater value is purchased - maximum discount $8.
Dine in only. All-you-can-eat excluded.

**Promotion valid now thru 12/30/2017**
See reverse side for additional conditions or restrictions.    **B114**

---

## UP TO $14 VALUE

### Enjoy one FREE LUNCH OR DINNER ENTREE when a second LUNCH OR DINNER ENTREE of equal or greater value is purchased - maximum discount $14.
Dine in only.

**Promotion valid now thru 12/30/2017**
See reverse side for additional conditions or restrictions.    **B115**

---

## UP TO $16 VALUE

www.SouthernStyleEatery.com

### Enjoy one FREE ENTREE when a second ENTREE of equal or greater value is purchased - maximum discount $16.
Dine in only.

**Promotion valid now thru 12/30/2017**
See reverse side for additional conditions or restrictions.    **B116**

---

## UP TO $13 VALUE

papapinnyspizzeria.com

### Enjoy one FREE PIZZA when a second PIZZA of equal or greater value is purchased - maximum discount $13.
Dine in only. Specials excluded.

**Promotion valid now thru 12/30/2017**
See reverse side for additional conditions or restrictions.    **B117**

# Buon Gusto Ristorante

- As featured on Food Network.
- Lunch specials.
- New York style pizza.
- Family owned & operated.
- Catering available.
- Serving beer & wine.
- Authentic homemade Italian cuisine in a casual environment.

2642 W Horizon Ridge Pkwy Ste A2
Henderson, NV
(702)407-6600

# El Mescal

- Come try our authentic homemade food and it will transport you to Mexico!
- Fresh seafood dishes along with some favorites like fajitas, tacos, and enchiladas.
- Open daily.
- Happy Hour everyday.
- We have lunch and dinner combinations or join us for breakfast.
- Full bar with delicious margaritas!

4460 S Durango Dr Ste H
(W Flamingo & S Durango)
Las Vegas, NV
(702)834-3702

# Mickie Finnz Las Vegas

425 Fremont St
Las Vegas, NV
(702)382-4204

# Extreme Sushi

- Curry dishes
- Appetizers
- Combo meals
- Noodle soup
- Salads
- Ala Carte sushi bar & all you can eat
- Rice bowls

10670 Southern Highlands Pkwy
(Inside Smith's shpg. Ctr.)
Las Vegas, NV
(702)437-8744

# Papa Pinny's Pizzeria

- Dine in, carry out and delivery
- Specialty pizzas, pastas, chicken and much more
- Children's menu available
- Large TVs for sports watching
- Beer and wine

8125 W Sahara Ave
Las Vegas, NV
(702)979-9222

# Southern Style Eatery

- Breakfast, Lunch & Dinner.
- Family & Kids Menu.
- Grilled or Fried…Your Choice!
- Catering.
- Open 8am - 10pm Daily.
- Direct from Louisiana!
- Seafood, Po-Boys, Burgers, and Southern Style Specials.

450 S Buffalo Dr Suite 114115
Las Vegas, NV
(702)545-0005

### UP TO $13 VALUE

PIZZA, WINGS & THINGS

**Enjoy one FREE PIZZA when a second PIZZA of equal or greater value is purchased - maximum discount $13.**

Delivery excluded.

**Promotion valid now thru 12/30/2017**
See reverse side for additional conditions or restrictions.     **B118**

---

### UP TO $16 VALUE

**DYNAMITE GRILL** ™

www.dynamitegrill.com

**Enjoy one FREE ENTREE when a second ENTREE of equal or greater value is purchased - maximum discount $16.**

Dine in only.

**Promotion valid now thru 12/30/2017**
See reverse side for additional conditions or restrictions.     **B119**

---

### UP TO $9 VALUE

# ESPRESSO KING KAFE

www.espressoking.com

**Enjoy one FREE ENTREE when a second ENTREE of equal or greater value is purchased - maximum discount $9.**

Dine in only.

**Promotion valid now thru 12/30/2017**
See reverse side for additional conditions or restrictions.     **B120**

---

### UP TO $10 VALUE

**Ginseng II**
Korean B.B.Q. Restaurant

www.ginsengbbq.com

**Enjoy one complimentary ENTREE when a second ENTREE of equal or greater value is purchased - maximum discount $10.**

Dine in only.

**Promotion valid now thru 12/30/2017**
See reverse side for additional conditions or restrictions.     **B121**

---

### UP TO $10 VALUE

HAMMER & ALES

www.hammeralesvegas.com

**Enjoy one FREE ENTREE when a second ENTREE of equal or greater value is purchased - maximum discount $10.**

**Promotion valid now thru 12/30/2017**
See reverse side for additional conditions or restrictions.     **B122**

---

### UP TO $14 VALUE

Pizza My Dear

www.pizzamydear.com

**Enjoy one FREE PIZZA when a second PIZZA of equal or greater value is purchased - maximum discount $14.**

**Promotion valid now thru 12/30/2017**
See reverse side for additional conditions or restrictions.     **B123**

# Dynamite Grill

- Hibachi & sushi
- Come dine and meet the World Series of Poker 2007 Winner!
- Open daily

10450 Decatur Blvd Ste 105
Las Vegas, NV
(702)399-9100

# Above the Crust Pizza

- Open 7 days.
- Calzones & Strombolis.
- Salads & Subs.
- New York Style Thin Crust.
- Dine In, Pick Up & Delivery.

7810 W Ann Rd
Las Vegas, NV
(702)749-7500

# Ginseng 2 Korean BBQ Restaurant

- House Specialties
- Open 24 Hours
- Hot Pot Dishes
- Full Bar
- Come try our authentic Korean BBQ!

3765 Las Vegas Blvd S
(Across from Monte Carlo Hotel & Casino & behind Walgreens)
Las Vegas, NV
(702)891-8403

# Espresso King Kafe

- All American Fare including Salads, Pizza, Sandwiches, Wraps and much more!
- Serving Breakfast, Lunch & Dinner.
- Dine In, Take Out or Delivery.
- Catering Available.

955 Grier Dr Ste D
Las Vegas, NV
(702)462-2433

# Pizza My Dear

- Catering
- Family & lunch specials
- Free Delivery (4 mile radius)
- Appetizers, salads, pastas, pizzas, and more!

1725 E Warm Springs Rd Ste 9
(Warm Springs & Spencer)
Las Vegas, NV
(702)368-3327

9320 W Flamingo Rd Ste 2
Las Vegas, NV
(702)435-3327

# Hammer & Ales

- American Classics including Burgers, Sandwiches & Salads
- Video Poker.
- HD TVs to Watch your Favorite Sports
- Full Bar.

3990 W Russell Rd Ste 1
Las Vegas, NV
(702)597-1550

## UP TO **50%** OFF

### *Anthony & Mario's* Broadway Pizzeria
*Authentic New York Pizza*

**Enjoy any one PIZZA at 50% off the regular price.**
Dine-in or carry out.

**Promotion valid now thru 12/30/2017**
See reverse side for additional conditions or restrictions.          **B124**

---

## UP TO **$5** VALUE

www.BarcelonaTapas-Bar.com

**Enjoy one complimentary TAPAS when a second TAPAS of equal or greater value is purchased - maximum discount $5.**
Excludes Happy Hour. Dine in only.

**Promotion valid now thru 12/30/2017**
See reverse side for additional conditions or restrictions.          **B125**

---

## UP TO **$25** VALUE

www.LaylaLV.com

**Enjoy 25% off the TOTAL BILL - maximum discount $25.**
Dine in only.

**Promotion valid now thru 12/30/2017**
See reverse side for additional conditions or restrictions.          **B126**

---

## UP TO **$5** VALUE

www.yassoulv.com

**Enjoy one FREE MENU ITEM when a second MENU ITEM of equal or greater value is purchased - maximum discount $5.**

**Promotion valid now thru 12/30/2017**
See reverse side for additional conditions or restrictions.          **B127**

---

## UP TO **$25** VALUE

www.MosRaceDayCafe.com

**Enjoy 25% off the TOTAL BILL - maximum discount $25.**
Dine in only.

**Promotion valid now thru 12/30/2017**
See reverse side for additional conditions or restrictions.          **B128**

---

## UP TO **$7** VALUE

www.IwantTiabi.com

**Enjoy one FREE ENTREE when a second ENTREE of equal or greater value is purchased - maximum discount $7.**
Specials Excluded. Dine in only.

**Promotion valid now thru 12/30/2017**
See reverse side for additional conditions or restrictions.          **B129**

# Barcelona Tapas & Bar

- Full Bar
- Try our homemade sangria & mojito
- Live band on weekends
- Open daily
- Hot, cold, seafood & meat tapas
- Entrees and desserts
- Happy hour Mon - Sat
- Join us for Football Sundays - $20 per person for all-you-can-eat and 2 drinks

10690 Southern Highlands Pkwy
Las Vegas, NV
(702)483-5764

# Broadway Pizzeria

- Catering Available
- Daily Lunch & Dinner Specials
- Cheese Sicilian
- Home of the Garlic Knot
- Vegetarian Special
- Hawaiian Special
- We Deliver

840 S Rancho Dr
(Rancho & Charleston)
Las Vegas, NV
(702)259-9002

# Yassou Greek Grill Cafe

- ·· Side orders include 2 kinds of fries, hummus, Saganaki, Dolmades, Tzatziki & more
- Sun 11am – 5pm
- ·· Gyros, chicken & steak Souvlaki, Spanakopita, pizzas, sandwiches, vegetarian plates & salads
- Family owned & operated
- Mon – Sat 11am – 8pm
- Baklava & rice pudding

7871 W Charleston Blvd
Las Vegas, NV
(702)798-8989

# Layla Grill & Hookah

- Desserts
- Salads
- Quality Restaurant & Lounge
- Sandwiches
- Appetizers
- Entrees
- Full Bar

8665 W Flamingo Rd Ste 107
(W Flamingo & Durango)
Las Vegas, NV
(702)202-4930

# Tiabi Coffee & Waffle Bar

- Breakfast & Lunch.
- Open 7 days.
- Waffles, Sandwiches & Desserts.
- Gluten Free & Vegan Options.
- Smoothies, Coffee & Tea.

3961 S Maryland Pkwy
Las Vegas, NV
(702)222-1722

# Mo's Race Day Cafe

- All American Fare
- Catering & Banquet Room
- Breakfast & Lunch
- Mon - Fri 7am - 4pm, Sat 9am - 3pm
- Extended hours during events

6825 Speedway Blvd Unit 101a
Las Vegas, NV
(702)632-1011

**UP TO $8 VALUE**

**Enjoy one complimentary ENTREE when a second ENTREE of equal or greater value is purchased - maximum discount $8.**

Dine in only.

**Promotion valid now thru 12/30/2017**
See reverse side for additional conditions or restrictions.     **B130**

**UP TO $10 VALUE**

www.tasteofchinalv.com

**Enjoy one FREE ENTREE when a second ENTREE of equal or greater value is purchased - maximum discount $10.**

Specials Excluded. Dine in only.

**Promotion valid now thru 12/30/2017**
See reverse side for additional conditions or restrictions.     **B131**

**UP TO $8 VALUE**

www.nakedcitylv.com

**Enjoy one complimentary MENU ITEM when a second MENU ITEM of equal or greater value is purchased - maximum discount $8.**

**Promotion valid now thru 12/30/2017**
See reverse side for additional conditions or restrictions.     **B132**

**UP TO $9 VALUE**

www.theculinaryacademy.org

**Enjoy one FREE BUFFET when a second BUFFET of equal or greater value is purchased - maximum discount $9.**

Dine in only.

**Promotion valid now thru 12/30/2017**
See reverse side for additional conditions or restrictions.     **B133**

**UP TO $13 VALUE**

www.vits-pizza.com

**Enjoy any one complimentary PIZZA when a second PIZZA of equal or greater value is purchased - maximum discount $13.**

Present coupon/card before ordering. Delivery excluded.

**Promotion valid now thru 12/30/2017**
See reverse side for additional conditions or restrictions.     **B134**

**UP TO $11 VALUE**

www.whatsuptups.com

**Enjoy one FREE ENTREE when a second ENTREE of equal or greater value is purchased - maximum discount $11.**

**Promotion valid now thru 12/30/2017**
See reverse side for additional conditions or restrictions.     **B135**

# Taste of China & Icy Bar

- Most Authentic Chinese Cuisine in Town!
- Party Trays and Catering
- Vegetarian dishes available
- Open daily
- Enjoy a refreshment and cool treats in our Icy Bar

4180 S Jones Blvd Ste 1
Las Vegas, NV
(702)527-6738

# Island Bar & Grill

- Burgers, sandwiches, pizza & breakfast
- Open 7 days a week
- We are your local tavern!

2660 S Maryland Pkwy
Las Vegas, NV
(702)737-1966

# Westside Bistro

- Buffet features freshly made soups, salads, entrees, and just-baked desserts.
- Open Monday-Friday, 11 a.m.-2 p.m
- Full-service restaurant serving seasonal cuisine

710 W Lake Mead Blvd
N Las Vegas, NV
(702)924-2115

# The Naked City Pizza Shop

- Carry out or delivery
- Sun-Thurs 11am - 10pm
- Home of the "Frickin Huge" pizza
- Starters, pastas, hot & cold subs, salads, chicken and desserts
- Buffalo, NY style pizza & wings
- Fri-Sat 11am - 11pm

3240 Arville St
(Corner of Desert Inn & Arville, inside Moondoggies Bar)
Las Vegas, NV
(702)243-6277

# Tups' Specialty Sandwiches

- Fresh & quality ingredients
- Catering
- Soups & salads
- Dine in or take out
- Paninis & sandwiches

2381 E Windmill Ln Ste 24
Las Vegas, NV
(702)776-8828

# Vit's Pizza

- Daily specials
- Open 7 days
- Pizzas
- Sandwiches
- Dine In, Pick Up & Delivery
- Appetizers
- Made to order salads
- Baked specialties

3390 Novat St
(Off of 215 & Cheyenne in Lone Mountain Village)
Las Vegas, NV
(702)242-8487

## UP TO $5 VALUE

### THAI PEPPER
Restaurant

www.thaipeppervegas.com

**Enjoy one FREE DINNER ENTREE when a second DINNER ENTREE of equal or greater value is purchased - maximum discount $5.**

Dine in only.

**Promotion valid now thru 12/30/2017**
See reverse side for additional conditions or restrictions. **B136**

---

## UP TO $15 VALUE

### brentwood
CAFE & TAVERN

**Enjoy one FREE ENTREE when a second ENTREE of equal or greater value is purchased - maximum discount $15.**

Dine in only.

**Promotion valid now thru 12/30/2017**
See reverse side for additional conditions or restrictions. **B137**

---

## UP TO $15 VALUE

### RED ROCK PIZZA
It's So Good!

**Enjoy one PIZZA at 50% OFF when a second PIZZA of equal or greater value is purchased - maximum discount $15.**

Delivery excluded.

**Promotion valid now thru 12/30/2017**
See reverse side for additional conditions or restrictions. **B138**

---

## $10 OFF

**$10 off any purchase of $30 or more. Valid for food, non-alcoholic beverage or merchandise.**

Minimum purchase of $30 required excluding tax and gratuity. Not valid with any other offers or discounts. One coupon per visit, per table. Unauthorized internet distribution, replication or resale is strictly prohibited. No cash value or return. Excludes banquet and group menus, alcohol and purchase of gift cards. Valid at participating Planet Hollywood locations. Valid for Dine In or To Go. Expires 12/31/2017.

**Promotion valid now thru 12/30/2017**
See reverse side for additional conditions or restrictions. **B139**

---

## UP TO $5 VALUE

### Tasty Island
Jamaican Restaurant

www.TastyIslandLv.com

**Enjoy one complimentary MENU ITEM when a second MENU ITEM of equal or greater value is purchased - maximum discount $5.**

Excludes Lunch Specials.

**Promotion valid now thru 12/30/2017**
See reverse side for additional conditions or restrictions. **B140**

---

## UP TO $13 VALUE

### Mad Matty's
CASINO

www.madmattyslv.com

**Enjoy one FREE ENTREE when a second ENTREE of equal or greater value is purchased - maximum discount $13.**

Dine in only.

**Promotion valid now thru 12/30/2017**
See reverse side for additional conditions or restrictions. **B141**

## Brentwood Cafe & Tavern

- Dinner Specials.
- Breakfast served all day.
- Catering available.
- Pizza, Salads, Burgers, Sandwiches.

7325 W Warm Springs Rd
(W. Warm Springs & Tenaya)
Las Vegas, NV
(702)656-3000

## Thai Pepper Restaurant

- Lunch specials.
- Traditional Thai cuisine.
- Dine in, Take out and Delivery.
- Open daily 11am - 10pm.

2226 Paradise Rd
(Corner of Sahara & Paradise, behind McDonalds)
Las Vegas, NV
(702)696-9107

13020-1080-0000

Valid at Participating Locations.

## Red Rock Pizza

- Fast delivery
- Where to go gourmet!
- Create your own pizza
- Featuring designer pizza, traditional & vegetarian

8455 W Lake Mead Blvd
Las Vegas, NV
(702)304-0400

## Mad Matty's Bar & Grill

- Large TVs.
- Delicious American favorites.
- Wide selection of spirits, wine and beer.
- Open 24 hours.

8100 W Sahara Ave
Las Vegas, NV
(702)254-9997

## Tasty Island Jamaican Restaurant

- The best authentic Jamaican food in town!
- Catering for all occasions
- Serving breakfast, lunch & dinner

6820 W Flamingo Rd Ste H
Las Vegas, NV
(702)222-0002

**UP TO $12 VALUE**

# COYOTES
## Cafe & Cantina

**Enjoy one complimentary MENU ITEM when a second MENU ITEM of equal or greater value is purchased - maximum discount $12.**

Dine in only.

**Promotion valid now thru 12/30/2017**
See reverse side for additional conditions or restrictions. **B142**

---

**UP TO $16 VALUE**

**Enjoy one complimentary LUNCH OR DINNER ENTREE when a second LUNCH OR DINNER ENTREE of equal or greater value is purchased - maximum discount $16.**

Dine in only.

**Promotion valid now thru 12/30/2017**
See reverse side for additional conditions or restrictions. **B143**

---

**UP TO $10 VALUE**

www.giannasvillapizza.com

**Enjoy one complimentary ENTREE when a second ENTREE of equal or greater value is purchased - maximum discount $10.**

Specials Excluded. Dine in only.

**Promotion valid now thru 12/30/2017**
See reverse side for additional conditions or restrictions. **B144**

---

**UP TO $8 VALUE**

www.thetangerinecafe.com

**Enjoy one FREE ENTREE when a second ENTREE of equal or greater value is purchased - maximum discount $8.**

**Promotion valid now thru 12/30/2017**
See reverse side for additional conditions or restrictions. **B145**

---

**UP TO $10 VALUE**

www.702kabob.com

**Enjoy one FREE ENTREE when a second ENTREE of equal or greater value is purchased - maximum discount $10.**

Dine in only.

**Promotion valid now thru 12/30/2017**
See reverse side for additional conditions or restrictions. **B146**

---

**UP TO $10 VALUE**

miperugrill.com

**Enjoy one FREE ENTREE when a second ENTREE of equal or greater value is purchased - maximum discount $10.**

Dine in only. Specials Excluded.

**Promotion valid now thru 12/30/2017**
See reverse side for additional conditions or restrictions. **B147**

# Hennesey's Tavern

425 Fremont St
Las Vegas, NV
(702)382-4421

# Coyote's Cafe & Cantina

• Lunch specials available
• Appetizers, soups & salads
• Tacos, enchiladas, combo plates, burritos, fajitas, chile rellenos, platillos Mexican

4350 E Sunset Rd
Henderson, NV
(702)458-3739

# The Tangerine Cafe

• Delivery & catering
• Open daily
• Panini, salads, homemade soups & more!
• Serving LAVAZZA coffee
• Breakfast available

10895 S Eastern Ave Ste 100
Henderson, NV
(702)407-8118

# Gianna's Pizza

• Dine- in, pick up & delivery
• Beer & wine, catering available
• Come check out our daily happy hour 2-5pm
• Your neighborhood family restaurant

3620 W Sahara Ave
Las Vegas, NV
(702)368-0368

# Mi Peru South American Grill

• Since 2008.
• …It's your turn!
• The World has already discovered the wonderful Peruvian Cuisine!
• Open daily.
• Steak, Seafood, Chicken & Pasta Meals.

1450 W Horizon Ridge Pkwy Ste B314
(Just off I-215 Exit Stephanie; in Foothills Plaza)
Henderson, NV
(702)220-4652

# Kabob Grill

• Mon - Sat 11am - 9pm
• Sun 11am - 8pm
• Pita Wraps
• Fresh & Healthy
• Vegetarian Options
• Kabob Platters
• Catering Available

9550 S Eastern Ave Ste 195
Las Vegas, NV
(702)435-2262

**UP TO $14 VALUE**

www.bostonpizzavegas.com

**Enjoy any one complimentary PIZZA when a second PIZZA of equal or greater value is purchased - maximum discount $14.**

Limit one coupon per person per day. Not valid with any other discounts or promotions.

**Promotion valid now thru 12/30/2017**
See reverse side for additional conditions or restrictions.     **B148**

---

**UP TO $9 VALUE**

**Enjoy one FREE ENTREE when a second ENTREE of equal or greater value is purchased - maximum discount $9.**

Dine in only.

**Promotion valid now thru 12/30/2017**
See reverse side for additional conditions or restrictions.     **B149**

---

**UP TO $13 VALUE**

www.codyssmokinbbq.com

**Enjoy one FREE ENTREE when a second ENTREE of equal or greater value is purchased - maximum discount $13.**

Bulk food excluded.

**Promotion valid now thru 12/30/2017**
See reverse side for additional conditions or restrictions.     **B150**

---

**UP TO $13 VALUE**

www.IndiaMasalaLV.com

**Enjoy one FREE ENTREE when a second ENTREE of equal or greater value is purchased - maximum discount $13.**

Dine in only.

**Promotion valid now thru 12/30/2017**
See reverse side for additional conditions or restrictions.     **B151**

---

**UP TO $6 VALUE**

Authentic Mexican Food

**Enjoy one FREE ENTREE when a second ENTREE of equal or greater value is purchased - maximum discount $6.**

Specials Excluded. Dine in only.

**Promotion valid now thru 12/30/2017**
See reverse side for additional conditions or restrictions.     **B152**

---

**UP TO $9 VALUE**

Home of "THE CHEESESTEAK"
www.tripleplayamericangrill.com

**Enjoy one FREE ENTREE when a second ENTREE of equal or greater value is purchased - maximum discount $9.**

Dine in only.

**Promotion valid now thru 12/30/2017**
See reverse side for additional conditions or restrictions.     **B153**

# Biscuits 2 Burgers

- Closed Monday
- Breakfast & Lunch
- Tue - Sun 8am - 2:30pm
- Catering
- Reservations Accepted

9700 W Tropicana Ave Ste 100
(W Tropicana & Grand Canyon)
Las Vegas, NV
(702)570-6877

# Boston Pizza

- Dine In, Pick Up or Delivery
- Pizzas, Wings, Philly Cheesesteaks, Grinders & More!
- Serving Beer
- Catering available
- Open 7 days a week
- 10am to 4am

1507 Las Vegas Blvd S
Las Vegas, NV
(702)385-2595

# India Masala Bar & Grill

- Catering available.
- Lunch buffet.
- We are the only restaurant in Las Vegas to serve Southern & Northern Indian cuisine.
- Open daily: 11:30am – 3pm; 5pm-10pm
- Dine in, take out or delivery.

1040 E Flamingo Rd
Las Vegas, NV
(702)431-8313

# Cody's Smokin' BBQ

- Best BBQ in Town!
- Meats, sandwiches & combos
- Delivery & catering available
- Homemade sides

1675 Industrial Rd
Las Vegas, NV
(702)863-7252

# Triple Play American Grill

- Kids Menu
- Sandwiches
- Build A Burger
- Soups & Salads
- Signature Cheesesteaks
- Chicken Wings & Fingers

7006 W Charleston Blvd
Las Vegas, NV
(702)255-1200

# Pancho's Kitchen

- Homemade Authentic Mexican Food
- Closed Sunday
- Serving Breakfast, Lunch and Dinner
- Vegan & Vegetarian Menu
- Catering Available
- Open Mon - Sat 10am - 8pm

3655 S Durango Dr Ste 27
Las Vegas, NV
(702)370-0987

**UP TO $25 VALUE**

sunsetpizzeriaonline.com

**Enjoy 25% off the TOTAL BILL - maximum discount $25.**
Specials Excluded. Delivery Excluded.

**Promotion valid now thru 12/30/2017**
See reverse side for additional conditions or restrictions.          B154

---

**UP TO $9 VALUE**

www.theviewmexicangrill.com

**Enjoy one FREE ENTREE when a second ENTREE of equal or greater value is purchased - maximum discount $9.**
Dine in only.

**Promotion valid now thru 12/30/2017**
See reverse side for additional conditions or restrictions.          B155

---

**UP TO $13 VALUE**

# MJ Food Nigerian Cuisine

**Enjoy one FREE JOLLOF RICE DISH or PLANTAIN MEAL when a second JOLLOF RICE DISH or PLANTAIN MEAL of equal or greater value - maximum discount $13.**
Dine in only.

**Promotion valid now thru 12/30/2017**
See reverse side for additional conditions or restrictions.          B156

---

**UP TO $15 VALUE**

**Enjoy one complimentary ENTREE when a second ENTREE of equal or greater value is purchased - maximum discount $15.**
Dine in only.

**Promotion valid now thru 12/30/2017**
See reverse side for additional conditions or restrictions.          B157

---

**UP TO $9 VALUE**

www.bajabargrilllv.com

**Enjoy one FREE ENTREE when a second ENTREE of equal or greater value is purchased - maximum discount $9.**
Dine in only.

**Promotion valid now thru 12/30/2017**
See reverse side for additional conditions or restrictions.          B158

---

**UP TO $7 VALUE**

www.villapizza.com

**Enjoy any one complimentary PIZZA when a second PIZZA of equal or greater value is purchased - maximum discount $7.**
Not valid with any other discounts or promotions. Present coupon/card before ordering. This location only. Specials excluded. Dine-in or carry out.

**Promotion valid now thru 12/30/2017**
See reverse side for additional conditions or restrictions.          B159

# The View Mexican Grill

- Catering Available
- Quality Ingredients.
- Everything Homemade Daily
- Breakfast, Lunch & Dinner

3231 N Decatur Blvd Ste 101
Las Vegas, NV
(702)629-5610

# Sunset Pizzeria

- Dine In, Take out & Delivery.
- Serving beer & wine.
- Pizza, pasta, calzones, chicken, salad & much more!
- Lunch & daily specials.
- 11am - 9pm everyday.

9730 W Tropicana Ave Ste 140
(W Tropicana & Ft Apache)
Las Vegas, NV
(702)778-4444

# Janelas Restaurant & Bar

- Call for availability, certain days closed to the public
- Available for company parties, meetings, weddings & banquets
- Classy, elegant dining at affordable prices
- Come eat where Butch Harmon & all his star students enjoy their lunches
- Open for breakfast & lunch

2851 Grand Hills Dr
(S Eastern - right on Grand Hills in Seven Hills at Rio Secco Golf Club)
Henderson, NV
(702)777-2400

# Nigerian Cuisine My Joy Food

- Authentic Nigerian cuisine
- Dine in, take out or delivery
- Wine & beer

5006 South Maryland Parkway, Unit 11
Las Vegas, NV
(702)798-0303

# VILLA PIZZA

- We Deliver!
- Open 7 days
- Serving authentic New York style pizza since 1976
- Kids and Team Parties
- Serving salads, subs, pastas, pizzas, appetizers and more
- Catering Available
- Daily Lunch and Dinner Specials

3385 S Durango Dr
(Just S. of Desert Inn)
Las Vegas, NV
(702)878-7889

# Baja Bar & Grill

- Happy Hour Mon-Fri
- Home of The Fish Taco!
- Free WiFi
- Come watch your favorite sports game here!
- Beer, Wine & Tequila
- Catering Available
- Mexican Favorites

4755 S Maryland Pkwy
Las Vegas, NV
(702)736-8830

**UP TO $12 VALUE**

**ELY'S RESTAURANT**
BREAKFAST & LUNCH
elysrestaurantlv.com

**Enjoy one FREE ENTREE when a second ENTREE of equal or greater value is purchased - maximum discount $12.**

**Promotion valid now thru 12/30/2017**
See reverse side for additional conditions or restrictions.   **B160**

**UP TO $13 VALUE**

**EL PATIO MEXICO**
AUTHENTIC MEXICAN CUISINE

**Enjoy one complimentary ENTREE when a second ENTREE of equal or greater value is purchased - maximum discount $13.**

Not valid with any other discounts or promotions. Specials excluded. Dine in only.

**Promotion valid now thru 12/30/2017**
See reverse side for additional conditions or restrictions.   **B161**

---

**UP TO $10 VALUE**

— All You Can Eat B.B.Q. —
**KIMCHI**

**Enjoy $10 off any purchase of $40 or more.**
Dine in only.

**Promotion valid now thru 12/30/2017**
See reverse side for additional conditions or restrictions.   **B162**

**UP TO $13 VALUE**

*BOMAS*

**Enjoy one complimentary ENTREE when a second ENTREE of equal or greater value is purchased - maximum discount $13.**

Not valid with any other discount offer. Specials excluded. Dine in only.

**Promotion valid now thru 12/30/2017**
See reverse side for additional conditions or restrictions.   **B163**

---

**UP TO $9 VALUE**

**MANHATTAN PIZZA**
www.manhattanpizza1lv.com

**Enjoy any one complimentary PIZZA when a second PIZZA of equal or greater value is purchased - maximum discount $9.**
Carry out only.

**Promotion valid now thru 12/30/2017**
See reverse side for additional conditions or restrictions.   **B164**

**UP TO $7 VALUE**

*Salsa Loca*
MEXICAN GRILL
salsalocarestaurant.com

**Enjoy one FREE ENTREE when a second ENTREE of equal or greater value is purchased - maximum discount $7.**
Specials Excluded. Happy Hour Excluded. Dine in only.

**Promotion valid now thru 12/30/2017**
See reverse side for additional conditions or restrictions.   **B165**

# El Patio Mexico

- Authentic Mexican food
- Serving breakfast, lunch & dinner
- House specialties
- Appetizers, super burritos, tortas, tacos and much more
- Open daily from 10am to 10pm
- Full bar
- Daily specials

4550 S Maryland Pkwy
(near Harmon)
Las Vegas, NV
(702)597-1155

# Ely's Restaurant

- Breakfast, Lunch & Dinner.
- Homemade Dishes with Friendly Servers.
- Kids Meal.
- Omelets, Waffles, Burgers, Salads, & Much More!

2477 E Tropicana Avenue
Las Vegas, NV
(702)201-1115

# Bomas Bar & Grill

- 24 hour gaming and restaurant
- New BBQ menu
- Daily Happy Hour
- Daily Specials
- Come watch your favorite sports with us!
Special pricing on drinks & food

8020 S Durango Dr
(Corner of Durango & Windmill)
Las Vegas, NV
(702)361-7913

# Kimchi

- All You Can Eat BBQ
- Hot Pot Dishes
- Come try our authentic Korean BBQ!
- Open 24 Hours
- House Specialties
- Full Bar

3049 Las Vegas Blvd S
(Next to Encore Hotel & Casino)
Las Vegas, NV
(702)894-9944

# Salsa Loca Mexican Grill

- Catering
- Authentic Mexican Cuisine
- Fresh & delicious seafood, tacos, tostadas, quesadillas, burritos & salads
- Combination & children's plates

4130 S Sandhill Rd Ste A3
Las Vegas, NV
(702)383-0563

# Manhattan Pizza

- Open 7 Days
- Dine in, Pick up, Delivery & Catering
- Pizza, Wings, Pastas, Subs, Burgers and Much More
- Everyday Lunch Specials
- Home of the 28" COLOSSAL PIZZA!

8550 W Charleston Blvd
(Charleston & Durango)
Las Vegas, NV
(702)233-0490

# Fast Food & Carryout Index

FAST FOOD & CARRYOUT INDEX

# Fast Food & Carryout Index

# Get More

## Get thousands more discounts to use at home or when traveling.

Download the mobile app now, included with this membership. Search for "Entertainment® Coupons" in your app store.

www.papajohns.com

Valid at participating U.S. Locations.

## Hungry Howie's
Valid at all Participating Locations

**FREE** WITH PURCHASE

### Enjoy Free Howie Bread with any purchase of $12 or more.

Valid at participating locations. Each store is independently owned & operated. One coupon per customer per visit. Not valid with any other discount or promotion. Additional toppings are extra. Excludes delivery fee & sales tax.

www.hungryhowies.com

**Promotion valid now thru 12/30/2017**
See reverse side for additional conditions or restrictions.

C2

---

## Hungry Howie's
Valid at all Participating Locations

**BUY ONE GET ONE**

### Enjoy one FREE Medium 1 Topping Pizza with the purchase of a Medium 1 Topping Pizza at regular menu price.

Valid at participating locations. Each store is independently owned & operated. One coupon per customer per visit. Not valid with any other discount or promotion. Additional toppings are extra. Excludes delivery fee & sales tax.

www.hungryhowies.com

**Promotion valid now thru 12/30/2017**
See reverse side for additional conditions or restrictions.

C3

---

## Hungry Howie's
Valid at all Participating Locations

**SPECIAL PRICE**

### Enjoy One Large 1 Topping Pizza for just $7.99.

Valid at participating locations. Each store is independently owned & operated. One coupon per customer per visit. Not valid with any other discount or promotion. Additional toppings are extra. Excludes delivery fee & sales tax.

www.hungryhowies.com

**Promotion valid now thru 12/30/2017**
See reverse side for additional conditions or restrictions.

C4

Valid at all Participating Locations

0000001S46V

This promotional offer is not valid on any other discount/promotion or on defined holidays. See Rules of Use for more details. Offer valid at all participating locations. Excludes tax, tip, alcohol, and some sale items.

Valid at all Participating Locations

0000001S452

This promotional offer is not valid on any other discount/promotion or on defined holidays. See Rules of Use for more details. Offer valid at all participating locations. Excludes tax, tip, alcohol, and some sale items.

Valid at all Participating Locations

0000001S450

This promotional offer is not valid on any other discount/promotion or on defined holidays. See Rules of Use for more details. Offer valid at all participating locations. Excludes tax, tip, alcohol, and some sale items.

# EAT LIKE YOU MEAN IT®

**Made from Scratch Biscuits™ &
Thickburgers® served on Fresh Baked Buns**

---

**Enjoy a FREE SAUSAGE BISCUIT with the purchase of a SAUSAGE BISCUIT at regular price.**

Served during breakfast hours. Offer not available with Combo purchase. Sales tax not included. Oregon is exempt from sales tax. One coupon per customer per visit. Limit one discount per coupon. Not valid with any other offer, discount or combo. Price and participation may vary. Coupon may not be transferred, auctioned, sold or duplicated in any way or transmitted via electronic media. Not for resale. ©2016 Carl's Jr. Restaurants LLC, Inc. All rights reserved.

**Coupon Code: 7734**

 **Promotion valid now thru 12/30/2017**
See reverse side for additional conditions or restrictions.

---

**Enjoy a FREE SMALL BEVERAGE & SMALL FRY with the purchase of any THICKBURGER® at regular price.**

Offer not available with Combo purchase. Sales tax not included. Oregon is exempt from sales tax. One coupon per customer per visit. Limit one discount per coupon. Not valid with any other offer, discount or combo. Price and participation may vary. Coupon may not be transferred, auctioned, sold or duplicated in any way or transmitted via electronic media. Not for resale. ©2016 Carl's Jr. Restaurants LLC, Inc. All rights reserved.

**Coupon Code: 8681**

 **Promotion valid now thru 12/30/2017**
See reverse side for additional conditions or restrictions.

---

**Enjoy a FREE COOL KIDS COMBO KIDS MEAL with purchase of a REGULAR COMBO MEAL.**

Not valid with Big Hamburger or Spicy Chicken Sandwich Combo Meals. Good for one Hamburger or Chicken Stars Cool Kids Combo Meal. Sales tax not included. Oregon is exempt from sales tax. One coupon per customer per visit. Limit one discount per coupon. Not valid with any other offer, discount or combo. Price and participation may vary. Coupon may not be transferred, auctioned, sold or duplicated in any way or transmitted via electronic media. Not for resale. ©2016 Carl's Jr. Restaurants LLC, Inc. All rights reserved.

**Coupon Code: 5911**

 **Promotion valid now thru 12/30/2017**
See reverse side for additional conditions or restrictions.

---

**Enjoy $1 OFF the purchase of any HAND-SCOOPED ICE CREAM SHAKE or MALT™ at regular price.**

Sales tax not included. Oregon is exempt from sales tax. One coupon per customer per visit. Limit one discount per coupon. Not valid with any other offer, discount or combo. Price and participation may vary. Coupon may not be transferred, auctioned, sold or duplicated in any way or transmitted via electronic media. Not for resale. ©2016 Carl's Jr. Restaurants LLC, Inc. All rights reserved.

**Coupon Code: 7354**

 **Promotion valid now thru 12/30/2017**
See reverse side for additional conditions or restrictions.

# Carl's Jr.®

**Sign up for exclusive offers & emails at carlsjr.com**

---

Valid at All Participating Locations.

---

Valid at All Participating Locations.

---

Valid at All Participating Locations.

---

Valid at All Participating Locations.

dq.com

### Enjoy $3 Off Any DQ® Cake or Blizzard® Cake (8" Round or Larger) at regular menu price.

Limit one coupon per customer, per visit. Not valid with any other coupon, offer, discount, combo, promotion or special offering. Plus tax if applicable. Valid only at participating locations listed on back. Void if altered, copied, transferred, exchanged, purchased, sold, scanned, uploaded, restricted, or prohibited by law. No cash value. Trademarks owned or licensed by Am. D.Q. Corp. ©2016.

**Coupon Code: 25051**

 **Promo valid 08/01/2016 thru 12/30/2017**
See reverse side for additional conditions or restrictions.

dq.com

### Enjoy one Free DQ® Cone when a second DQ® Cone of equal or greater value is purchased at regular menu price.

Limit one coupon per customer, per visit. Not valid with any other coupon, offer, discount, combo, promotion or special offering. Plus tax if applicable. Valid only at participating locations listed on back. Void if altered, copied, transferred, exchanged, purchased, sold, scanned, uploaded, restricted, or prohibited by law. No cash value. Trademarks owned or licensed by Am. D.Q. Corp. ©2016.

**Coupon Code: 25195**

 **Promo valid 08/01/2016 thru 12/30/2017**
See reverse side for additional conditions or restrictions.

dq.com

### Enjoy one 12oz. Small or Larger DQ Blizzard® Treat for 99¢ when you purchase a DQ Blizzard® Treat of equal or greater value at regular menu price.

Limit one coupon per customer, per visit. Not valid with any other coupon, offer, discount, combo, promotion or special offering. Plus tax if applicable. Valid only at participating locations listed on back. Void if altered, copied, transferred, exchanged, purchased, sold, scanned, uploaded, restricted, or prohibited by law. No cash value. Trademarks owned or licensed by Am. D.Q. Corp. ©2016.

**Coupon Code: 25047**

 **Promo valid 08/01/2016 thru 12/30/2017**
See reverse side for additional conditions or restrictions.

dq.com

### Enjoy one Free DQ® Small Sundae when a second DQ® Small Sundae of equal or greater value is purchased at regular menu price.

Limit one coupon per customer, per visit. Not valid with any other coupon, offer, discount, combo, promotion or special offering. Plus tax if applicable. Valid only at participating locations listed on back. Void if altered, copied, transferred, exchanged, purchased, sold, scanned, uploaded, restricted, or prohibited by law. No cash value. Trademarks owned or licensed by Am. D.Q. Corp. ©2016.

**Coupon Code: 25480**

 **Promo valid 08/01/2016 thru 12/30/2017**
See reverse side for additional conditions or restrictions.

Valid only at participating locations in the
Las Vegas and surrounding areas.

This promotional offer is not valid on any other discount/promotion or on defined
holidays. See Rules of Use for more details. Offer valid at all participating locations.
Excludes tax, tip, alcohol, and some sale items.                    49781920

Valid only at participating locations in the
Las Vegas and surrounding areas.

This promotional offer is not valid on any other discount/promotion or on defined
holidays. See Rules of Use for more details. Offer valid at all participating locations.
Excludes tax, tip, alcohol, and some sale items.                    49781914

Valid only at participating locations in the
Las Vegas and surrounding areas.

This promotional offer is not valid on any other discount/promotion or on defined
holidays. See Rules of Use for more details. Offer valid at all participating locations.
Excludes tax, tip, alcohol, and some sale items.                    49781934

Valid only at participating locations in the
Las Vegas and surrounding areas.

This promotional offer is not valid on any other discount/promotion or on defined
holidays. See Rules of Use for more details. Offer valid at all participating locations.
Excludes tax, tip, alcohol, and some sale items.                    49781922

## Orange Julius.

orangejulius.com

**Enjoy one Free Premium Fruit Smoothie when a second Premium Fruit Smoothie of equal or greater value is purchased at regular menu price.**

Limit one coupon per customer, per visit. Not valid with any other coupon, offer, discount, combo, promotion or special offering. Plus tax if applicable. Valid only at participating locations listed on back. Void if altered, copied, transferred, exchanged, purchased, sold, scanned, uploaded, restricted, or prohibited by law. No cash value. Trademarks owned or licensed by Am. D.Q. Corp. ©2016.

**Coupon Code: 29192**

**Promo valid 08/01/2016 thru 12/30/2017**
See reverse side for additional conditions or restrictions.

## Orange Julius.

orangejulius.com

**Enjoy one Free Julius® Original when a second Julius® Original of equal or greater value is purchased at regular menu price.**

Limit one coupon per customer, per visit. Not valid with any other coupon, offer, discount, combo, promotion or special offering. Plus tax if applicable. Valid only at participating locations listed on back. Void if altered, copied, transferred, exchanged, purchased, sold, scanned, uploaded, restricted, or prohibited by law. No cash value. Trademarks owned or licensed by Am. D.Q. Corp. ©2016.

**Coupon Code: 25043**

**Promo valid 08/01/2016 thru 12/30/2017**
See reverse side for additional conditions or restrictions.

C7

C8

**Perfection**

starts with fire-grilled, citrus-marinated chicken!

©2016 El Pollo Loco, Inc.

Valid at Participating Locations.

Valid at Participating Locations.

Valid at Participating Locations.

C9

# CATERING *by* Quiznos®

## LET US CATER YOUR NEXT EVENT

QLSM-ENTBOOK-AD-1115

**www.quiznos.com**

Valid at US Quiznos®

0000001MHLT

Valid at US Quiznos®

0000001MHR4

Valid at US Quiznos®

0000001MHOY

**Auntie Anne's®**

See reverse side for location information

### FREE SIGNATURE PRETZEL with the purchase of Pretzel Nuggets and a Drink.

Not valid at select airports and travel plaza locations. One time use only. One discount per customer per visit.

**Promotion valid now thru 12/31/2017**
See reverse side for additional conditions or restrictions.

C10

---

**Auntie Anne's®**

See reverse side for location information

### FREE SIGNATURE PRETZEL with the purchase of any Pretzel Dog and a Drink.

Not valid at select airports and travel plaza locations. One time use only. One discount per customer per visit.

**Promotion valid now thru 12/31/2017**
See reverse side for additional conditions or restrictions.

C11

---

**Auntie Anne's®**

See reverse side for location information

### FREE SIGNATURE PRETZEL with the purchase of any Two Pretzel Items.

Not valid at select airports and travel plaza locations. One time use only. One discount per customer per visit.

**Promotion valid now thru 12/31/2017**
See reverse side for additional conditions or restrictions.

C12

# AuntieAnne's

3200 Las Vegas Blvd.
Fashion Show Mall
Las Vegas, NV

4300 Meadows Lane
The Meadows Mall
Las Vegas, NV

Maryland Pkwy btwn
Desert Inn Rd & Twain
Boulevard Mall
Las Vegas, NV

3663 Las Vegas Blvd.
Miracle Mile Shops
Las Vegas, NV

7400 Las Vegas Blvd.
Las Vegas Outlet Center
Las Vegas, NV

This promotional offer is not valid on any other discount/promotion or on defined holidays. See Rules of Use for more details. Offer valid at all participating locations. Excludes tax, tip, alcohol, and some sale items.
49781196

# AuntieAnne's

3200 Las Vegas Blvd.
Fashion Show Mall
Las Vegas, NV

4300 Meadows Lane
The Meadows Mall
Las Vegas, NV

Maryland Pkwy btwn
Desert Inn Rd & Twain
Boulevard Mall
Las Vegas, NV

3663 Las Vegas Blvd.
Miracle Mile Shops
Las Vegas, NV

7400 Las Vegas Blvd.
Las Vegas Outlet Center
Las Vegas, NV

This promotional offer is not valid on any other discount/promotion or on defined holidays. See Rules of Use for more details. Offer valid at all participating locations. Excludes tax, tip, alcohol, and some sale items.
49781202

# AuntieAnne's

3200 Las Vegas Blvd.
Fashion Show Mall
Las Vegas, NV

4300 Meadows Lane
The Meadows Mall
Las Vegas, NV

Maryland Pkwy btwn
Desert Inn Rd & Twain
Boulevard Mall
Las Vegas, NV

3663 Las Vegas Blvd.
Miracle Mile Shops
Las Vegas, NV

7400 Las Vegas Blvd.
Las Vegas Outlet Center
Las Vegas, NV

This promotional offer is not valid on any other discount/promotion or on defined holidays. See Rules of Use for more details. Offer valid at all participating locations. Excludes tax, tip, alcohol, and some sale items.
49781205

# You're drooling.

## The Pastrami Burger

### Sammy's
L.A. Pastrami & Burgers

---

## BUY ONE GET ONE

### Long John Silver's
*Think Fish*
www.longjohnsilvers.com

**Enjoy one FREE FISH & MORE when a second FISH & MORE of equal or greater value is purchased.**

**Promotion valid now thru 12/30/2017**
See reverse side for additional conditions or restrictions.          **C14**

## SAVE

**in the box®**
www.jackinthebox.com

### Enjoy a FREE MEDIUM CURLY FRY with any Purchase.

Valid at participating Jack in the Box® Restaurants. Please present coupon when ordering. One coupon per guest, per visit. No duplicates accepted. Not valid with any other offer. This coupon has no cash value and is not redeemable for cash. Jack in the Box is a registered trademark of Jack in the Box Inc. ©2016 Jack in the Box Inc.

**Coupon Code: 289**

**Promotion valid now thru 12/30/2017**
See reverse side for additional conditions or restrictions.          **C15**

## BUY ONE GET ONE

### Long John Silver's
*Think Fish*
www.longjohnsilvers.com

**Enjoy one FREE MENU ITEM when a second MENU ITEM of equal or greater value is purchased.**

**Promotion valid now thru 12/30/2017**
See reverse side for additional conditions or restrictions.          **C16**

## BUY ONE GET ONE

**in the box®**
www.jackinthebox.com

### Enjoy one FREE HOMESTYLE CHICKEN SANDWICH when a second HOMESTYLE CHICKEN SANDWICH of equal or greater value is purchased.

Valid at participating Jack in the Box® Restaurants. Please present coupon when ordering. One coupon per guest, per visit. No duplicates accepted. Not valid with any other offer. This coupon has no cash value and is not redeemable for cash. Jack in the Box is a registered trademark of Jack in the Box Inc. ©2016 Jack in the Box Inc.

**Coupon Code: 547**

**Promotion valid now thru 12/30/2017**
See reverse side for additional conditions or restrictions.          **C17**

## BUY ONE GET ONE

*Think Fish*
www.longjohnsilvers.com

**Enjoy one FREE MENU ITEM when a second MENU ITEM of equal or greater value is purchased.**

**Promotion valid now thru 12/30/2017**
See reverse side for additional conditions or restrictions.          **C18**

## BUY ONE GET ONE

**in the box®**
www.jackinthebox.com

### Enjoy one FREE DOUBLE JACK when a second DOUBLE JACK of equal or greater value is purchased.

Valid at participating Jack in the Box® Restaurants. Please present coupon when ordering. One coupon per guest, per visit. No duplicates accepted. Not valid with any other offer. This coupon has no cash value and is not redeemable for cash. Jack in the Box is a registered trademark of Jack in the Box Inc. ©2016 Jack in the Box Inc.

**Coupon Code: 840**

**Promotion valid now thru 12/30/2017**
See reverse side for additional conditions or restrictions.          **C19**

# Jack in the Box®

Valid at participating Jack in the Box®
Restaurants.

# Long John Silver's

Henderson
240 E Lake Mead
Pkwy
(702)233-3217

Las Vegas
2207 E Windmill
Ln
(702)616-7282

3270 N Durango
Dr
(702)656-0828

401 S Decatur
Blvd
(702)870-4717

4765 W
Charleston Blvd
(702)258-0678

4966 Boulder
Hwy
(702)451-8653

734 N Nellis Blvd
(702)438-2385

North Las Vegas
1025 W Craig Rd
(702)642-6741

---

# Jack in the Box®

Valid at participating Jack in the Box®
Restaurants.

# Long John Silver's

Henderson
240 E Lake Mead
Pkwy
(702)233-3217

Las Vegas
2207 E Windmill
Ln
(702)616-7282

3270 N Durango
Dr
(702)656-0828

401 S Decatur
Blvd
(702)870-4717

4765 W
Charleston Blvd
(702)258-0678

4966 Boulder
Hwy
(702)451-8653

734 N Nellis Blvd
(702)438-2385

North Las Vegas
1025 W Craig Rd
(702)642-6741

---

# Jack in the Box®

Valid at participating Jack in the Box®
Restaurants.

# Long John Silver's

Henderson
240 E Lake Mead
Pkwy
(702)233-3217

Las Vegas
2207 E Windmill
Ln
(702)616-7282

3270 N Durango
Dr
(702)656-0828

401 S Decatur
Blvd
(702)870-4717

4765 W
Charleston Blvd
(702)258-0678

4966 Boulder
Hwy
(702)451-8653

734 N Nellis Blvd
(702)438-2385

North Las Vegas
1025 W Craig Rd
(702)642-6741

**BUY ONE GET ONE**

# Wetzel's Pretzels

www.wetzels.com

## FREE WETZEL BITZ with the purchase of a WETZEL BITZ.

Offer valid at participating mall locations. Free item must be of equal or lesser value than purchased item. One coupon per person per visit only. Not Valid with any other offers.

**Promotion valid now thru 12/30/2017**
See reverse side for additional conditions or restrictions.　　**C20**

---

 **$1 OFF**

# SAMURAI SAM'S
### TERIYAKI GRILL

www.samuraisams.net
### Enjoy $1 OFF any BOWL or SALAD.

Excludes kids meals and side salads. Must present coupon when ordering. Limit one coupon per visit. Not valid with any other offer or discount. Valid at participating locations only. ©2016 Kahala Franchising L.L.C. SAMURAI SAM'S TERIYAKI GRILL and WOK THE HEALTHY PATH are registered trademarks of Kahala Franchising, L.L.C.

**Promotion valid now thru 12/30/2017**
See reverse side for additional conditions or restrictions.　　**C21**

---

 **BUY ONE GET ONE**

# Wetzel's Pretzels

www.wetzels.com

## FREE PRETZEL with the purchase of a PRETZEL.

Offer valid at participating mall locations. Free item must be of equal or lesser value than purchased item. One coupon per person per visit only. Not Valid with any other offers.

**Promotion valid now thru 12/30/2017**
See reverse side for additional conditions or restrictions.　　**C22**

---

 **SAVE**

# SAMURAI SAM'S
### TERIYAKI GRILL

www.samuraisams.net
### Enjoy one FREE REGULAR DARK CHICKEN TERIYAKI BOWL with purchase of a REGULAR DARK CHICKEN TERIYAKI BOWL & 2 DRINKS.

Regular Dark Chicken Teriyaki Bowls come with white rice & dark meat chicken. Must present coupon upon ordering. Limit one coupon per visit. No cash value. Not valid with any other offer or discount. Valid at participating locations only. ©2016 Kahala Franchising, L.L.C. SAMURAI SAM'S TERIYAKI GRILL and WOK THE HEALTHY PATH are registered trademarks of Kahala Franchising, L.L.C.

**Promotion valid now thru 12/30/2017**
See reverse side for additional conditions or restrictions.　　**C23**

---

 **BUY ONE GET ONE**

# Wetzel's Pretzels

www.wetzels.com

## FREE WETZEL DOG with the purchase of a WETZEL DOG.

Offer valid at participating mall locations. Free item must be of equal or lesser value than purchased item. One coupon per person per visit only. Not Valid with any other offers.

**Promotion valid now thru 12/30/2017**
See reverse side for additional conditions or restrictions.　　**C24**

---

 **SPECIAL PRICE**

www.samuraisams.net

### Enjoy a Regular Teriyaki Dark Chicken Bowl for only $3.99.

Regular Dark Chicken Teriyaki bowls come with white rice and dark chicken meat. Must present coupon upon ordering. Excludes kids and side salads. Limit one coupon per visit. No cash value. Not valid with any other offer or discount. ©2016 Kahala Franchising, L.L.C. SAMURAI SAM'S TERIYAKI GRILL and WOK THE HEALTHY PATH are registered trademarks of Kahala Franchising, L.L.C.

**Promotion valid now thru 12/30/2017**
See reverse side for additional conditions or restrictions.　　**C25**

# Samurai Sam's Teriyaki Grill

Valid at Participating Locations.

# Wetzel's Pretzels

· Knot your average pretzel

Offer valid at participating mall locations. Visit our website for a list of locations.

# Samurai Sam's Teriyaki Grill

Valid at Participating Locations.

# Wetzel's Pretzels

· Knot your average pretzel

Offer valid at participating mall locations. Visit our website for a list of locations.

# Samurai Sam's Teriyaki Grill

Valid at Participating Locations.

# Wetzel's Pretzels

· Knot your average pretzel

Offer valid at participating mall locations. Visit our website for a list of locations.

## BUY ONE GET ONE

www.haagendazs.com

**Enjoy one complimentary MILKSHAKE when a second MILKSHAKE of equal or greater value is purchased.**

Valid Holidays.

**Promotion valid now thru 12/30/2017**
See reverse side for additional conditions or restrictions.

C26

## FREE WITH PURCHASE

littlecaesars.com

**FREE Crazy Bread® with the purchase of any DEEP!DEEP!™ Dish Pizza (8-Piece Order).**

8 Piece Order. Crazy Sauce® extra. Valid only at participating Tucson and Las Vegas area Little Caesars® locations. Not valid with any other offers. Plus tax where applicable. ©2016 LCE, INC.

**Promotion valid now thru 12/30/2017**
See reverse side for additional conditions or restrictions.

C27

---

## UP TO $8 VALUE

www.haagendazs.com

**Enjoy one complimentary MENU ITEM when a second MENU ITEM of equal or greater value is purchased - maximum discount $8.**

Valid Holidays.

**Promotion valid now thru 12/30/2017**
See reverse side for additional conditions or restrictions.

C28

## FREE WITH PURCHASE

littlecaesars.com

**FREE Crazy Bread® with the purchase of any DEEP!DEEP!™ Dish Pizza (8-Piece Order).**

8 Piece Order. Crazy Sauce® extra. Valid only at participating Tucson and Las Vegas area Little Caesars® locations. Not valid with any other offers. Plus tax where applicable. ©2016 LCE, INC.

**Promotion valid now thru 12/30/2017**
See reverse side for additional conditions or restrictions.

C29

---

## UP TO $8 VALUE

www.haagendazs.com

**Enjoy one complimentary DAZZLER ICE CREAM SUNDAE when a second DAZZLER ICE CREAM SUNDAE of equal or greater value is purchased - maximum discount $8.**

Valid Holidays.

**Promotion valid now thru 12/30/2017**
See reverse side for additional conditions or restrictions.

C30

## FREE WITH PURCHASE

littlecaesars.com

**FREE Crazy Bread® with the purchase of any DEEP!DEEP!™ Dish Pizza (8-Piece Order).**

8 Piece Order. Crazy Sauce® extra. Valid only at participating Tucson and Las Vegas area Little Caesars® locations. Not valid with any other offers. Plus tax where applicable. ©2016 LCE, INC.

**Promotion valid now thru 12/30/2017**
See reverse side for additional conditions or restrictions.

C31

# Little Caesars®

Valid only at participating Tucson and Las Vegas area Little Caesars® locations.

# Haagen-Dazs

Jean
31700 Las Vegas Blvd S
(Buffalo Bills Resort & Casino)
(702)386-7867

31900 Las Vegas Blvd S
(Primm Valley Resort & Casino)
(702)874-1376

Las Vegas
3200 Las Vegas Blvd S
(Fashion Show Mall)
(702)699-5426

3377 Las Vegas Blvd S
(The Venetian Resort Hotel & Casino)
(702)733-5000

3645 Las Vegas Blvd S
(Bally's Resort)
(702)699-7896

3770 Las Vegas Blvd S
(Monte Carlo Resort & Casino)
(702)730-7777

3790 Las Vegas Blvd S
(New York-New York Hotel & Casino)
(702)740-6969

3799 Las Vegas Blvd S
(MGM Grand Star Lane Mall)
(702)597-0689

---

# Little Caesars®

Valid only at participating Tucson and Las Vegas area Little Caesars® locations.

This promotional offer is not valid on any other discount/promotion or on defined holidays. See Rules of Use for more details. Offer valid at all participating locations. Excludes tax, tip, alcohol, and some sale items.          49781671

# Haagen-Dazs

Jean
31700 Las Vegas Blvd S
(Buffalo Bills Resort & Casino)
(702)386-7867

31900 Las Vegas Blvd S
(Primm Valley Resort & Casino)
(702)874-1376

Las Vegas
3200 Las Vegas Blvd S
(Fashion Show Mall)
(702)699-5426

3377 Las Vegas Blvd S
(The Venetian Resort Hotel & Casino)
(702)733-5000

3645 Las Vegas Blvd S
(Bally's Resort)
(702)699-7896

3770 Las Vegas Blvd S
(Monte Carlo Resort & Casino)
(702)730-7777

3790 Las Vegas Blvd S
(New York-New York Hotel & Casino)
(702)740-6969

3799 Las Vegas Blvd S
(MGM Grand Star Lane Mall)
(702)597-0689

---

# Little Caesars®

Valid only at participating Tucson and Las Vegas area Little Caesars® locations.

This promotional offer is not valid on any other discount/promotion or on defined holidays. See Rules of Use for more details. Offer valid at all participating locations. Excludes tax, tip, alcohol, and some sale items.          49781671

# Haagen-Dazs

Jean
31700 Las Vegas Blvd S
(Buffalo Bills Resort & Casino)
(702)386-7867

31900 Las Vegas Blvd S
(Primm Valley Resort & Casino)
(702)874-1376

Las Vegas
3200 Las Vegas Blvd S
(Fashion Show Mall)
(702)699-5426

3377 Las Vegas Blvd S
(The Venetian Resort Hotel & Casino)
(702)733-5000

3645 Las Vegas Blvd S
(Bally's Resort)
(702)699-7896

3770 Las Vegas Blvd S
(Monte Carlo Resort & Casino)
(702)730-7777

3790 Las Vegas Blvd S
(New York-New York Hotel & Casino)
(702)740-6969

3799 Las Vegas Blvd S
(MGM Grand Star Lane Mall)
(702)597-0689

## UP TO **$8** VALUE

hotheadburritos.com

**Enjoy one FREE BURRITO or BOWL when a second BURRITO or BOWL of equal or greater value and a DRINK are purchased - maximum discount $8.**

**Promotion valid now thru 12/30/2017**
See reverse side for additional conditions or restrictions.　　**C32**

---

## FREE

hotheadburritos.com

**Enjoy one FREE TACO.**
No purchase necessary.

**Promotion valid now thru 12/30/2017**
See reverse side for additional conditions or restrictions.　　**C33**

---

## FREE

hotheadburritos.com

**Enjoy one FREE TACO.**
No purchase necessary.

**Promotion valid now thru 12/30/2017**
See reverse side for additional conditions or restrictions.　　**C34**

---

## UP TO **$1** VALUE

hotheadburritos.com

**Enjoy $1 off any MEAL - maximum discount $1.**

**Promotion valid now thru 12/30/2017**
See reverse side for additional conditions or restrictions.　　**C35**

---

## 50% OFF

hotheadburritos.com

**Enjoy 50% off one BURRITO or BOWL when a second BURRITO or BOWL of equal or greater value is purchased.**

**Promotion valid now thru 12/30/2017**
See reverse side for additional conditions or restrictions.　　**C36**

---

## UP TO **$3** VALUE

hotheadburritos.com

**Enjoy a FREE CHIPS & SALSA with the purchase of any BURRITO or BOWL - maximum discount $3.**

**Promotion valid now thru 12/30/2017**
See reverse side for additional conditions or restrictions.　　**C37**

# Hot Head Burritos

- Burritos, Bowls, Tacos, & Quesadillas
- Vegan Options
- Kids Meal
- Catering.
- Mild to Wild

725 Green Valley Parkway, Suite 150 (Green Valley & W. Horizon Ridge) Henderson, NV (702)263-7281

10550 Southern Highlands Parkway (Southern Highland & Cactus) Las Vegas, NV (702)410-5030

This promotional offer is not valid on any other discount/promotion or on defined holidays. See Rules of Use for more details. Offer valid at all participating locations. Excludes tax, tip, alcohol, and some sale items.     49786649

---

# Hot Head Burritos

- Burritos, Bowls, Tacos, & Quesadillas
- Vegan Options
- Kids Meal
- Catering.
- Mild to Wild

725 Green Valley Parkway, Suite 150 (Green Valley & W. Horizon Ridge) Henderson, NV (702)263-7281

10550 Southern Highlands Parkway (Southern Highland & Cactus) Las Vegas, NV (702)410-5030

This promotional offer is not valid on any other discount/promotion or on defined holidays. See Rules of Use for more details. Offer valid at all participating locations. Excludes tax, tip, alcohol, and some sale items.     49786647

---

# Hot Head Burritos

- Burritos, Bowls, Tacos, & Quesadillas
- Vegan Options
- Kids Meal
- Catering.
- Mild to Wild

725 Green Valley Parkway, Suite 150 (Green Valley & W. Horizon Ridge) Henderson, NV (702)263-7281

10550 Southern Highlands Parkway (Southern Highland & Cactus) Las Vegas, NV (702)410-5030

This promotional offer is not valid on any other discount/promotion or on defined holidays. See Rules of Use for more details. Offer valid at all participating locations. Excludes tax, tip, alcohol, and some sale items.     49786650

---

# Hot Head Burritos

- Burritos, Bowls, Tacos, & Quesadillas
- Vegan Options
- Kids Meal
- Catering.
- Mild to Wild

725 Green Valley Parkway, Suite 150 (Green Valley & W. Horizon Ridge) Henderson, NV (702)263-7281

10550 Southern Highlands Parkway (Southern Highland & Cactus) Las Vegas, NV (702)410-5030

This promotional offer is not valid on any other discount/promotion or on defined holidays. See Rules of Use for more details. Offer valid at all participating locations. Excludes tax, tip, alcohol, and some sale items.     49786649

---

# Hot Head Burritos

- Burritos, Bowls, Tacos, & Quesadillas
- Vegan Options
- Kids Meal
- Catering.
- Mild to Wild

725 Green Valley Parkway, Suite 150 (Green Valley & W. Horizon Ridge) Henderson, NV (702)263-7281

10550 Southern Highlands Parkway (Southern Highland & Cactus) Las Vegas, NV (702)410-5030

This promotional offer is not valid on any other discount/promotion or on defined holidays. See Rules of Use for more details. Offer valid at all participating locations. Excludes tax, tip, alcohol, and some sale items.     49786656

---

# Hot Head Burritos

- Burritos, Bowls, Tacos, & Quesadillas
- Vegan Options
- Kids Meal
- Catering.
- Mild to Wild

725 Green Valley Parkway, Suite 150 (Green Valley & W. Horizon Ridge) Henderson, NV (702)263-7281

10550 Southern Highlands Parkway (Southern Highland & Cactus) Las Vegas, NV (702)410-5030

This promotional offer is not valid on any other discount/promotion or on defined holidays. See Rules of Use for more details. Offer valid at all participating locations. Excludes tax, tip, alcohol, and some sale items.     49786653

# SAVE

**Enjoy one FREE 2 PC LEG & THIGH or 2 PC TENDER STRIPS® with the purchase of any Value Combo Meal at regular price.**

Present coupon when ordering. Limit one per coupon. Void where prohibited. Not Valid with any other discounts or promotions. Offer valid only at participating U.S. Church's restaurants. Prices may vary. Substitution extra charge.

**Promotion valid now thru 12/30/2017**
See reverse side for additional conditions or restrictions.　　**C38**

# SAVE

**Enjoy 2 FREE LARGE SIDES with purchase of 10 PC or more CHICKEN or TENDER STRIPS® at regular menu price.**

Present coupon when ordering. Limit one per coupon. Void where prohibited. Not Valid with any other discounts or promotions. Offer valid only at participating U.S. Church's restaurants. Prices may vary. Substitution extra charge.

**Promotion valid now thru 12/30/2017**
See reverse side for additional conditions or restrictions.　　**C39**

# BUY ONE GET ONE

**Enjoy one FREE MENU ITEM when a second MENU ITEM of equal or greater value is purchased.**

**Promotion valid now thru 12/30/2017**
See reverse side for additional conditions or restrictions.　　**C40**

# BUY ONE GET ONE

**Enjoy one FREE MENU ITEM when a second MENU ITEM of equal or greater value is purchased.**

**Promotion valid now thru 12/30/2017**
See reverse side for additional conditions or restrictions.　　**C41**

# BUY ONE GET ONE

**Enjoy one FREE MENU ITEM when a second MENU ITEM of equal or greater value is purchased.**

**Promotion valid now thru 12/30/2017**
See reverse side for additional conditions or restrictions.　　**C42**

# UP TO $25 VALUE

**Enjoy 20% off the TOTAL BILL - maximum discount $25.**

**Promotion valid now thru 12/30/2017**
See reverse side for additional conditions or restrictions.　　**C43**

# Church's Chicken

Valid at all participating locations.

This promotional offer is not valid on any other discount/promotion or on defined holidays. See Rules of Use for more details. Offer valid at all participating locations. Excludes tax, tip, alcohol, and some sale items.    0000001IGJC

# Church's Chicken

Valid at all participating locations.

This promotional offer is not valid on any other discount/promotion or on defined holidays. See Rules of Use for more details. Offer valid at all participating locations. Excludes tax, tip, alcohol, and some sale items.    0000001IGJK

# Ben & Jerry's

3411 Las Vegas Blvd S
(inside Casino Royale on the Strip)
Las Vegas, NV
(702)737-3500

1301 W Sunset Rd (inside Sunset
Station)
Henderson, NV
(702)435-1010

3663 Las Vegas Blvd S
Ste 520
(inside Miracle Mile Shops, inside Planet Hollywood Hotel & Casino)
Las Vegas, NV
(702)732-2942

This promotional offer is not valid on any other discount/promotion or on defined holidays. See Rules of Use for more details. Offer valid at all participating locations. Excludes tax, tip, alcohol, and some sale items.    C00_17EE0149_2

# Ben & Jerry's

2225 Village Walk Dr
(at the District at Green
Valley Ranch)
Henderson, NV
(702)437-3300

1301 W Sunset Rd (inside
Sunset
Station)
Henderson, NV
(702)435-1010

3411 Las Vegas Blvd S
(inside Casino Royale on
the Strip)
Las Vegas, NV
(702)737-3500

3663 Las Vegas Blvd S
Ste 520
(inside Miracle Mile Shops,
inside Planet Hollywood
Hotel & Casino)
Las Vegas, NV
(702)732-2942

This promotional offer is not valid on any other discount/promotion or on defined holidays. See Rules of Use for more details. Offer valid at all participating locations. Excludes tax, tip, alcohol, and some sale items.    C00_17EE0149_1

# Ben & Jerry's

2225 Village Walk Dr
(at the District at Green
Valley Ranch)
Henderson, NV
(702)437-3300

1301 W Sunset Rd (inside
Sunset
Station)
Henderson, NV
(702)435-1010

3411 Las Vegas Blvd S
(inside Casino Royale on
the Strip)
Las Vegas, NV
(702)737-3500

3663 Las Vegas Blvd S
Ste 520
(inside Miracle Mile Shops,
inside Planet Hollywood
Hotel & Casino)
Las Vegas, NV
(702)732-2942

This promotional offer is not valid on any other discount/promotion or on defined holidays. See Rules of Use for more details. Offer valid at all participating locations. Excludes tax, tip, alcohol, and some sale items.    C00_17EE0149_4

# Ben & Jerry's

3411 Las Vegas Blvd S
(inside Casino Royale on the Strip)
Las Vegas, NV
(702)737-3500

1301 W Sunset Rd (inside Sunset
Station)
Henderson, NV
(702)435-1010

3663 Las Vegas Blvd S
Ste 520
(inside Miracle Mile Shops, inside Planet Hollywood Hotel & Casino)
Las Vegas, NV
(702)732-2942

This promotional offer is not valid on any other discount/promotion or on defined holidays. See Rules of Use for more details. Offer valid at all participating locations. Excludes tax, tip, alcohol, and some sale items.    C00_17EE0149_1

## UP TO $5 VALUE

www.EndlessSwirls.com

**Enjoy one FREE MENU ITEM when a second MENU ITEM of equal or greater value is purchased - maximum discount $5.**

**Promotion valid now thru 12/30/2017**
See reverse side for additional conditions or restrictions.    **C44**

## BUY ONE GET ONE

www.tropicalsmoothiecafe.com

**Enjoy one FREE GOURMET WRAP when a second GOURMET WRAP of equal or greater value is purchased.**

**Promotion valid now thru 12/30/2017**
See reverse side for additional conditions or restrictions.    **C45**

## UP TO $5 VALUE

www.EndlessSwirls.com

**Enjoy one FREE MENU ITEM when a second MENU ITEM of equal or greater value is purchased - maximum discount $5.**

**Promotion valid now thru 12/30/2017**
See reverse side for additional conditions or restrictions.    **C46**

## BUY ONE GET ONE

www.tropicalsmoothiecafe.com

**Enjoy one FREE BISTRO SANDWICH when a second BISTRO SANDWICH of equal or greater value is purchased.**

**Promotion valid now thru 12/30/2017**
See reverse side for additional conditions or restrictions.    **C47**

## UP TO $5 VALUE

www.EndlessSwirls.com

**Enjoy one FREE MENU ITEM when a second MENU ITEM of equal or greater value is purchased - maximum discount $5.**

**Promotion valid now thru 12/30/2017**
See reverse side for additional conditions or restrictions.    **C48**

## BUY ONE GET ONE

www.tropicalsmoothiecafe.com

**Enjoy one FREE SMOOTHIE when a second SMOOTHIE of equal or greater value is purchased.**

**Promotion valid now thru 12/30/2017**
See reverse side for additional conditions or restrictions.    **C49**

# Tropical Smoothie Café

• Healthy, fast food!
• Let us cater your next event
• Smoothies made with real fruit
• Sandwiches, Wraps, Salads & Breakfast.

Valid at all Nevada locations.

# Endless Swirls

• Open 7 days.
• Fresh fruit & dry toppings.
• Party/meeting room available.
• Frozen Yogurt & Custard.
• Pay by ounce.

4500 E Sunset Rd Ste 8
(Located next to Galaxy Theaters)
Henderson, NV
(702)856-2888

# Tropical Smoothie Café

• Healthy, fast food!
• Let us cater your next event
• Smoothies made with real fruit
• Sandwiches, Wraps, Salads & Breakfast.

Valid at all Nevada locations.

# Endless Swirls

• Open 7 days.
• Fresh fruit & dry toppings.
• Party/meeting room available.
• Frozen Yogurt & Custard.
• Pay by ounce.

4500 E Sunset Rd Ste 8
(Located next to Galaxy Theaters)
Henderson, NV
(702)856-2888

# Tropical Smoothie Café

• Healthy, fast food!
• Let us cater your next event
• Smoothies made with real fruit
• Sandwiches, Wraps, Salads & Breakfast.

Valid at all Nevada locations.

# Endless Swirls

• Open 7 days.
• Fresh fruit & dry toppings.
• Party/meeting room available.
• Frozen Yogurt & Custard.
• Pay by ounce.

4500 E Sunset Rd Ste 8
(Located next to Galaxy Theaters)
Henderson, NV
(702)856-2888

**UP TO $8 VALUE**

www.sammyspastrami.com

**Enjoy one FREE MENU ITEM when a second MENU ITEM of equal or greater value is purchased - maximum discount $8.**

**Promotion valid now thru 12/30/2017**
See reverse side for additional conditions or restrictions.

C50

**UP TO $5 VALUE**

www.sammyspastrami.com

**Enjoy $5 off any LARGE SANDWICH, FRY & DRINK - maximum discount $5.**

**Promotion valid now thru 12/30/2017**
See reverse side for additional conditions or restrictions.

C51

**UP TO $25 VALUE**

www.ritasspringvalley.com

**Enjoy 25% off the TOTAL BILL - maximum discount $25.**

**Promotion valid now thru 12/30/2017**
See reverse side for additional conditions or restrictions.

C52

**UP TO $5 VALUE**

www.ritasspringvalley.com

**Enjoy one FREE MENU ITEM when a second MENU ITEM of equal or greater value is purchased - maximum discount $5.**

**Promotion valid now thru 12/30/2017**
See reverse side for additional conditions or restrictions.

C53

**UP TO $5 VALUE**

www.schlotzskys.com

**Enjoy one complimentary MENU ITEM when a second MENU ITEM of equal or greater value is purchased - maximum discount $5.**

**Promotion valid now thru 12/30/2017**
See reverse side for additional conditions or restrictions.

C54

**UP TO $5 VALUE**

www.schlotzskys.com

**Enjoy one complimentary MENU ITEM when a second MENU ITEM of equal or greater value is purchased - maximum discount $5.**

**Promotion valid now thru 12/30/2017**
See reverse side for additional conditions or restrictions.

C55

# Sammy's L.A. Pastrami & Burgers

- Famous Garlic Fries
- Home of "The 502 Fry"
- Outrageous Burgers
- Handmade Lemonade
- L.A. Style Pastrami

2191 E Tropicana Ave
(1 block W. of Eastern on Tropicana)
Las Vegas, NV
(702)482-8192

This promotional offer is not valid on any other discount/promotion or on defined holidays. See Rules of Use for more details. Offer valid at all participating locations. Excludes tax, tip, alcohol, and some sale items.     49786685

# Sammy's L.A. Pastrami & Burgers

- Famous Garlic Fries
- Home of "The 502 Fry"
- Outrageous Burgers
- Handmade Lemonade
- L.A. Style Pastrami

2191 E Tropicana Ave
(1 block W. of Eastern on Tropicana)
Las Vegas, NV
(702)482-8192

This promotional offer is not valid on any other discount/promotion or on defined holidays. See Rules of Use for more details. Offer valid at all participating locations. Excludes tax, tip, alcohol, and some sale items.     00000001P4Q

# Rita's Italian Ice

- Catering
- Drive Thru at Rainbow Location
- Cookie Sandwiches, Milkshakes & Sundaes
- Italian Ice & Frozen Custard

5415 S Rainbow Blvd          725 Las Vegas Blvd S
Ste D                        Las Vegas, NV
Las Vegas, NV                (702)462-6210
(702)462-6210

This promotional offer is not valid on any other discount/promotion or on defined holidays. See Rules of Use for more details. Offer valid at all participating locations. Excludes tax, tip, alcohol, and some sale items.     0000000RRKI

# Rita's Italian Ice

- Catering
- Drive Thru at Rainbow Location
- Cookie Sandwiches, Milkshakes & Sundaes
- Italian Ice & Frozen Custard

5415 S Rainbow Blvd          725 Las Vegas Blvd S
Ste D                        Las Vegas, NV
Las Vegas, NV                (702)462-6210
(702)462-6210

This promotional offer is not valid on any other discount/promotion or on defined holidays. See Rules of Use for more details. Offer valid at all participating locations. Excludes tax, tip, alcohol, and some sale items.     0000000RRKN

# Schlotzsky's Better

- Seriously good dining in a fresh, casual atmosphere
- Kids meals & catering available
- Sandwiches, pizza, salads, soups, and more

5119 W Charleston Blvd
Las Vegas, NV
(702)877-8768

This promotional offer is not valid on any other discount/promotion or on defined holidays. See Rules of Use for more details. Offer valid at all participating locations. Excludes tax, tip, alcohol, and some sale items.     35417

# Schlotzsky's Better

- Seriously good dining in a fresh, casual atmosphere
- Kids meals & catering available
- Sandwiches, pizza, salads, soups, and more

5119 W Charleston Blvd
Las Vegas, NV
(702)877-8768

This promotional offer is not valid on any other discount/promotion or on defined holidays. See Rules of Use for more details. Offer valid at all participating locations. Excludes tax, tip, alcohol, and some sale items.     35417

## 10% OFF

www.goldenspoon.com

**Enjoy 10% off your TOTAL BILL - maximum discount $10.**

**Promotion valid now thru 12/30/2017**
See reverse side for additional conditions or restrictions.　　C56

## 20% OFF

www.poppedcornshop.com

**Enjoy 20% off the TOTAL PURCHASE.**
Excludes holiday orders.

**Promotion valid now thru 12/30/2017**
See reverse side for additional conditions or restrictions.　　C57

## BUY ONE GET ONE

www.goldenspoon.com

**Enjoy one FREE Small Yogurt Cup with the purchase of any Large Yogurt.**
Free small cup only; Cones and toppings additional.

**Promotion valid now thru 12/30/2017**
See reverse side for additional conditions or restrictions.　　C58

## 20% OFF

www.poppedcornshop.com

**Enjoy 20% off the TOTAL PURCHASE.**
Excludes holiday orders.

**Promotion valid now thru 12/30/2017**
See reverse side for additional conditions or restrictions.　　C59

## BUY ONE GET ONE

www.goldenspoon.com

**Enjoy one FREE Regular Yogurt Cup when a second Regular Yogurt of equal or greater value is purchased.**
Free regular cup only; Cones and toppings additional.

**Promotion valid now thru 12/30/2017**
See reverse side for additional conditions or restrictions.　　C60

## 20% OFF

www.poppedcornshop.com

**Enjoy 20% off the TOTAL PURCHASE.**
Excludes holiday orders.

**Promotion valid now thru 12/30/2017**
See reverse side for additional conditions or restrictions.　　C61

# Popped

- Gourmet Savory & Sweet Popcorn.
- Try our Frozen Popcorn!
- Great for Corporate Gifts, Birthdays, Baby Shower, Weddings
- Online Ordering
- Open Daily

3700 S HUALAPAI WAY STE 108 LAS VEGAS, NV (702)207-0985

6649 Las Vegas Blvd S (In Town Square) Las Vegas, NV (702)207-0985

9480 S Eastern Ave., Ste 110 (S Eastern & Richmar) Las Vegas, NV (702)998-9234

This promotional offer is not valid on any other discount/promotion or on defined holidays. See Rules of Use for more details. Offer valid at all participating locations. Excludes tax, tip, alcohol, and some sale items.    0000000RRTM

---

# Golden Spoon Frozen Yogurt

Valid at all participating locations.

This promotional offer is not valid on any other discount/promotion or on defined holidays. See Rules of Use for more details. Offer valid at all participating locations. Excludes tax, tip, alcohol, and some sale items.    0000001GXYZ

---

# Popped

- Gourmet Savory & Sweet Popcorn.
- Try our Frozen Popcorn!
- Great for Corporate Gifts, Birthdays, Baby Shower, Weddings
- Online Ordering
- Open Daily

3700 S HUALAPAI WAY STE 108 LAS VEGAS, NV (702)207-0985

6649 Las Vegas Blvd S (In Town Square) Las Vegas, NV (702)207-0985

9480 S Eastern Ave., Ste 110 (S Eastern & Richmar) Las Vegas, NV (702)998-9234

This promotional offer is not valid on any other discount/promotion or on defined holidays. See Rules of Use for more details. Offer valid at all participating locations. Excludes tax, tip, alcohol, and some sale items.    0000000RRTM

---

# Golden Spoon Frozen Yogurt

Valid at all participating locations.

This promotional offer is not valid on any other discount/promotion or on defined holidays. See Rules of Use for more details. Offer valid at all participating locations. Excludes tax, tip, alcohol, and some sale items.    0000001GXYD

---

# Popped

- Gourmet Savory & Sweet Popcorn.
- Try our Frozen Popcorn!
- Great for Corporate Gifts, Birthdays, Baby Shower, Weddings
- Online Ordering
- Open Daily

3700 S HUALAPAI WAY STE 108 LAS VEGAS, NV (702)207-0985

6649 Las Vegas Blvd S (In Town Square) Las Vegas, NV (702)207-0985

9480 S Eastern Ave., Ste 110 (S Eastern & Richmar) Las Vegas, NV (702)998-9234

This promotional offer is not valid on any other discount/promotion or on defined holidays. See Rules of Use for more details. Offer valid at all participating locations. Excludes tax, tip, alcohol, and some sale items.    0000000RRTM

---

# Golden Spoon Frozen Yogurt

Valid at all participating locations.

This promotional offer is not valid on any other discount/promotion or on defined holidays. See Rules of Use for more details. Offer valid at all participating locations. Excludes tax, tip, alcohol, and some sale items.    0000001GXUN

### UP TO $7 VALUE

# BOB'S
## EAST SIDE DELI

www.BobsEastSideDeli.com

**Enjoy one FREE SANDWICH when a second SANDWICH of equal or greater value is purchased - maximum discount $7.**

Delivery Excluded.

**Promotion valid now thru 12/30/2017**
See reverse side for additional conditions or restrictions.　　**C62**

---

### UP TO $11 VALUE

**Enjoy one FREE 12" THIN CRUST CHEESE PIZZA with the purchase of any 18" PIZZA - maximum discount $11.**

**Promotion valid now thru 12/30/2017**
See reverse side for additional conditions or restrictions.　　**C63**

---

### UP TO $14 VALUE

www.sicilyspizza.com

**Enjoy one FREE PIZZA when a second PIZZA of equal or greater value is purchased - maximum discount $14.**

Delivery excluded.

**Promotion valid now thru 12/30/2017**
See reverse side for additional conditions or restrictions.　　**C64**

---

### 10% OFF

sienadeli.com

**Enjoy 10% off any DELI purchase.**

Including sandwiches, market items, bakery items, coffee & pastries.

**Promotion valid now thru 12/30/2017**
See reverse side for additional conditions or restrictions.　　**C65**

---

### UP TO $7 VALUE

www.abuelastacos.com

**Enjoy one complimentary MENU ITEM when a second MENU ITEM of equal or greater value is purchased - maximum discount $7.**

**Promotion valid now thru 12/30/2017**
See reverse side for additional conditions or restrictions.　　**C66**

---

### BUY ONE GET ONE

**Enjoy one complimentary CLUCK E' TOS when a second CLUCK E' TOS of equal or greater value is purchased.**

**Promotion valid now thru 12/30/2017**
See reverse side for additional conditions or restrictions.　　**C67**

# Rosati's

- Authentic Chicago Pizza
- Thin Crust, Double Dough, Pan, Stuffed Crust and Specialty
- Pastas, Sandwiches, Wings, Calzones, Salads & Desserts
- Lunch Specials & Kids Menu
- Catering.

430 East Silverado Ranch Boulevard, Suite 110
Las Vegas, NV
(702)735-1122

# Bob's East Side Deli

- Hot & cold subs, sandwiches, wraps and burgers
- Bagels, muffins, cookies baked fresh daily on premise
- Mon - Sat 6 am - 4 pm
- Proudly serving your breakfast & lunch needs since 1990
- Sun 7 am - 1 pm
- Free delivery!
- Homemade salads

2900 E Patrick Ln Ste 9
Las Vegas, NV
(702)739-5860

# Siena Deli

- Celebrating over 25 years as a Las Vegas tradition
- Daily happy hour
- Authentic Trattoria
- Specialty market
- Deli
- Bakery

9500 West Sahara Avenue
Las Vegas, NV
(702)736-8424

# Sicily's Pizza

- Pick up and catering available.
- Quality food, fast delivery & great customer service.
- Pizza, pasta, salad, wings, subs and more.
- 24 hour delivery!

3585 S Durango Dr Ste 106
Las Vegas, NV
(702)333-8000

# Farm Basket

- We're carried away with quality
- Great sandwiches--the best in Las Vegas!
- Family owned & operated in Las Vegas for over 25 years

6148 W Charleston Blvd
Las Vegas, NV
(702)878-6343

# Abuelas Tacos

- Handmade tortillas
- Tacos, burritos, quesadillas and bowls
- Open daily
- Authentic recipe
- Combo plates and kids menu available

4225 E Sahara Ave
Las Vegas, NV
(702)431-0284

## UP TO $30 VALUE

www.highrollerpizza.com

**Enjoy one FREE PIZZA when a second PIZZA of equal or greater value is purchased - maximum discount $30.**

Delivery Excluded.

**Promotion valid now thru 12/30/2017**
See reverse side for additional conditions or restrictions.　　　C68

---

## UP TO 50% OFF

# Mixers Ice Cream & Boba

**Enjoy 50% off the regular price of any FOOD ORDER.**

**Promotion valid now thru 12/30/2017**
See reverse side for additional conditions or restrictions.　　　C70

---

## UP TO $5 VALUE

www.loshuicholeslv.com

**Enjoy one FREE MENU ITEM when a second MENU ITEM of equal or greater value is purchased - maximum discount $5.**

Specials Excluded. Delivery Excluded.

**Promotion valid now thru 12/30/2017**
See reverse side for additional conditions or restrictions.　　　C72

---

## BUY ONE GET ONE

www.hotdogonastick.com/

**Enjoy one FREE MENU ITEM when a second MENU ITEM of equal or greater value is purchased.**

Combo meals & kids meals excluded. All Fish and/or Zucchini items excluded.

**Promotion valid now thru 12/30/2017**
See reverse side for additional conditions or restrictions.　　　C69

---

## UP TO $7 VALUE

www.stephanoslv.com

**Enjoy one FREE GYRO WRAP when a second GYRO WRAP of equal or greater value is purchased - maximum discount $7.**

**Promotion valid now thru 12/30/2017**
See reverse side for additional conditions or restrictions.　　　C71

---

## SAVE

www.mrsfields.com

**Enjoy 2 COOKIES FREE with purchase of 3 COOKIES at regular price.**

**Promotion valid now thru 12/30/2017**
See reverse side for additional conditions or restrictions.　　　C73

# Hot Dog On A Stick

VALID AT ALL PARTICIPATING LOCATIONS.

# High Roller Pizza

- We deliver!
- Made with natural ingredients
- Specialty pizzas and sub sandwiches
- We use high-quality organic vegetables and humanely-raised animal products
- Daily lunch specials

8174 Las Vegas Blvd S Ste 101
Las Vegas, NV
(702)960-7788

# Stephano's Greek & Mediterranean Grill

- Pita wraps, plates, Greek favorites, salads, & rice bowls
- We Deliver!
- Catering & private parties available
- Many vegetarian choices
- Free WiFi

10612 S Eastern Ave
Henderson, NV
(702)795-8444

4632 S Maryland Pkwy
Ste 14
Las Vegas, NV
(702)795-8444

# Mixers Ice Cream & Boba

- Milkshake, Sundaes & Smoothies
- Homemade Ice Cream & Gelato
- Sugar Free Available
- Shaved Ice
- Boba

5625 S Rainbow Blvd Ste D
Las Vegas, NV
(702)368-3770

# Mrs. Fields

3680 S Maryland Pkwy
(Boulevard Mallnext to JC Penney)
Las Vegas, NV
(702)369-8030

# Los Huicholes Mexican Restaurant

- Delicious Mexican and American food.
- Open 7 days.
- Catering available.
- We Deliver.

546 N Eastern Ave Ste 100
Las Vegas, NV
(702)227-1515

**UP TO $7 VALUE**

**Enjoy one complimentary MENU ITEM when a second MENU ITEM of equal or greater value is purchased - maximum discount $7.**

Must purchase 2 drinks.

**Promotion valid now thru 12/30/2017**
See reverse side for additional conditions or restrictions.  **C74**

**UP TO $7 VALUE**

www.bahamabucks.com

**Enjoy one FREE MENU ITEM when a second MENU ITEM of equal or greater value is purchased - maximum discount $7.**

Excludes Paradise Fruit, Party Packs & Sno 2 Throw.

**Promotion valid now thru 12/30/2017**
See reverse side for additional conditions or restrictions.  **C75**

**UP TO $9 VALUE**

www.johnnyvegasgrill.com

**Enjoy one FREE MENU ITEM when a second MENU ITEM of equal or greater value is purchased - maximum discount $9.**

**Promotion valid now thru 12/30/2017**
See reverse side for additional conditions or restrictions.  **C76**

**UP TO $5 VALUE**

www.CJsIce.com

**Enjoy one FREE ITALIAN ICE or FROZEN CUSTARD when a second ITALIAN ICE or FROZEN CUSTARD of equal or greater value is purchased - maximum discount $5.**

**Promotion valid now thru 12/30/2017**
See reverse side for additional conditions or restrictions.  **C77**

**UP TO $5 VALUE**

# Maribel Mexican Food & More

**Enjoy one FREE MENU ITEM when a second MENU ITEM of equal or greater value is purchased - maximum discount $5.**

Exclude daily & kids specials.

**Promotion valid now thru 12/30/2017**
See reverse side for additional conditions or restrictions.  **C78**

**UP TO $5 VALUE**

www.saltedmalted.com

**Enjoy one FREE MENU ITEM when a second MENU ITEM of equal or greater value is purchased - maximum discount $5.**

**Promotion valid now thru 12/30/2017**
See reverse side for additional conditions or restrictions.  **C79**

# Bahama Buck's

- Lemonades
- Island Smoothies
- Party Packs
- Coffee
- Open 7 Days
- Shaved Ice
- Fresh Fruit

7345 Arroyo Crossing Pkwy Ste 105
Las Vegas, NV
(702)478-7700

# El Burrito Loco

- Seafood
- Breakfast Available
- Open Daily from 8am to 10pm
- Drive Thru
- Tacos, Tortas, Burritos, Tostadas, Sopes
- Combination Plates

2401 S Valley View Blvd
(located on Sahara & Valley View)
Las Vegas, NV
(702)257-0812

# CJ's Italian Ice & Custard

- Open Mon. - Sun. 12pm - 10pm.
- Catering available.
- Sundae.
- Root Beer Float & Banana Float.
- Italian Ice & Custard.
- Pies & Cakes.

3555 S Durango Dr
Las Vegas, NV
(702)240-1880

# Johnny Vegas Grill

- House Specials.
- Charbroiled Angus Beef Burgers, Cheese Steaks, Pizza, Subs, Wings and Fingers.
- Dine In, Take Out or Delivery.
- Open Daily.

3342 S Sandhill Rd
Las Vegas, NV
(702)570-5458

# Salted Malted

- Breakfast sandwiches & fry bar
- Dole whip
- Baked goods & ice cream treats
- Custom ice cream sandwiches
- Mini donuts, cookies, poutine, grilled cheese

6584 N Decatur Blvd
Las Vegas, NV
(702)754-6500

# Maribel Mexican Food & More

- Seafood Specialties.
- Burgers & Chicken Fingers.
- Daily & Kids Specials.
- Open Mon – Sun 11am – 9pm.
- Tacos & Fajitas.
- All Day Breakfast.

9821 S Eastern Ave
Las Vegas, NV
(702)431-5485

www.greatamericancookiesnwa.com

## Enjoy $3.00 off the purchase of ANY MEDIUM OR LARGE COOKIE CAKE.

Not Valid with any other discounts or promotions.
Delivery Excluded.

**Promotion valid now thru 12/30/2017**
See reverse side for additional conditions or restrictions.          **C80**

www.potatocornerusa.com

## Enjoy one FREE MENU ITEM when a second MENU ITEM of equal or greater value is purchased - maximum discount $8.

Excludes chicken items. This location only.

**Promotion valid now thru 12/30/2017**
See reverse side for additional conditions or restrictions.          **C81**

## BUY ONE GET ONE

www.icecreamatsamslv.com

## Enjoy one FREE ICE CREAM SCOOP when a second ICE CREAM SCOOP of equal or greater value is purchased.

**Promotion valid now thru 12/30/2017**
See reverse side for additional conditions or restrictions.          **C82**

## SAVE

www.teriyakimadness.com

## Enjoy one FREE ENTREE with purchase of a second ENTREE & TWO DRINKS - maximum discount $9.

**Promotion valid now thru 12/30/2017**
See reverse side for additional conditions or restrictions.          **C83**

## Sorrento Pizza

## Enjoy one FREE PIZZA when a second PIZZA of equal or greater value is purchased - maximum discount $25.

Specials Excluded. Delivery Excluded.

**Promotion valid now thru 12/30/2017**
See reverse side for additional conditions or restrictions.          **C84**

www.vivalasarepas.com

## Enjoy $5 off any purchase of $15 or more.

**Promotion valid now thru 12/30/2017**
See reverse side for additional conditions or restrictions.          **C85**

# Potato Corner

- Chicken & fries combo
- Always fresh to order
- World's Best Flavored French Fries

1300 W Sunset Rd Ste K05
Henderson, NV
(702)750-9746

# Great American Cookies

- Open Daily
- We make everything by hand to ensure that old-fashioned homemade taste
- We are confident that our cookies are the best!
- Great American Cookies makes delicious gourmet cookie gifts, cookie tins & gourmet cookie cakes
- Our chewy gourmet cookies are made with the finest ingredients

1300 W Sunset Rd
(Galleria Mall)
Henderson, NV
(702)433-5588

4300 Meadows Ln
(Meadows Mall)
Las Vegas, NV
(702)870-5588

7400 Las Vegas Blvd
S
(Las Vegas Outlet
Center)
Las Vegas, NV
(702)897-7229

# Teriyaki Madness

- Sunday 11am – 9:30pm.
- Fast and Friendly Service.
- Fresh Asian Grill.
- Dine In or Take Out.
- High Protein & Low Carb.
- Mon – Sat 10am – 9:30pm.

2548 Wigwam Pkwy
Ste 150
Henderson, NV
(702)898-8623

43 S Stephanie St
Henderson, NV
(702)228-8623

5705 Centennial
Center Blvd Ste 190
Las Vegas, NV
(702)331-0999

7481 W Lake Mead
Blvd
Las Vegas, NV
(702)982-8623

9845 S Maryland
Pkwy Ste C
(at Silverado Ranch
Blvd)
Las Vegas, NV
(702)252-8623

725 W Craig Rd Ste
132
N Las Vegas, NV
(702)341-8623

# Sam's Ice Cream

- Frozen yogurt and sorbet.
- Floats and freezes.
- Smoothies, sundaes, shakes & malts.
- We serve Blue Bunny Ice Cream.
- Ice cream cakes.

3760 E Desert Inn Rd
(Sandhill & Desert Inn)
Las Vegas, NV
(702)456-0588

# Viva Las Arepas

- Arepas, wood-fired chicken, ribs, and empanadas.
- Fri & Sat 9am – 12am.
- Natural drinks.
- Authentic Venezuelan food.
- Sun – Thur 9am – 10pm.

1616 Las Vegas Blvd S Ste 120
Las Vegas, NV
(702)366-9696

# Sorrento Pizza

- Halal & Vegan pizza available
- Pick up & Delivery
- Wings, Fingers, Hot & Cold Subs, Salads & Pasta
- Open daily 11am - 1am

860 N Rainbow Blvd
Las Vegas, NV
(702)870-1205

## UP TO $5 VALUE

www.averyscoffee.com

**Enjoy one FREE MENU ITEM when a second MENU ITEM of equal or greater value is purchased - maximum discount $5.**

**Promotion valid now thru 12/30/2017**
See reverse side for additional conditions or restrictions.     **C86**

---

## UP TO $5 VALUE

**CREAM**

www.creamnation.com

**Enjoy one FREE MENU ITEM when a second MENU ITEM of equal or greater value is purchased - maximum discount $5.**

**Promotion valid now thru 12/30/2017**
See reverse side for additional conditions or restrictions.     **C87**

---

## UP TO $5 VALUE

**Enjoy one FREE MENU ITEM when a second MENU ITEM of equal or greater value is purchased - maximum discount $5.**

**Promotion valid now thru 12/30/2017**
See reverse side for additional conditions or restrictions.     **C88**

---

## UP TO $11 VALUE

www.pineappleparklv.com

**Enjoy one FREE MENU ITEM when a second MENU ITEM of equal or greater value is purchased - maximum discount $11.**

Exclude souvenir cups.

**Promotion valid now thru 12/30/2017**
See reverse side for additional conditions or restrictions.     **C89**

---

## UP TO $6 VALUE

**Enjoy one FREE MENU ITEM when a second MENU ITEM of equal or greater value is purchased - maximum discount $6.**

**Promotion valid now thru 12/30/2017**
See reverse side for additional conditions or restrictions.     **C90**

---

## UP TO $7 VALUE

www.teriyakiboyhealthygrill.com

**Enjoy one FREE MENU ITEM when a second MENU ITEM of equal or greater value is purchased - maximum discount $7.**

**Promotion valid now thru 12/30/2017**
See reverse side for additional conditions or restrictions.     **C91**

# Cream

- Gluten Free & Vegan Options
- Freshly Bake HOMEMADE Cookies.
- Gourmet Ice Cream Sandwiches!
- Shakes & Floats

1980 Festival Plaza Dr Ste 165
(Located in Downtown Summerlin)
Las Vegas, NV
(702)272-0072

# Avery's Coffee

- Sandwiches, salads & pastries
- We roast coffee!
- Teas & smoothies
- Open daily
- Locally owned & operated Espresso Bar

9440 W Sahara Ave Ste 145
Las Vegas, NV
(702)476-2063

# Pineapple Park

- Crepes
- Smoothies & Juice.
- Dole Whip & Dole Soft Serve!
- Dessert Treats

10550 Southern Highlands Pkwy Ste 110
Las Vegas, NV
(702)331-6110

# Senor Pollo

- Take out & delivery
- Sandwiches, burritos, tacos & salads
- Chicken wings
- Fresh, whole roasted chicken
- Homemade sides

5485 W Flamingo Rd
Las Vegas, NV
(702)706-1667

# Teriyaki Boy Healthy Grill

- Growing healthy bodies one great meal at a time!
- Dine In or Carry Out
- Catering Available
- Open 7 days
- Bowls, Wraps, Salads, Vegetarian and BOBA Smoothies

1725 N Rainbow
Blvd Ste 170b
(Next to LV
Athletic Club)
Las Vegas, NV
(702)722-2155

4441 E Bonanza
Rd
(Located in the
Cardenas
Shopping Center)
Las Vegas, NV
(702)453-1111

9055 S Eastern
Ave Ste 1b
(Next to LV
Athletic Club)
Las Vegas, NV
(702)260-1148

# Froggies Snow Cone Shack

- Open daily
- Shaved ice, snow cones, snow balls, powder balls
- 44 premium flavors along with 9 sugar free

780 E Pyle Ave
Las Vegas, NV
(702)491-8288

8150 S Maryland Pkwy
Las Vegas, NV
(702)491-8288

**UP TO $5 VALUE**

# Al's D•nuts

www.als-donuts.com

**Enjoy 50% off the regular price of any BAKERY ORDER - maximum discount $5.**

**Promotion valid now thru 12/30/2017**
See reverse side for additional conditions or restrictions.          **C92**

**UP TO $5 VALUE**

Al's Donuts | Cafe Burger

www.cafeburgergroup.com

**Enjoy 50% off the regular price of any BAKERY ORDER - maximum discount $5.**

**Promotion valid now thru 12/30/2017**
See reverse side for additional conditions or restrictions.          **C93**

---

**BUY ONE GET ONE**

www.lilbrownsugarscupcakecafe.com

**Enjoy one complimentary CAKE POP when a second CAKE POP of equal or greater value is purchased.**

**Promotion valid now thru 12/30/2017**
See reverse side for additional conditions or restrictions.          **C94**

**UP TO $5 VALUE**

www.crepeexpectations.com

**Enjoy $5 off any purchase of $15 or more.**

**Promotion valid now thru 12/30/2017**
See reverse side for additional conditions or restrictions.          **C95**

---

**UP TO $5 VALUE**

EURO Market & Deli

www.euromarketanddeli.com

**Enjoy one FREE SANDWICH when a second SANDWICH of equal or greater value is purchased - maximum discount $5.**

**Promotion valid now thru 12/30/2017**
See reverse side for additional conditions or restrictions.          **C96**

**UP TO $7 VALUE**

Coney Island Gourmet Hot Dogs

www.coneyislandhotdoglv.net

**Enjoy one FREE MENU ITEM when a second MENU ITEM of equal or greater value is purchased - maximum discount $7.**

**Promotion valid now thru 12/30/2017**
See reverse side for additional conditions or restrictions.          **C97**

## Al's Donuts & Cafe Burger

- Come try our Kroussant! (aka Cronut or Kronut)
- Best selection of pastries
- We are rated the best donuts in Las Vegas!
- Donuts & Burgers
- Open daily

7280 W Azure Dr Ste 150
Las Vegas, NV
(702)655-7280

## Al's Donuts

- Best selection of pastries
- Come try our Kroussant! (aka Cronut or Kronut)
- Open daily
- We are rated the best donuts in Las Vegas!

1220 E Harmon Ave
Las Vegas, NV
(702)735-3039

## Crepe Expectations

- Savory & Sweet Crepes.
- Wine, Beer & Champagne.
- Mon – Fri 9am – 3pm.
- Coffee & Tea.
- Sat & Sun 8am – 3pm.

9500 S Eastern Ave Ste 150
Las Vegas, NV
(702)583-4939

## Lil Brown Sugar's Cupcake Cafe

- Cupcakes, cookies, bagels & muffins
- Cake pop bouquets
- Cakes for all occasions
- We deliver!

55 S Gibson Rd Ste 110
Henderson, NV
(702)203-7376

## Coney Island Gourmet Hot Dogs

- New York Red Onion Sauce.
- Fresh bread.
- Homemade Chili made everyday.
- Square Potato Knish.
- We feature Sabrett All Beef natural casing franks.

3480 S Maryland Pkwy Ste 102
Las Vegas, NV
(702)822-2619

## Euro Market & Deli

- Imported European groceries.
- Fresh pastries.
- Open daily til 9pm.
- Fresh brew & premium coffees.
- All our sandwiches are made featuring Boars Head Brand Products.

5625 S Rainbow Blvd
Las Vegas, NV
(702)464-5022

## UP TO $9 VALUE

www.froyotimevegas.com

**Enjoy one FREE MENU ITEM when a second MENU ITEM of equal or greater value is purchased - maximum discount $9.**

**Promotion valid now thru 12/30/2017**
See reverse side for additional conditions or restrictions.   **C98**

## UP TO $5 VALUE

www.eiscreamcafe.com

**Enjoy one FREE MENU ITEM when a second MENU ITEM of equal or greater value is purchased - maximum discount $5.**

**Promotion valid now thru 12/30/2017**
See reverse side for additional conditions or restrictions.   **C99**

## BUY ONE GET ONE

# Bubbles
## SHAVED ICE

**Enjoy one complimentary SHAVED ICE when a second SHAVED ICE of equal or greater value is purchased.**

**Promotion valid now thru 12/30/2017**
See reverse side for additional conditions or restrictions.   **C100**

## UP TO $5 VALUE

**Enjoy 50% off the regular price of any FROZEN YOGURT - maximum discount $5.**

**Promotion valid now thru 12/30/2017**
See reverse side for additional conditions or restrictions.   **C101**

## UP TO $6 VALUE

**Enjoy one FREE MENU ITEM when a second MENU ITEM of equal or greater value is purchased - maximum discount $6.**

**Promotion valid now thru 12/30/2017**
See reverse side for additional conditions or restrictions.   **C102**

## UP TO $5 VALUE

**Enjoy one FREE MENU ITEM when a second MENU ITEM of equal or greater value is purchased - maximum discount $5.**

**Promotion valid now thru 12/30/2017**
See reverse side for additional conditions or restrictions.   **C103**

# Eis Cream Cafe

- Traditional & unique gourmet ice cream and sherbert flavors.
- Ice Cream Sandwich, Sundaes & Banana Splits.
- Smoothies & Shakes.
- Kronuts & Macaroons.
- Now serving the yummiest ice cream in Las Vegas!

9711 S Eastern Ave Ste H1
(Located in the Target Plaza, facing Silverado Ranch Blvd.)
Las Vegas, NV
(702)270-2191

# Froyo Time Frozen Yogurt

- 50+ Fresh & Dry Toppings
- Open Daily
- 12+ Flavors.
- We Deliver!
- Grab a Cup! Mix it Up

3310 E Flamingo Rd Ste 3a
Las Vegas, NV
(702)750-0100

# Chill-n-Yogurt

- Free WiFi.
- Open 7 days.
- Sit back on our sofas & watch TV.
- New flavors everyday!
- Fresh fruit & dry toppings.

3310 E Flamingo Rd Suite 3a
Las Vegas, NV
(702)547-0151

# Bubbles Shaved Ice

- Assortment of flavors
- Open Mon - Sun 12pm - 6pm

2535 S Torrey Pines Dr
Las Vegas, NV
(702)489-7990

# Swirlicious

- Crepes
- Self-serve frozen yogurt
- Open daily
- Fresh fruit and dry toppings

2505 Anthem Village Dr Ste B
Henderson, NV
(702)776-8755

# Lab Hawaiian Shave Ice

- Cotton Candy, Drinks, & more!
- Dole Whip
- Thrifty Ice Cream
- Real Hawaiian Shave Ice

4300 Meadows Ln Ste 5150
Las Vegas, NV
(702)221-8003

## UP TO $5 VALUE

www.yumzfrozenyogurt.com

**Enjoy one FREE MENU ITEM when a second MENU ITEM of equal or greater value is purchased - maximum discount $5.**

**Promotion valid now thru 12/30/2017**
See reverse side for additional conditions or restrictions.　**C104**

## UP TO $6 VALUE

**tops n bottoms**
frozen yogurt

www.topsnbottomsfrozenyogurt.com

**Enjoy one FREE FROZEN YOGURT ORDER when a second FROZEN YOGURT ORDER of equal or greater value is purchased - maximum discount $6.**

**Promotion valid now thru 12/30/2017**
See reverse side for additional conditions or restrictions.　**C105**

## UP TO $9 VALUE

**THE GREEN REGIME**
wellness cafe
www.thegreenregime.com

**Enjoy one FREE MENU ITEM when a second MENU ITEM of equal or greater value - maximum discount $9.**
Delivery excluded.

**Promotion valid now thru 12/30/2017**
See reverse side for additional conditions or restrictions.　**C106**

## BUY ONE GET ONE

sweetaddictionlv.com

**Enjoy FREE 2 COOKIES when another 2 COOKIES of equal or greater value is purchased.**

**Promotion valid now thru 12/30/2017**
See reverse side for additional conditions or restrictions.　**C107**

## UP TO $5 VALUE

## FROZEN TREATS KINGDOM

**Enjoy one FREE MENU ITEM when a second MENU ITEM of equal or greater value is purchased - maximum discount $5.**

**Promotion valid now thru 12/30/2017**
See reverse side for additional conditions or restrictions.　**C108**

## BUY ONE GET ONE

www.LuvItFrozenCustard.com

**Enjoy one FREE MENU ITEM when a second MENU ITEM of equal or greater value is purchased.**
Excludes Pints, Quarts, Half-Gallons & Merchandise.

**Promotion valid now thru 12/30/2017**
See reverse side for additional conditions or restrictions.　**C109**

# tops n bottoms frozen yogurt

- Fresh fruit & dry toppings
- Open 7 days a week
- Lots of great flavors to choose from!

| | |
|---|---|
| 1181 S Buffalo Dr Ste 150 | 6070 S Rainbow Blvd Ste 6 |
| (SW Corner of Charleston & Buffalo) | (NE Corner of Rainbow & Patrick) |
| Las Vegas, NV | Las Vegas, NV |
| (702)838-2893 | (702)838-2893 |

# Yumz Frozen Yogurt

- High in pro biotics, has less than 100 calories per serving and is fat-free.
- Kosher certified and Gluten free.
- Over 85 fruit, nut & dry toppings.
- Self-serve frozen yogurt with a variety of amazing flavors.

6135 S Fort Apache Rd Ste 400
Las Vegas, NV
(702)201-1155

# Sweet Addiction

- Proudly serving Thrifty Ice Cream
- Homemade cookies
- Milkshakes & Root beer floats
- Ice cream sandwiches
- We cater parties & social events!

| | |
|---|---|
| 2291 N. Green Valley Parkway | 5165 S. Fort Apache Rd., Ste. 160 |
| (Next to Starbucks) | (Across from Walmart/Panera Bread) |
| Henderson, NV | Las Vegas, NV |
| (702)547-9244 | (702)570-6993 |

# The Green Regime

- Paleo Friendly.
- Protein Shakes.
- Juice Bar.
- Wraps & Sandwiches.

| | | |
|---|---|---|
| 5835 South Eastern Avenue, Suite 101 | 6980 West Warm Springs Road, Suite 190 | 8751 West Charleston Boulevard, Suite 120 |
| Las Vegas, NV | Las Vegas, NV | Las Vegas, NV |
| (702)802-5555 | (702)706-6889 | (702)706-5081 |

# Luv It Frozen Custard

- Serving the Las Vegas community since 1973!
- Many flavors to choose from.
- Open 7 days.
- Toppings available.

505 E Oakey Blvd
(Just E. of Las Vegas Blvd.)
Las Vegas, NV
(702)384-6452

# Frozen Treats Kingdom

- Chicago favorites including hot dogs and more
- Ice cream, shakes, floats, sandwiches, and desserts
- Famous alligator sausage
- Closed Sunday

3347 E Russell Rd Ste C1
(E Russell & Pecos)
Las Vegas, NV
(702)547-0557

UP TO **$5** VALUE

www.cornfusionpopcornandtreats.com

**Enjoy one FREE MENU ITEM when a second MENU ITEM of equal or greater value is purchased - maximum discount $5.**

**Promotion valid now thru 12/30/2017**
See reverse side for additional conditions or restrictions.  **C110**

---

UP TO **$5** VALUE

www.showboybakeshop.com

**Enjoy one FREE MENU ITEM when a second MENU ITEM of equal or greater value is purchased - maximum discount $5.**

**Promotion valid now thru 12/30/2017**
See reverse side for additional conditions or restrictions.  **C111**

---

# BUY ONE GET ONE

www.pastrypalacelv.com

**Enjoy one FREE BAKERY ITEM when a second BAKERY ITEM of equal or greater value is purchased.**

Special occasion cakes excluded.

**Promotion valid now thru 12/30/2017**
See reverse side for additional conditions or restrictions.  **C112**

---

UP TO **$5** VALUE

**Enjoy one FREE MENU ITEM when a second MENU ITEM of equal or greater value is purchased - maximum discount $5.**

**Promotion valid now thru 12/30/2017**
See reverse side for additional conditions or restrictions.  **C113**

---

UP TO **$6** VALUE

bonjourbakerylasvegas.com

**Enjoy one FREE MENU ITEM when a second MENU ITEM of equal or greater value is purchased - maximum discount $6.**

**Promotion valid now thru 12/30/2017**
See reverse side for additional conditions or restrictions.  **C114**

---

UP TO **$5** VALUE

the thoughtful food company

www.vegan-bites.com

**Enjoy one FREE MENU ITEM when a second MENU ITEM of equal or greater value is purchased - maximum discount $5.**

**Promotion valid now thru 12/30/2017**
See reverse side for additional conditions or restrictions.  **C115**

# Showboy Bake Shop

- Consultations & Tastings
- Closed Mondays
- Gluten Free Available
- Gourmet Cupcakes and Custom Cakes

2591 Anthem Village Dr Ste B4
Henderson, NV
(702)359-0200

# CornFusion

- Gourmet Popcorn & Sweet Shop.
- Perfect to celebrate any occasion, from Birthday to Graduation.
- We also have caramel apples, marshmallow pops & treats, candies and Krispy delights.
- Over 40 flavors of delicious gourmet popcorn hand-crafted daily by our chefs in Las Vegas!

5130 S Fort Apache Rd Ste 205
Las Vegas, NV
(702)220-5090

# Tasty Crepes

- Frozen Treats
- Savory & Sweet Crepes.
- Smoothies & Cold Drinks
- Thrifty Ice Cream
- Hawaiian Ice.

4845 S Fort Apache Rd Ste F
Las Vegas, NV
(702)818-5517

# Pastry Palace

- Home of the finest cakes in Las Vegas.
- Call us for your next special occasion cake.
- Cupcakes, cookies, cake pops & pastries.
- Sunday 10am – 2pm.
- Mon – Sat 10am – 7pm.

4523 W SAHARA AVE
Las Vegas, NV
(702)251-1555

# Veganbites

- Cakes, cookies, loaves, and candies
- Come and taste amazing!
- Closed Monday
- Las Vegas' first and only organic all vegan bakery
- Dark chocolate covered strawberries
- Savory snacks

8876 S Eastern Ave Ste 101
Las Vegas, NV
(702)487-3111

# Bonjour Bakery

- Breakfast, Sandwiches, Salads, Pastries
- Mon - Sat 7:00 am - 6:00 pm
- Wedding & Specialty Cakes
- Sun 8:00 am - 4:00 pm
- French Bakery & Coffee Shop

4012 S Rainbow Blvd Ste J
Las Vegas, NV
(702)889-0611

**UP TO $7 VALUE**

**Enjoy one FREE MENU ITEM when a
second MENU ITEM of equal or
greater value is purchased -
maximum discount $7.**

**Promotion valid now thru 12/30/2017**
See reverse side for additional conditions or restrictions.    **C116**

---

 **UP TO $10 VALUE**

**Enjoy one FREE MENU ITEM when a
second MENU ITEM of equal or
greater value is purchased -
maximum discount $10.**

**Promotion valid now thru 12/30/2017**
See reverse side for additional conditions or restrictions.    **C117**

---

 **UP TO $5 VALUE**

www.raspadosinlasvegasnv.com

**Enjoy one FREE MENU ITEM when a
second MENU ITEM of equal or
greater value is purchased -
maximum discount $5.**

**Promotion valid now thru 12/30/2017**
See reverse side for additional conditions or restrictions.    **C118**

---

 **UP TO $5 VALUE**

www.tipsycoffeehouse.com

**Enjoy one FREE MENU ITEM when a
second MENU ITEM of equal or
greater value is purchased -
maximum discount $5.**

**Promotion valid now thru 12/30/2017**
See reverse side for additional conditions or restrictions.    **C119**

---

 **BUY ONE GET ONE**

www.globecafelv.com

**Enjoy one MENU ITEM when a
second MENU ITEM of equal or
greater value is purchased -
maximum discount $5.**

**Promotion valid now thru 12/30/2017**
See reverse side for additional conditions or restrictions.    **C120**

---

 **UP TO $7 VALUE**

**Enjoy one FREE MENU ITEM when a
second MENU ITEM of equal or
greater value is purchased -
maximum discount $7.**

**Promotion valid now thru 12/30/2017**
See reverse side for additional conditions or restrictions.    **C121**

# Illumilatte Brew Society

- Free Wi-Fi
- Sandwiches, pastries, desserts
- Open late
- Gourmet coffee
- Loose leaf tea

6825 W Russell Rd Ste 155
Las Vegas, NV
(702)900-9290

# Espression Cafe

- Omelets, Sandwiches, Burgers, Salads & Flatbreads.
- Sweets Treats & Baked Goods.
- Delivery & Catering Available.
- Open Mon - Fri 6:30am - 5:30pm
- Illy Coffee, Tea & Smoothies.
- Serving Breakfast & Lunch.

321 S Casino Center Blvd Suite 120
Las Vegas, NV
(702)366-0665

# Tipsy Coffee House

- Fresh Baked Pastries
- Specialty Espresso Drinks & Liquor Filled Chocolates
- Dessert & Coffee House
- Breakfast & Lunch Specials

6496 Medical Center St Ste 102
Las Vegas, NV
(702)754-1239

# Mexicali Raspados

- Cool Raspados, Clamatos, and savory Hot Dogs
- Thrifty Ice Cream
- Banana Splits, Shaved Ice & Fruit Salads

4865 S Pecos Rd
Las Vegas, NV
(702)547-6125

# Coffee, Tea or Me

- Espresso Drinks.
- Mon-Fri 9am - 7pm.
- Thrifty Brand Ice Cream.
- Teas.
- Happy Hour Frappes.
- Sat 10am - 7pm.
- Sandwiches & Krispy Kreme Donuts.

2600 W Sahara Ave Ste 121
Las Vegas, NV
(702)776-7220

# Globe Cafe

- Coffee, Espresso, Tea, Hot Chocolate and Frappes
- Breakfast Omelets, Waffles & Crepes
- Sandwiches, Paninis & Salads
- Pastry
- Open Daily

8545 S. Eastern Ave
#101
Las Vegas, NV
(702)722-3272

## UP TO $6 VALUE

**Enjoy one FREE MENU ITEM when a second MENU ITEM of equal or greater value is purchased - maximum discount $6.**

**Promotion valid now thru 12/30/2017**
See reverse side for additional conditions or restrictions.        C122

## UP TO $5 VALUE

www.freshkabob.com

**Enjoy one FREE GYRO when a second GYRO of equal or greater value is purchased - maximum discount $5.**

Dine in only.

**Promotion valid now thru 12/30/2017**
See reverse side for additional conditions or restrictions.        C123

## FREE WITH PURCHASE

www.houseofvino.com

**Enjoy one FREE SANDWICH when a second SANDWICH of equal or greater value and 2 beverages are purchased.**

**Promotion valid now thru 12/30/2017**
See reverse side for additional conditions or restrictions.        C124

## UP TO $6 VALUE

www.whichwich.com

**Enjoy one FREE MENU ITEM when a second MENU ITEM of equal or greater value is purchased - maximum discount $6.**

**Promotion valid now thru 12/30/2017**
See reverse side for additional conditions or restrictions.        C125

## UP TO $5 VALUE

www.sofiascafe.com

**Enjoy one FREE MENU ITEM when a second MENU ITEM of equal or greater value is purchased - maximum discount $5.**

Specials Excluded. Dine in only.

**Promotion valid now thru 12/30/2017**
See reverse side for additional conditions or restrictions.        C126

## UP TO $8 VALUE

WRAPS • SALADS • BOWLS
zikizwraps.com

**Enjoy one FREE MENU ITEM when a second MENU ITEM of equal or greater value is purchased - maximum discount $8.**

**Promotion valid now thru 12/30/2017**
See reverse side for additional conditions or restrictions.        C127

# Fresh Kabob

- Always Halal.
- Kabob Platters.
- Featured twice on Las Vegas Review Journal.
- Open 7 Days.
- Always Fresh.
- We Cater.

1405 E Sunset Rd Ste 130
(E Sunset Rd & Paradise)
Las Vegas, NV
(702)868-9096

# Super B Super Burrito

- Burritos, quesadillas, and combo plates
- Best Burrito in Town!
- Open Daily
- Made fresh & cooked to order

8899 S Eastern Ave
Las Vegas, NV
(702)364-8226

# Which Wich

- Catering available
- Vegan options
- Sandwiches & more
- Shakes & Sweets

2192 N Rainbow Blvd
Las Vegas, NV
(702)648-8100

# House of Vino
# Neighborhood Market

- Daily house specials
- Pizzas, breakfast items & fresh baked goods
- Featuring Boar's Head meats and cheeses
- Sandwiches made to order
- Open daily

8053 N Durango Dr
Las Vegas, NV
(702)834-8466

# Zikiz

- Catering Available
- All Ingredients Prepared Fresh Daily
- Made To Order Wraps, Salads & Bowls.

1500 N Green Valley Pkwy Ste 230
Henderson, NV
(702)565-9727

# Sofia's Cafe

- Italian & Mediterranean cuisine.
- Lunch and dinner specials.
- We deliver!
- Closed Sunday.
- Catering available.

3380 Arville St Ste C
(Arville & Spring Mountain)
Las Vegas, NV
(702)221-0005

## UP TO **$8** VALUE

www.manhattanpizza4LV.com

### Enjoy one FREE PIZZA when a second PIZZA of equal or greater value is purchased - maximum discount $8.

Discount taken off regular price menu Delivery Excluded. This location only. Excludes 24" & 28" Colossal.

**Promotion valid now thru 12/30/2017**
See reverse side for additional conditions or restrictions.     **C128**

---

## UP TO **$10** VALUE

**LAZY JOE'S
FISH & CHIPS**

www.lazyjoesfishandchips.com

### Enjoy one FREE MENU ITEM when a second MENU ITEM of equal or greater value is purchased - maximum discount $10.

Delivery Excluded. Specials Excluded. All-you-can-eat excluded.

**Promotion valid now thru 12/30/2017**
See reverse side for additional conditions or restrictions.     **C129**

---

## UP TO **$12** VALUE

# Backyard BBQ

### Enjoy one FREE ENTREE when a second ENTREE of equal or greater value is purchased - maximum discount $12.

**Promotion valid now thru 12/30/2017**
See reverse side for additional conditions or restrictions.     **C130**

---

## UP TO **$8** VALUE

# INDIAN BOWL

indianbowlcuisine.com

### Enjoy one FREE ENTREE when a second ENTREE of equal or greater value is purchased - maximum discount $8.

Specials Excluded.

**Promotion valid now thru 12/30/2017**
See reverse side for additional conditions or restrictions.     **C131**

---

## UP TO **$14** VALUE

www.avantipizzalv.com/

### Enjoy one FREE PIZZA when a second PIZZA of equal or greater value is purchased - maximum discount $14.

Delivery excluded.

**Promotion valid now thru 12/30/2017**
See reverse side for additional conditions or restrictions.     **C132**

---

## UP TO **$15** VALUE

www.mreatz.com

### Enjoy one complimentary MENU ITEM when a second MENU ITEM of equal or greater value is purchased - maximum discount $15.

Not Valid with any other discounts or promotions. Carry out only.

**Promotion valid now thru 12/30/2017**
See reverse side for additional conditions or restrictions.     **C133**

# Lazy Joe's Fish & Chips

- Mediterranean Bites
- Daily Specials
- Vienna Italian Beef & Chicago Style Hot Dog
- Open Daily
- Ipswich Clams, Lobster Roll and Much More!
- Dine In, Take Out & Delivery
- Gluten Free

7835 S Rainbow Blvd Ste 22
Las Vegas, NV
(702)489-6523

# Manhattan Pizza IV

- Delivery, dine-on or carry-out
- Philly steaks, calzones, hot & cold subs
- Pizza, pasta, salads, burgers, gyros
- Appetizers & desserts
- Lunch specials
- We make everything from scratch!
- Chicken wings & fingers

3950 N Tenaya Way Ste 150
Las Vegas, NV
(702)395-5244

# Indian Bowl Cuisine

- Lamb, chicken and vegetarian dishes
- Authentic Indian cuisine
- Open daily 11am-9:30pm
- Catering
- Lunch specials

4550 S Maryland Pkwy Ste D
Las Vegas, NV
(702)477-6706

# Backyard BBQ

- Mexican Favorites.
- Open Daily.
- BBQ Plates, Finger Foods, Burgers, Sandwiches and Salads.
- Breakfast Available.

1675 Industrial Rd
Las Vegas, NV
(702)812-5436

# Mr. Eat'z

- Linch time specials
- Delivery or carry out
- Subs
- Finger foods
- Pizza
- Seafood
- Desserts
- Phillys
- Ribs
- Chicken
- Burgers
- Soups & salads
- We cater parties big or small
- Pasta

6386 W Lake Mead Blvd
(at Torrey Pines & Lake Mead)
Las Vegas, NV
(702)636-0008

# Avanti Pizza

- Carry out, delivery & catering
- Chicago style pizza
- Thin crust & specialty pizza
- Chicken & wings, sandwiches, pastas and more!
- Open daily

2555 Wigwam Pkwy
Henderson, NV
(702)565-7575

## UP TO **$9** VALUE

*Tacos El Jefe's*

www.tacoseljefes.com

**Enjoy one FREE MENU ITEM when a second MENU ITEM of equal or greater value is purchased - maximum discount $9.**

**Promotion valid now thru 12/30/2017**
See reverse side for additional conditions or restrictions.     **C134**

## UP TO **$7** VALUE

www.onestopnutrition.com

**Enjoy one FREE MENU ITEM when a second MENU ITEM of equal or greater value is purchased - maximum discount $7.**

This location only.

**Promotion valid now thru 12/30/2017**
See reverse side for additional conditions or restrictions.     **C135**

## UP TO **$10** VALUE

### PAYLE$$ II Pizza & Ribs

www.paylesspizzalv.com/

**Enjoy one FREE PIZZA when a second PIZZA of equal or greater value is purchased - maximum discount $10.**

Specials Excluded. Delivery Excluded.

**Promotion valid now thru 12/30/2017**
See reverse side for additional conditions or restrictions.     **C136**

## UP TO **$5** VALUE

### PHAT PHRANK'S

MEXICAN FOOD

**Enjoy one complimentary MENU ITEM when a second MENU ITEM of equal or greater value is purchased - maximum discount $5.**

**Promotion valid now thru 12/30/2017**
See reverse side for additional conditions or restrictions.     **C137**

## UP TO **$16** VALUE

BONA PIZZA

bonapizzavegas.com/

**Enjoy one FREE PIZZA when a second PIZZA of equal or greater value is purchased - maximum discount $16.**

Specials Excluded. Delivery Excluded.

**Promotion valid now thru 12/30/2017**
See reverse side for additional conditions or restrictions.     **C138**

## UP TO **$9** VALUE

www.702wingspot.com

**Enjoy one FREE MENU ITEM when a second MENU ITEM of equal or greater value is purchased - maximum discount $9.**

**Promotion valid now thru 12/30/2017**
See reverse side for additional conditions or restrictions.     **C139**

# One Stop Nutrition

- All natural fruit nutritional shakes
- Gourmet coffee
- Free WiFi
- Smoothie and Juice Bar
- Open daily

6171 N Decatur Blvd
Las Vegas, NV
(702)431-7867

# Tacos El Jefe's

- Breakfast Available.
- Healthy Bowls.
- House Specialties.
- Tacos, Quesadillas, Burritos, Tortas and much more.
- We Cater & Deliver.

6475 W Charleston Blvd Ste 120
Las Vegas, NV
(702)248-6692

# Phat Phrank's Mexican Food

- "Not The Best, Just None Better"
- Closed Sundays
- Everything made in-house
- Fish tacos, tortas, burritos, tacos, tostadas
- Enchiladas made from scratch and hand rolled w/ New Mexico Chile
- Our breakfast burrito is second to none!
- Serving Menudo every Saturday

4850 W Sunset Rd
(On the NE corner of Sunset and Decatur)
Las Vegas, NV
(702)247-6528

# Payless Pizza #2 And Ribs

- Catering All Events.
- Burgers, Subs, Pizza, BBQ Ribs, Chicken, Fish & Shrimp, Pasta, and Much More!
- 5 stars on Yelp!
- Lunch & Family Specials.
- Voted Best NY Style Pizza in Las Vegas!

5785 W Tropicana Ave Ste 3
Las Vegas, NV
(702)316-1999

# 702 Wing Spot

- We Cater & Deliver.
- Wings and Fries.
- Party Platters.

6475 W Charleston Blvd Ste 150
Las Vegas, NV
(702)870-7768

# Bona Pizza

- Thur - Sat 10am - 2am
- Lunch & Family Specials
- Pizza, Philly Steaks, Strombolis, Calzone, Subs, Chicken & More
- Sun - Wed 10am - 12am
- Carry Out & Delivery

4080 Paradise Rd Ste 8
Las Vegas, NV
(702)722-6298

## UP TO $17 VALUE

www.vegaspizzadeli.com

**Enjoy one FREE PIZZA when a second PIZZA of equal or greater value is purchased - maximum discount $17.**

Delivery Excluded.

**Promotion valid now thru 12/30/2017**
See reverse side for additional conditions or restrictions.   **C140**

---

## UP TO $6 VALUE

www.zombiedogsfoodtruck.com

**Enjoy one FREE MENU ITEM when a second MENU ITEM of equal or greater value is purchased - maximum discount $6.**

**Promotion valid now thru 12/30/2017**
See reverse side for additional conditions or restrictions.   **C141**

---

## BUY ONE GET ONE

www.ThoseGuysPies.com

**Enjoy one FREE PIZZA when a second PIZZA of equal or greater value is purchased.**

Excludes Cheesesteak Pie. Delivery Excluded.

**Promotion valid now thru 12/30/2017**
See reverse side for additional conditions or restrictions.   **C142**

---

## UP TO $5 VALUE

www.ninjalasvegas.com

**Enjoy one FREE MENU ITEM when a second MENU ITEM of equal or greater value is purchased - maximum discount $5.**

**Promotion valid now thru 12/30/2017**
See reverse side for additional conditions or restrictions.   **C143**

---

## SAVE

www.fudgeryfudge.com

**Enjoy one FREE 1/2 LB. of FUDGE with purchase of 1 1/2 lbs. of FUDGE - maximum discount $9.**

**Promotion valid now thru 12/30/2017**
See reverse side for additional conditions or restrictions.   **C144**

---

## UP TO $6 VALUE

**Enjoy one FREE MENU ITEM when a second MENU ITEM of equal or greater value is purchased - maximum discount $6.**

**Promotion valid now thru 12/30/2017**
See reverse side for additional conditions or restrictions.   **C145**

# Zombie Dogs

- Best Hot Dog in Town!
- Otis Spunkmeyer Cookies
- Catering Available

2828 S Highland Dr
Las Vegas, NV
(702)403-7096

# Vegas Pizza & Deli

- Dine In, Take Out, and Delivery
- Sun 10am – 9pm
- Mon – Sat 10am –10pm
- Sandwiches, Pizza, & More

8480 Las Vegas Blvd S Ste 110
(Las Vegas Blvd S & Wigwam)
Las Vegas, NV
(702)685-2661

# Ninja Teriyaki & Sushi 2 Go

- Catering Available
- Bento Box
- Sun 11am - 8pm
- Sushi Rolls
- Mon - Sat 11am - 9pm
- Rice Bowls

3025 E Desert Inn Rd Ste 15
Las Vegas, NV
(702)982-5444

# Those Guys Pies Pizza, Fingers Cheesesteaks

- Pick up & Delivery.
- Cheesesteaks made with 100% Certified Angus Beef Ribeye.
- NY Style Pizza & Fingers.
- 100% Fresh & House-made Ingredients.

2916 Lake East Dr
(W Sahara & Lake East, in Lakes Town Shopping Center)
Las Vegas, NV
(702)629-2626

# Taqueria El Capullo

- Authentic Mexican Food
- Dine In & Pick Up
- Closed Monday
- Daily Specials

4825 W Flamingo Rd Ste 1
Las Vegas, NV
(702)901-7280

# The Fudgery

- The favorite since 1980
- Visit our website to order fudge online
- See fudge being made right in front of your eyes

855 S Grand Central Pkwy Ste 1504
Las Vegas, NV
(702)387-5553

# Activities & Attractions Index

**Get these offers, and thousands more, on the mobile app!**
Search for "Entertainment® Coupons" in your app store to download.

# Activities & Attractions Index

# Get More

**Get thousands more discounts to use at home or when traveling.**

Download the mobile app now, included with this membership. Search for "Entertainment® Coupons" in your app store.

**Get these offers, and thousands more, on the mobile app!**
Search for "Entertainment® Coupons" in your app store to download.

ACTIVITIES & ATTRACTIONS INDEX

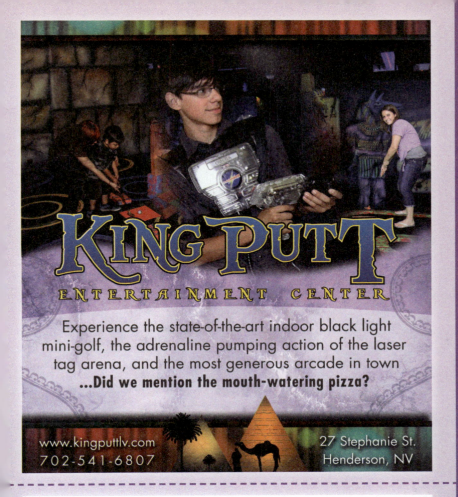

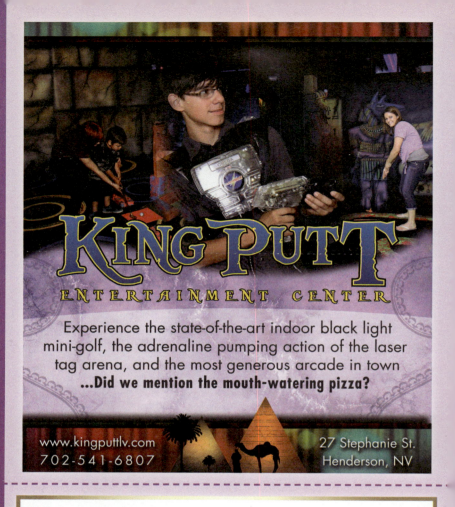

## Let's PARTY

Choose one of our great birthday party packages. Our all-inclusive packages include invitations, games, pizza, private party room, and more!

Get 30% Off Snack Menu Items

Book Your Party Online!

KING PUTT
ENTERTAINMENT CENTER

www.kingputtlv.com

# LET'S PARTY

Choose one of our great birthday party packages. Our all-inclusive packages include invitations, games, pizza, private party room, and more!

Get 30% Off Snack Menu Items

Book Your Party Online!

KING PUTT
ENTERTAINMENT CENTER

www.kingputtlv.com

# KING PUTT
## ENTERTAINMENT CENTER

www.kingputtlv.com

27 S. Stephanie St.
Henderson, NV

(702) 541-6807

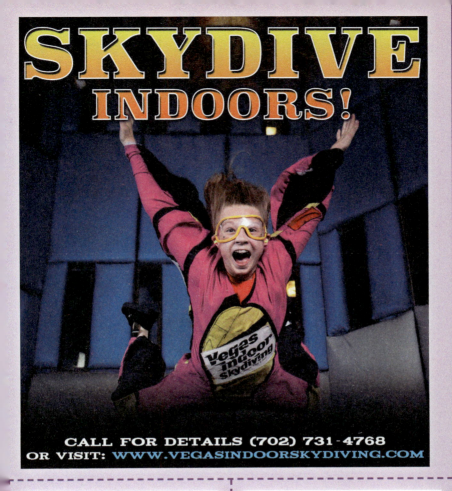

D3

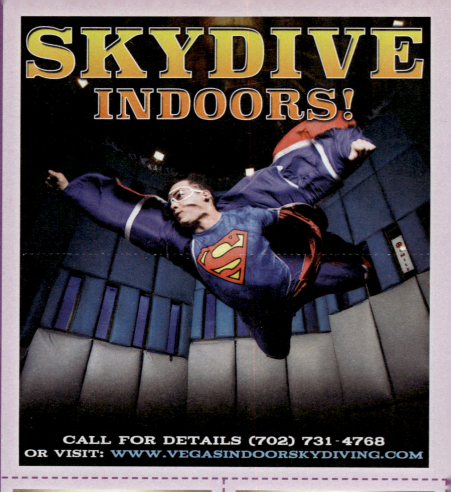

# LAS VEGAS MINI GRAN PRIX

## Race, Ride, Slide & Eat

www.lvmgp.com

---

  **www.lvmgp.com**

## OPEN YEAR-ROUND, 7 DAYS PER WEEK

❖ Adult Gran Prix Cars

❖ Sprint Kart Speedway

❖ Go-Karts

❖ Kiddie Karts

❖ Dragon Roller Coaster

❖ Super Fun Slide

❖ Tornado Twister

❖ Dive Bomber Airplanes

❖ Arcade Games

❖ Restaurant/Party Room

❖ Parties

❖ Group Events

---

### LAS VEGAS MINI GRAN PRIX

1401 N. Rainbow Blvd.
(at Vegas Drive)
Las Vegas, NV

(702) 259-7000

### LAS VEGAS MINI GRAN PRIX

1401 N. Rainbow Blvd.
(at Vegas Drive)
Las Vegas, NV

(702) 259-7000

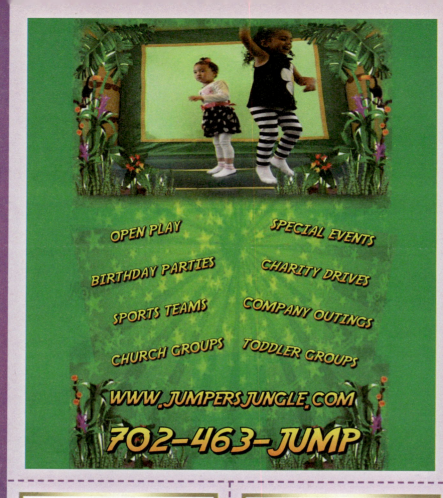

OPEN PLAY

SPECIAL EVENTS

BIRTHDAY PARTIES

CHARITY DRIVES

SPORTS TEAMS

COMPANY OUTINGS

CHURCH GROUPS

TODDLER GROUPS

WWW.JUMPERSJUNGLE.COM

702-463-JUMP

4005 W. Reno Ave.
Las Vegas, NV

(702) 463-5867

4220 W. Craig Rd.
North Las Vegas, NV

(702) 463-5867

4005 W. Reno Ave.
Las Vegas, NV

(702) 463-5867

4220 W. Craig Rd.
North Las Vegas, NV

(702) 463-5867

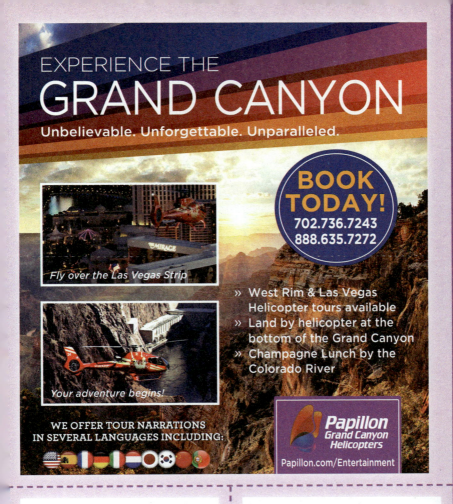

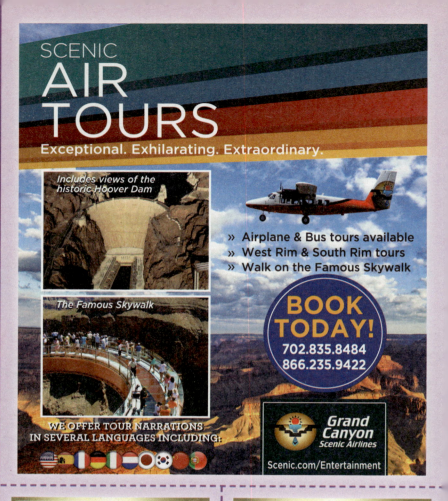

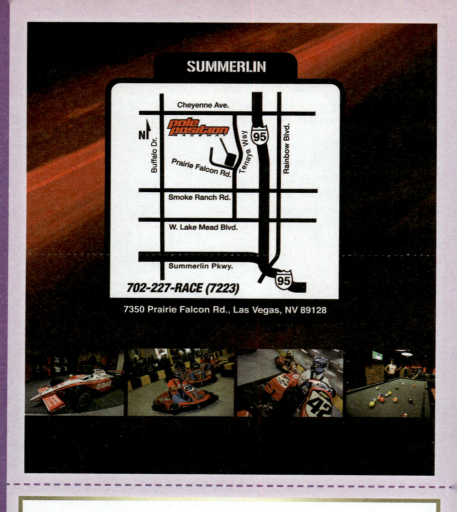

## SUMMERLIN

Cheyenne Ave.

Buffalo Dr.

Prairie Falcon Rd.

Tenaya Way

95

Rainbow Blvd.

Smoke Ranch Rd.

W. Lake Mead Blvd.

Summerlin Pkwy.

95

**702-227-RACE (7223)**

7350 Prairie Falcon Rd., Las Vegas, NV 89128

**INDOOR KARTING**

www.polepositionraceway.com

4175 South Arville St., Ste. 100
(Central/Strip: Located next to Palms Hotel & Casino)
Las Vegas, NV

(702) 227-7223

7350 Prairie Falcon Rd.
(Northwest/Summerlin: Tenaya N. of Smoke Ranch)
Las Vegas, NV

(702) 227-7223

UP TO **$8** VALUE

www.kingputtlv.com

**Enjoy $1 off 18 HOLES OF INDOOR MINIATURE GOLF (up to 8 people).**

**Promotion valid now thru 12/30/2017**
See reverse side for additional conditions or restrictions.          **D8**

UP TO **$8** VALUE

www.kingputtlv.com

**Enjoy $1 off 18 HOLES OF INDOOR MINIATURE GOLF (up to 8 people).**

**Promotion valid now thru 12/30/2017**
See reverse side for additional conditions or restrictions.          **D9**

UP TO **$8** VALUE

www.kingputtlv.com

**Enjoy $1 off 18 HOLES OF INDOOR MINIATURE GOLF (up to 8 people).**

**Promotion valid now thru 12/30/2017**
See reverse side for additional conditions or restrictions.          **D10**

UP TO **$5** VALUE

www.kingputtlv.com

**Enjoy one FREE 5 TOKENS when another 5 TOKENS of equal or greater value is purchased - maximum discount $5.**

**Promotion valid now thru 12/30/2017**
See reverse side for additional conditions or restrictions.          **D11**

UP TO **$30** VALUE

www.kingputtlv.com

**Enjoy $30 off TEAM PARTY/CORPORATE EVENT.**

**Promotion valid now thru 12/30/2017**
See reverse side for additional conditions or restrictions.          **D12**

UP TO **$30** VALUE

www.kingputtlv.com

**Enjoy $30 off the regular price of ULTIMATE PARTY PACKAGE.**

**Promotion valid now thru 12/30/2017**
See reverse side for additional conditions or restrictions.          **D13**

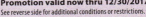

# King Putt Indoor Miniature Golf

- Arcade
- Indoor Mini Golf with Egyptian or Jungle Theme
- Birthday Parties & Corporate Events.
- Snacks

7230 W Lake Mead Blvd
(Lake Mead & Tenaya in Whole Foods
Shopping Center just off of I-95)
Las Vegas, NV
(702)823-1519

---

# King Putt Indoor Miniature Golf

- Arcade
- Indoor Mini Golf with Egyptian or Jungle Theme
- Birthday Parties & Corporate Events.
- Snacks

7230 W Lake Mead Blvd
(Lake Mead & Tenaya in Whole Foods
Shopping Center just off of I-95)
Las Vegas, NV
(702)823-1519

---

# King Putt Indoor Miniature Golf

- Arcade
- Indoor Mini Golf with Egyptian or Jungle Theme
- Birthday Parties & Corporate Events.
- Snacks

7230 W Lake Mead Blvd
(Lake Mead & Tenaya in Whole Foods
Shopping Center just off of I-95)
Las Vegas, NV
(702)823-1519

---

# King Putt Indoor Miniature Golf

- Arcade
- Indoor Mini Golf with Egyptian or Jungle Theme
- Birthday Parties & Corporate Events.
- Snacks

7230 W Lake Mead Blvd
(Lake Mead & Tenaya in Whole Foods
Shopping Center just off of I-95)
Las Vegas, NV
(702)823-1519

---

# King Putt Indoor Miniature Golf

- Arcade
- Indoor Mini Golf with Egyptian or Jungle Theme
- Birthday Parties & Corporate Events.
- Snacks

7230 W Lake Mead Blvd
(Lake Mead & Tenaya in Whole Foods
Shopping Center just off of I-95)
Las Vegas, NV
(702)823-1519

---

# King Putt Indoor Miniature Golf

- Arcade
- Indoor Mini Golf with Egyptian or Jungle Theme
- Birthday Parties & Coporate Events.
- Snacks

7230 W Lake Mead Blvd
(Lake Mead & Tenaya in Whole Foods
Shopping Center just off of I-95)
Las Vegas, NV
(702)823-1519

## BUY ONE GET ONE

www.CSIEXHIBIT.com

**Enjoy one complimentary
ADMISSION when a second
ADMISSION of equal or greater
value is purchased.**

**Promotion valid now thru 12/30/2017**
See reverse side for additional conditions or restrictions. **D14**

---

## UP TO $5 VALUE

www.kingputtlv.com

**Enjoy 5 FREE TOKENS when 5
TOKENS of equal or greater value
are purchased - maximum discount
$5.**

**Promotion valid now thru 12/30/2017**
See reverse side for additional conditions or restrictions. **D15**

---

## BUY ONE GET ONE

Clark County
Department of Parks & Recreation
Clark County Heritage Museum

**Enjoy one complimentary
ADMISSION when a second
ADMISSION of equal or greater
value is purchased.**

**Promotion valid now thru 12/30/2017**
See reverse side for additional conditions or restrictions. **D16**

---

## UP TO $8 VALUE

www.kingputtlv.com

**Enjoy $1 off 18 HOLES OF INDOOR
MINIATURE GOLF.**
Valid for up to 8 people.

**Promotion valid now thru 12/30/2017**
See reverse side for additional conditions or restrictions. **D17**

---

## UP TO $25 VALUE

www.wildwesthorsebackadventures.com

**Enjoy 25% off any Breakfast, Lunch
or Dinner HORSEBACK TOUR -
maximum discount $25.**

**Promotion valid now thru 12/30/2017**
See reverse side for additional conditions or restrictions. **D18**

---

## UP TO $8 VALUE

www.kingputtlv.com

**Enjoy $1 off LASER TAG.**
Valid for up to 8 people.

**Promotion valid now thru 12/30/2017**
See reverse side for additional conditions or restrictions. **D19**

# King Putt Entertainment Center

- Indoor Mini Golf with Egyptian or Jungle Theme
- Laser Tag
- Arcade
- Dining
- Great for Parties and Events

27 S Stephanie St
Henderson, NV
(702)541-6807

# CSI: The Experience

- Can you solve the Crime?
- 15 Suspects
- Interactive Attraction
- 3 Killers
- 3 Murders

3779 Las Vegas Blvd S
(Located in the Studio Walk at MGM Grand)
Las Vegas, NV
(702)891-1111

# King Putt Entertainment Center

- Indoor Mini Golf with Egyptian or Jungle Theme
- Laser Tag
- Arcade
- Dining
- Great for Parties and Events

27 S Stephanie St
Henderson, NV
(702)541-6807

# Clark County Heritage Museum

- The story of Southern Nevada comes to life at the Clark County Heritage Museum!
- Open daily 9am - 4:30pm
- Step inside a mining exhibit filled with mineral specimens...tour historic homes, complete with period furnishings
- Wander through a resurrected ghost town...see a 1905 Union Pacific steam engine...visit our timeline from prehistory through the 20th century

1830 S Boulder Hwy
(Between Las Vegas & Hoover Dam)
Henderson, NV
(702)455-7955

# King Putt Entertainment Center

- Indoor Mini Golf with Egyptian or Jungle Theme
- Laser Tag
- Arcade
- Dining
- Great for Parties and Events

27 S Stephanie St
Henderson, NV
(702)541-6807

# Wild West Horseback Adventures

- Fun for the whole family.
- Perfect for corporate events & parties.
- Call for details.
- Breakfast/Lunch ride includes 1 hour trail ride, delicious meal, petting zoo & cowboy town.
- Dinner ride includes sunset trail ride, BBQ steak dinner, cattle herding & relax under the stars by our campfire.
- Complimentary hotel pick up & drop off.
- Come be a Cowboy for a day!

2470 Chandler Ave Ste 11
Las Vegas, NV
(702)792-5050

### UP TO $13 OFF

flipnoutxtreme.com

**Enjoy one FREE ONE HOUR JUMP PASS when a second ONE HOUR JUMP PASS of equal or greater value is purchased - maximum discount $13.**

Must watch safety video and sign waiver before participating.

**Promotion valid now thru 12/30/2017**
See reverse side for additional conditions or restrictions.          **D20**

### UP TO $16 OFF

flipnoutxtreme.com

**Enjoy $4 off the regular price of our famous ALL-YOU-CAN-PLAY-PASS (up to 4 people).**

Not valid on weekends or holidays. Must watch safety video and sign waiver before participating.

**Promotion valid now thru 12/30/2017**
See reverse side for additional conditions or restrictions.          **D21**

### $25 OFF

flipnoutxtreme.com

**Enjoy $25 off the regular price of our SILVER, GOLD, OR PLATINUM PARTY PACKAGE.**

Not valid on weekends or holidays. Must watch safety video and sign waiver before participating.

**Promotion valid now thru 12/30/2017**
See reverse side for additional conditions or restrictions.          **D22**

### UP TO $8 OFF

flipnoutxtreme.com

**Enjoy one FREE GAME OF LASER TAG when a second GAME OF LASER TAG of equal or greater value is purchased - maximum discount $8.**

Must watch safety video and sign waiver before participating.

**Promotion valid now thru 12/30/2017**
See reverse side for additional conditions or restrictions.          **D23**

### UP TO $18 OFF

flipnoutxtreme.com

**Enjoy one (1) FREE ALL-YOU-CAN-PLAY ONE HOUR PASS on your birthday! - maximum discount $18.**

Must verify birthday with ID. Must watch safety video and sign waiver before participating.

**Promotion valid now thru 12/30/2017**
See reverse side for additional conditions or restrictions.          **D24**

### UP TO $16 OFF

flipnoutxtreme.com

**Enjoy $4 off the regular price of our famous ALL-YOU-CAN-PLAY-PASS (up to 4 people).**

Not valid on weekends or holidays. Must watch safety video and sign waiver before participating.

**Promotion valid now thru 12/30/2017**
See reverse side for additional conditions or restrictions.          **D25**

# FLIPnOUT Xtreme

- Trampolines, Laser Tag, Zip Line, Stunt Jump
- Climbing Walls, Obstacle Course, Trampoline Wall, Dodgeball
- Hoops, Slackline, Arcade, Laser Maze
- Private Party Room
- Free WiFi

4245 S Grand Canyon Dr Ste 111
Las Vegas, NV
(702)579-9999

This promotional offer is not valid on any other discount/promotion or on defined holidays. See Rules of Use for more details. Offer valid at all participating locations. Excludes tax, tip, alcohol, and some sale items.   49786339

# FLIPnOUT Xtreme

- Trampolines, Laser Tag, Zip Line, Stunt Jump
- Climbing Walls, Obstacle Course, Trampoline Wall, Dodgeball
- Hoops, Slackline, Arcade, Laser Maze
- Private Party Room
- Free WiFi

4245 S Grand Canyon Dr Ste 111
Las Vegas, NV
(702)579-9999

This promotional offer is not valid on any other discount/promotion or on defined holidays. See Rules of Use for more details. Offer valid at all participating locations. Excludes tax, tip, alcohol, and some sale items.   49786336

# FLIPnOUT Xtreme

- Trampolines, Laser Tag, Zip Line, Stunt Jump
- Climbing Walls, Obstacle Course, Trampoline Wall, Dodgeball
- Hoops, Slackline, Arcade, Laser Maze
- Private Party Room
- Free WiFi

4245 S Grand Canyon Dr Ste 111
Las Vegas, NV
(702)579-9999

This promotional offer is not valid on any other discount/promotion or on defined holidays. See Rules of Use for more details. Offer valid at all participating locations. Excludes tax, tip, alcohol, and some sale items.   49786345

# FLIPnOUT Xtreme

- Trampolines, Laser Tag, Zip Line, Stunt Jump
- Climbing Walls, Obstacle Course, Trampoline Wall, Dodgeball
- Hoops, Slackline, Arcade, Laser Maze
- Private Party Room
- Free WiFi

4245 S Grand Canyon Dr Ste 111
Las Vegas, NV
(702)579-9999

This promotional offer is not valid on any other discount/promotion or on defined holidays. See Rules of Use for more details. Offer valid at all participating locations. Excludes tax, tip, alcohol, and some sale items.   49786342

# FLIPnOUT Xtreme

- Trampolines, Laser Tag, Zip Line, Stunt Jump
- Climbing Walls, Obstacle Course, Trampoline Wall, Dodgeball
- Hoops, Slackline, Arcade, Laser Maze
- Private Party Room
- Free WiFi

4245 S Grand Canyon Dr Ste 111
Las Vegas, NV
(702)579-9999

This promotional offer is not valid on any other discount/promotion or on defined holidays. See Rules of Use for more details. Offer valid at all participating locations. Excludes tax, tip, alcohol, and some sale items.   49786339

# FLIPnOUT Xtreme

- Trampolines, Laser Tag, Zip Line, Stunt Jump
- Climbing Walls, Obstacle Course, Trampoline Wall, Dodgeball
- Hoops, Slackline, Arcade, Laser Maze
- Private Party Room
- Free WiFi

4245 S Grand Canyon Dr Ste 111
Las Vegas, NV
(702)579-9999

This promotional offer is not valid on any other discount/promotion or on defined holidays. See Rules of Use for more details. Offer valid at all participating locations. Excludes tax, tip, alcohol, and some sale items.   49786348

**UP TO $32 VALUE**

www.csn.edu

**Enjoy one complimentary ADMISSION when a second ADMISSION of equal or greater value is purchased - maximum discount $32.**

For up to 8 people.

**Promotion valid now thru 12/30/2017**
See reverse side for additional conditions or restrictions.          **D26**

---

**UP TO $10 VALUE**

www.lvmgp.com

**Enjoy $10 OFF a PARTY PACKAGE - maximum discount $10.**
One coupon per party.

**Promotion valid now thru 12/30/2017**
See reverse side for additional conditions or restrictions.          **D27**

---

**UP TO $32 VALUE**

www.csn.edu

**Enjoy one complimentary ADMISSION when a second ADMISSION of equal or greater value is purchased - maximum discount $32.**

For up to 8 people.

**Promotion valid now thru 12/30/2017**
See reverse side for additional conditions or restrictions.          **D28**

---

**UP TO $8 VALUE**

www.lvmgp.com

**Enjoy a FREE RIDE TICKET with purchase of TWO RIDE TICKETS at regular price - maximum discount $8.**
One coupon per person per day.

**Promotion valid now thru 12/30/2017**
See reverse side for additional conditions or restrictions.          **D29**

---

**UP TO $32 VALUE**

www.csn.edu

**Enjoy one complimentary ADMISSION when a second ADMISSION of equal or greater value is purchased - maximum discount $32.**

For up to 8 people.

**Promotion valid now thru 12/30/2017**
See reverse side for additional conditions or restrictions.          **D30**

---

**UP TO $59 VALUE**

www.lvmgp.com

**Enjoy $35 for ONE or $59 for TWO MEAL AND RIDE PACKAGE (includes a 2 hour Ride Band, small one item pizza, & a small drink) - maximum discount $59.**

**Promotion valid now thru 12/30/2017**
See reverse side for additional conditions or restrictions.          **D31**

## Las Vegas Mini Gran Prix

- Open Year Round--7 Days a Week.
- Adult Gran Prix Cars.
- Sprint Kart Speedway & Kiddie Karts.
- Dragon Roller Coaster & Tornado Twister.
- Super Fun Slide.
- Arcade Games.
- Restaurant & Party Room.
- Parties & Group Events.

1401 N Rainbow Blvd
(at Vegas Drive)
Las Vegas, NV
(702)259-7000

## CSN Planetarium

- Open Fri. 6 p.m. & 7:30 p.m., Sat. 3:30 p.m. & 7:30 p.m.
- Call for current programming (702)651-4-SKY

3200 E Cheyenne Ave
(South entrance)
North Las Vegas, NV
(702)651-4759

## Las Vegas Mini Gran Prix

- Open Year Round--7 Days a Week.
- Adult Gran Prix Cars.
- Sprint Kart Speedway & Kiddie Karts.
- Dragon Roller Coaster & Tornado Twister.
- Super Fun Slide.
- Arcade Games.
- Restaurant & Party Room.
- Parties & Group Events.

1401 N Rainbow Blvd
(at Vegas Drive)
Las Vegas, NV
(702)259-7000

## CSN Planetarium

- Open Fri. 6 p.m. & 7:30 p.m., Sat. 3:30 p.m. & 7:30 p.m.
- Call for current programming (702)651-4-SKY

3200 E Cheyenne Ave
(South entrance)
North Las Vegas, NV
(702)651-4759

## Las Vegas Mini Gran Prix

- Open Year Round--7 Days a Week.
- Adult Gran Prix Cars.
- Sprint Kart Speedway & Kiddie Karts.
- Dragon Roller Coaster & Tornado Twister.
- Super Fun Slide.
- Arcade Games.
- Restaurant & Party Room.
- Parties & Group Events.

1401 N Rainbow Blvd
(at Vegas Drive)
Las Vegas, NV
(702)259-7000

## CSN Planetarium

- Open Fri. 6 p.m. & 7:30 p.m., Sat. 3:30 p.m. & 7:30 p.m.
- Call for current programming (702)651-4-SKY

3200 E Cheyenne Ave
(South entrance)
North Las Vegas, NV
(702)651-4759

## SPECIAL OFFER

**CHUCK E. CHEESE'S.**
Where A Kid Can Be A Kid.*
chuckecheese.com

### Enjoy Medium 1-Topping Pizza, 2 Soft Drinks, and 35 Tokens for $19.99.

Valid with coupon only in participating stores excluding Hawaii. No cash value.©2016 CEC Entertainment, L.P.

**Coupon Code: 5202**

**Promotion valid thru 12/31/2017**
See reverse side for additional conditions or restrictions.          **D32**

---

## SPECIAL OFFER

**CHUCK E. CHEESE'S.**
Where A Kid Can Be A Kid.*
chuckecheese.com

### Enjoy Large 1-Topping Pizza, 4 Soft Drinks and 55 Tokens for $29.99.

Valid with coupon only in participating stores excluding Hawaii. No cash value.©2016 CEC Entertainment, L.P.

**Coupon Code: 5205**

**Promotion valid thru 12/31/2017**
See reverse side for additional conditions or restrictions.          **D33**

---

## SPECIAL OFFER

**CHUCK E. CHEESE'S.**
Where A Kid Can Be A Kid.*
chuckecheese.com

### Enjoy Large 1-Topping Pizza, 4 Soft Drinks and 110 Tokens for $39.99.

Valid with coupon only in participating stores excluding Hawaii. No cash value.©2016 CEC Entertainment, L.P.

**Coupon Code: 5206**

**Promotion valid thru 12/31/2017**
See reverse side for additional conditions or restrictions.          **D34**

---

## SPECIAL OFFER

**CHUCK E. CHEESE'S.**
Where A Kid Can Be A Kid.*
chuckecheese.com

### Enjoy 2 Large 1-Topping Pizzas, 4 Soft Drinks and 110 Tokens for $49.99.

Valid with coupon only in participating stores excluding Hawaii. No cash value.©2016 CEC Entertainment, L.P.

**Coupon Code: 5207**

**Promotion valid thru 12/31/2017**
See reverse side for additional conditions or restrictions.          **D35**

---

## SPECIAL OFFER

**CHUCK E. CHEESE'S.**
Where A Kid Can Be A Kid.*
chuckecheese.com

### Enjoy 110 Tokens for $20.

Valid with coupon only in participating stores excluding Hawaii. No cash value.©2016 CEC Entertainment, L.P.

**Coupon Code: 5208**

**Promotion valid thru 12/31/2017**
See reverse side for additional conditions or restrictions.          **D36**

---

## UP TO $9 VALUE

www.potteryshopstudio.com

### Enjoy one FREE PAINT TIME when a second PAINT TIME of equal or greater value is purchased - maximum discount $9.

**Promotion valid now thru 12/30/2017**
See reverse side for additional conditions or restrictions.          **D37**

# Chuck E. Cheese's

Valid only in participating Chuck E. Cheese's
U.S. locations.

# Chuck E. Cheese's

Valid only in participating Chuck E. Cheese's
U.S. locations.

# Chuck E. Cheese's

Valid only in participating Chuck E. Cheese's
U.S. locations.

# Chuck E. Cheese's

Valid only in participating Chuck E. Cheese's
U.S. locations.

# The Pottery Shop

- Home parties
- Parties available
- Open 7 days
- No appointment necessary
- School fundraisers
- Kids camp
- Classroom workshops
- Pieces range from $8 to $70
- Weekly specials
- Story time

6623 LAS VEGAS BLVD S UNIT 140
(In Town Square)
LAS VEGAS, NV
(702)699-5600

# Chuck E. Cheese's

Valid only in participating Chuck E. Cheese's
U.S. locations.

## UP TO $35 VALUE

www.vegaslockdown.com

**Enjoy one FREE ADMISSION when a second ADMISSION of equal or greater value is purchased - maximum discount $35.**

**Promotion valid now thru 12/30/2017**
See reverse side for additional conditions or restrictions.

**D38**

## UP TO $25 VALUE

www.polepositionraceway.com

**Enjoy one FREE RACE when a second RACE of equal or greater value is purchased - maximum discount $25.**
Saturdays excluded.

**Promotion valid now thru 12/30/2017**
See reverse side for additional conditions or restrictions.

**D39**

## UP TO $35 VALUE

www.vegaslockdown.com

**Enjoy one FREE ADMISSION when a second ADMISSION of equal or greater value is purchased - maximum discount $35.**

**Promotion valid now thru 12/30/2017**
See reverse side for additional conditions or restrictions.

**D40**

## UP TO $25 VALUE

www.polepositionraceway.com

**Enjoy one FREE RACE when a second RACE of equal or greater value is purchased - maximum discount $25.**
Saturdays excluded.

**Promotion valid now thru 12/30/2017**
See reverse side for additional conditions or restrictions.

**D41**

## UP TO $10 VALUE

**Enjoy one complimentary ADMISSION when an ADULT ADMISSION is purchased - maximum discount $10.**

Special events excluded. Special events excluded. One coupon per customer per visit. Not valid with any other discounts or promotions.

**Promotion valid now thru 12/30/2017**
See reverse side for additional conditions or restrictions.

**D42**

## UP TO $25 VALUE

www.polepositionraceway.com

**Enjoy one FREE RACE when a second RACE of equal or greater value is purchased - maximum discount $25.**
Saturdays excluded.

**Promotion valid now thru 12/30/2017**
See reverse side for additional conditions or restrictions.

**D43**

# Pole Position Raceway

- Experience the thrill of real racing!
- Video arcade & snack bar.
- Kart speeds up to 45 mph.
- State-of-the-art event & meeting rooms.
- Over 1 million dollars of racing memorabilia on display.

| | |
|---|---|
| 4175 S Arville St (Central/Strip: Located next to Palms Hotel & Casino) Las Vegas, NV (702)227-7223 | 7350 Prairie Falcon Rd (Northwest/Summerlin: Tenaya N of Smoke Ranch) Las Vegas, NV (702)227-7223 |

# Lock Down

- Great for parties and events
- 60 minutes to escape... Do you have what it takes?
- Three thematic rooms
- Try the ultimate escape adventure game!

3271 S Highland Dr Ste 715
Las Vegas, NV
(702)998-8723

# Pole Position Raceway

- Experience the thrill of real racing!
- Video arcade & snack bar.
- Kart speeds up to 45 mph.
- State-of-the-art event & meeting rooms.
- Over 1 million dollars of racing memorabilia on display.

| | |
|---|---|
| 4175 S Arville St (Central/Strip: Located next to Palms Hotel & Casino) Las Vegas, NV (702)227-7223 | 7350 Prairie Falcon Rd (Northwest/Summerlin: Tenaya N of Smoke Ranch) Las Vegas, NV (702)227-7223 |

# Lock Down

- Great for parties and events
- 60 minutes to escape... Do you have what it takes?
- Three thematic rooms
- Try the ultimate escape adventure game!

3271 S Highland Dr Ste 715
Las Vegas, NV
(702)998-8723

# Pole Position Raceway

- Experience the thrill of real racing!
- Video arcade & snack bar.
- Kart speeds up to 45 mph.
- State-of-the-art event & meeting rooms.
- Over 1 million dollars of racing memorabilia on display.

| | |
|---|---|
| 4175 S Arville St (Central/Strip: Located next to Palms Hotel & Casino) Las Vegas, NV (702)227-7223 | 7350 Prairie Falcon Rd (Northwest/Summerlin: Tenaya N of Smoke Ranch) Las Vegas, NV (702)227-7223 |

# Las Vegas Natural History Museum

900 Las Vegas Blvd N
Las Vegas, NV
(702)384-3466

## UP TO $30 VALUE

www.combatzonepblv.com

**Enjoy one FREE 4 HOUR RENTAL PACKAGE SESSION when a second 4 HOUR RENTAL PACKAGE SESSION of equal or greater value is purchased - maximum discount $30.**

Exclude Paintballs.

**Promotion valid now thru 12/30/2017**
See reverse side for additional conditions or restrictions.          **D44**

## UP TO $14 OFF

lasvegas.rockinjump.com

**Enjoy one FREE ONE FULL HOUR JUMP when a second ONE FULL HOUR JUMP of equal or greater value is purchased - maximum discount $14.**

Limit one coupon per visit.

**Promotion valid now thru 12/30/2017**
See reverse side for additional conditions or restrictions.          **D45**

## UP TO $30 VALUE

www.combatzonepblv.com

**Enjoy one FREE 4 HOUR RENTAL PACKAGE SESSION when a second 4 HOUR RENTAL PACKAGE SESSION of equal or greater value is purchased - maximum discount $30.**

Exclude Paintballs.

**Promotion valid now thru 12/30/2017**
See reverse side for additional conditions or restrictions.          **D46**

## UP TO $11 OFF

lasvegas.rockinjump.com

**Enjoy 50% off 2 HOURS OF JUMP - maximum discount $11.**
Limit one coupon per visit.

**Promotion valid now thru 12/30/2017**
See reverse side for additional conditions or restrictions.          **D47**

## UP TO $30 VALUE

www.combatzonepblv.com

**Enjoy one FREE 4 HOUR RENTAL PACKAGE SESSION when a second 4 HOUR RENTAL PACKAGE SESSION of equal or greater value is purchased - maximum discount $30.**

Exclude Paintballs.

**Promotion valid now thru 12/30/2017**
See reverse side for additional conditions or restrictions.          **D48**

## $50 OFF

lasvegas.rockinjump.com

**Enjoy $50 off a PARTY OR EVENT.**
Limit one coupon per visit.

**Promotion valid now thru 12/30/2017**
See reverse side for additional conditions or restrictions.          **D49**

# Rockin' Jump

- 30 ft. Rock Tower
- Dodgeball
- Extreme Air
- Slam Dunk Zone
- Free WiFi
- Lounge Area

7200 Montessouri St Ste 160
Las Vegas, NV
(702)553-0744

This promotional offer is not valid on any other discount/promotion or on defined
holidays. See Rules of Use for more details. Offer valid at all participating locations.
Excludes tax, tip, alcohol, and some sale items.       49786325

---

# Combat Zone Paintball

- Food & Beverage Concession
- 2 Airball Fields & 2 Scenario Fields
- Huge Staging Area
- Open Daily
- Retail Store
- Ages 10 and up
- Memberships, Fundraisers & Events
- Rental Includes 4 Hour Session, Air, Marker, Mask, Hopper and Tank

13011 Las Vegas Blvd S
(one mile S. of the M Resort)
Las Vegas, NV
(702)388-9663

This promotional offer is not valid on any other discount/promotion or on defined
holidays. See Rules of Use for more details. Offer valid at all participating locations.
Excludes tax, tip, alcohol, and some sale items.       00000001P5R

---

# Rockin' Jump

- 30 ft. Rock Tower
- Dodgeball
- Extreme Air
- Slam Dunk Zone
- Free WiFi
- Lounge Area

7200 Montessouri St Ste 160
Las Vegas, NV
(702)553-0744

This promotional offer is not valid on any other discount/promotion or on defined
holidays. See Rules of Use for more details. Offer valid at all participating locations.
Excludes tax, tip, alcohol, and some sale items.       49786328

---

# Combat Zone Paintball

- Food & Beverage Concession
- 2 Airball Fields & 2 Scenario Fields
- Huge Staging Area
- Open Daily
- Retail Store
- Ages 10 and up
- Memberships, Fundraisers & Events
- Rental Includes 4 Hour Session, Air, Marker, Mask, Hopper and Tank

13011 Las Vegas Blvd S
(one mile S. of the M Resort)
Las Vegas, NV
(702)388-9663

This promotional offer is not valid on any other discount/promotion or on defined
holidays. See Rules of Use for more details. Offer valid at all participating locations.
Excludes tax, tip, alcohol, and some sale items.       00000001P5R

---

# Rockin' Jump

- 30 ft. Rock Tower
- Dodgeball
- Extreme Air
- Slam Dunk Zone
- Free WiFi
- Lounge Area

7200 Montessouri St Ste 160
Las Vegas, NV
(702)553-0744

This promotional offer is not valid on any other discount/promotion or on defined
holidays. See Rules of Use for more details. Offer valid at all participating locations.
Excludes tax, tip, alcohol, and some sale items.       49786331

---

# Combat Zone Paintball

- Food & Beverage Concession
- 2 Airball Fields & 2 Scenario Fields
- Huge Staging Area
- Open Daily
- Retail Store
- Ages 10 and up
- Memberships, Fundraisers & Events
- Rental Includes 4 Hour Session, Air, Marker, Mask, Hopper and Tank

13011 Las Vegas Blvd S
(one mile S. of the M Resort)
Las Vegas, NV
(702)388-9663

This promotional offer is not valid on any other discount/promotion or on defined
holidays. See Rules of Use for more details. Offer valid at all participating locations.
Excludes tax, tip, alcohol, and some sale items.       00000001P5R

## BUY ONE GET ONE

**Enjoy one complimentary CLOUD NINE COURSE FEE when a second CLOUD NINE COURSE FEE of equal or greater value is purchased.**

Call for t-times.

**Promotion valid now thru 12/30/2017**
See reverse side for additional conditions or restrictions.     **D50**

---

UP TO **$42** VALUE

wetnwildlasvegas.com

**Enjoy $7 off the regular price of a General Admission ticket - maximum discount $42.**
Valid for up to 6 tickets. Valid during public operating days of 2016-2017 season only. Present this coupon at the park or enter promo code 13021 online & save $7 off each general admission ticket (over 42", under 65 years old) up to six (6) people. Call or visit online to confirm public operating dates and hours as they are subject to change. Not valid on park company rentals/special events. Additional terms & conditions apply.

**PLU #: 13021**

**Promotion valid now thru 12/30/2017**
See reverse side for additional conditions or restrictions.     **D51**

---

## BUY ONE GET ONE

**Enjoy ONE HOUR OF DRIVING RANGE TIME when a second HOUR OF DRIVING RANGE TIME of equal or greater value is purchased.**

**Promotion valid now thru 12/30/2017**
See reverse side for additional conditions or restrictions.     **D52**

---

UP TO **$42** VALUE

wetnwildlasvegas.com

**Enjoy $7 off the regular price of a General Admission ticket - maximum discount $42.**
Valid for up to 6 tickets. Valid during public operating days of 2016-2017 season only. Present this coupon at the park or enter promo code 13021 online & save $7 off each general admission ticket (over 42", under 65 years old) up to six (6) people. Call or visit online to confirm public operating dates and hours as they are subject to change. Not valid on park company rentals/special events. Additional terms & conditions apply.

**PLU #: 13021**

**Promotion valid now thru 12/30/2017**
See reverse side for additional conditions or restrictions.     **D53**

---

## BUY ONE GET ONE

**Enjoy one complimentary PUTTING COURSE FEE when a second PUTTING COURSE FEE of equal or greater value is purchased.**

**Promotion valid now thru 12/30/2017**
See reverse side for additional conditions or restrictions.     **D54**

---

UP TO **$42** VALUE

wetnwildlasvegas.com

**Enjoy $7 off the regular price of a General Admission ticket - maximum discount $42.**
Valid for up to 6 tickets. Valid during public operating days of 2016-2017 season only. Present this coupon at the park or enter promo code 13021 online & save $7 off each general admission ticket (over 42", under 65 years old) up to six (6) people. Call or visit online to confirm public operating dates and hours as they are subject to change. Not valid on park company rentals/special events. Additional terms & conditions apply.

**PLU #: 13021**

**Promotion valid now thru 12/30/2017**
See reverse side for additional conditions or restrictions.     **D55**

# Wet'n'Wild Las Vegas

- Huge interactive 3-story children's spray structure with heated water.
- Featuring Tornado, the world's premier funnel water slide that simulates a natural storm experience.
- Visit us online to confirm operating dates and hours.
- Nevada's biggest'n'best water park!
- Over 25 slides & attractions for the entire family.

7055 S Fort Apache Rd
Las Vegas, NV
(702)979-1600

This promotional offer is not valid on any other discount/promotion or on defined holidays. See Rules of Use for more details. Offer valid at all participating locations. Excludes tax, tip, alcohol, and some sale items.     000000026TC

# Angel Park Golf Club

- Lighted for night play
- Play the most incredible par 3 course in America displaying shot concepts of the world's famous par 3 holes
- Our new Cloud Nine par 3 course is lighted for night play!
- Open to the public
- Golf shop, full service restaurant & lounge, catered events
- World's finest 18-hole natural grass putting course & lighted driving range
- Two 18-hole Arnold Palmer designed championship golf courses

100 S Rampart Blvd
Las Vegas, NV
(702)254-4653

This promotional offer is not valid on any other discount/promotion or on defined holidays. See Rules of Use for more details. Offer valid at all participating locations. Excludes tax, tip, alcohol, and some sale items.     111047

---

# Wet'n'Wild Las Vegas

- Huge interactive 3-story children's spray structure with heated water.
- Featuring Tornado, the world's premier funnel water slide that simulates a natural storm experience.
- Visit us online to confirm operating dates and hours.
- Nevada's biggest'n'best water park!
- Over 25 slides & attractions for the entire family.

7055 S Fort Apache Rd
Las Vegas, NV
(702)979-1600

This promotional offer is not valid on any other discount/promotion or on defined holidays. See Rules of Use for more details. Offer valid at all participating locations. Excludes tax, tip, alcohol, and some sale items.     000000026TC

# Angel Park Golf Club

- Lighted for night play
- Play the most incredible par 3 course in America displaying shot concepts of the world's famous par 3 holes
- Our new Cloud Nine par 3 course is lighted for night play!
- Open to the public
- Golf shop, full service restaurant & lounge, catered events
- World's finest 18-hole natural grass putting course & lighted driving range
- Two 18-hole Arnold Palmer designed championship golf courses

100 S Rampart Blvd
Las Vegas, NV
(702)254-4653

This promotional offer is not valid on any other discount/promotion or on defined holidays. See Rules of Use for more details. Offer valid at all participating locations. Excludes tax, tip, alcohol, and some sale items.     135624

---

# Wet'n'Wild Las Vegas

- Huge interactive 3-story children's spray structure with heated water.
- Featuring Tornado, the world's premier funnel water slide that simulates a natural storm experience.
- Visit us online to confirm operating dates and hours.
- Nevada's biggest'n'best water park!
- Over 25 slides & attractions for the entire family.

7055 S Fort Apache Rd
Las Vegas, NV
(702)979-1600

This promotional offer is not valid on any other discount/promotion or on defined holidays. See Rules of Use for more details. Offer valid at all participating locations. Excludes tax, tip, alcohol, and some sale items.     000000026TC

# Angel Park Golf Club

- Lighted for night play
- Play the most incredible par 3 course in America displaying shot concepts of the world's famous par 3 holes
- Our new Cloud Nine par 3 course is lighted for night play!
- Open to the public
- Golf shop, full service restaurant & lounge, catered events
- World's finest 18-hole natural grass putting course & lighted driving range
- Two 18-hole Arnold Palmer designed championship golf courses

100 S Rampart Blvd
Las Vegas, NV
(702)254-4653

This promotional offer is not valid on any other discount/promotion or on defined holidays. See Rules of Use for more details. Offer valid at all participating locations. Excludes tax, tip, alcohol, and some sale items.     111048

**UP TO $229 VALUE**

*"The Las Vegas Tour and Wedding Authority!"*

www.lasvegastourdesk.com

**Enjoy one complimentary ZION NATIONAL PARK TOUR when a second ZION NATIONAL PARK TOUR of equal or greater value is purchased - maximum discount $229.**

**Code: Entertainment**

**Promotion valid now thru 12/30/2017**
See reverse side for additional conditions or restrictions.    **D56**

---

**$50 VALUE**

www.scenic.com/entertainment

**Enjoy $50 Off one GRAND CANYON SOUTH AIRPLANE TOUR LANDING - maximum discount $50.**

Limit 6 per coupon. Additional fuel surcharge may be collected at check-in. Must call direct and mention code: ENTERTAINMENT. Offer based off of full retail price per person.

**Tracking Code: ENTERTAINMENT**

**Promotion valid now thru 12/30/2017**
See reverse side for additional conditions or restrictions.    **D57**

---

**BUY ONE GET ONE**

www.BounceU.com/Henderson

**Enjoy one complimentary ADMISSION when a second ADMISSION of equal or greater value is purchased.**

**Promotion valid now thru 12/30/2017**
See reverse side for additional conditions or restrictions.    **D58**

---

**$50 VALUE**

www.scenic.com/entertainment

**Enjoy $50 Off a GRAND CANYON AIRPLANE TOUR WITH HOOVER DAM BUS - maximum discount $50.**

Limit 6 per coupon. Additional fuel surcharge may be collected at check-in. Must call direct and mention code: ENTERTAINMENT. Offer based off of full retail price per person.

**Tracking Code: ENTERTAINMENT**

**Promotion valid now thru 12/30/2017**
See reverse side for additional conditions or restrictions.    **D59**

---

**UP TO $12 VALUE**

**Adventure Indoor Playground**

**Enjoy one FREE ADMISSION when a second ADMISSION of equal or greater value is purchased - maximum discount $12.**

**Promotion valid now thru 12/30/2017**
See reverse side for additional conditions or restrictions.    **D60**

---

**BUY ONE GET ONE**

www.scenic.com/entertainment

**Enjoy one FREE GRAND CANYON AIRPLANE TOUR when a second GRAND CANYON AIRPLANE TOUR of equal or greater value is purchased.**

Limit 6 per coupon. Additional fuel surcharge may be collected at check-in. Must call direct and mention code: ENTERTAINMENT. Offer based off of full retail price per person.

**Tracking Code: ENTERTAINMENT**

**Promotion valid now thru 12/30/2017**
See reverse side for additional conditions or restrictions.    **D61**

# Scenic Airlines

- Seating and windows customized to allow perfect picture taking opportunities
- Amazing views of Hoover Dam, Lake Mead, the Colorado River and the Grand Canyon
- Multi-lingual narrations

1265 Airport Rd
Boulder City, NV
(702)835-8484

# Las Vegas Tour Desk

- Hotel to Hotel Pick Up & Drop Off
- Refreshments on the Bus
- Lunch
- Morning Snack
- Narrated Tour of Mojave Desert & Zion National Park

3014 S Rancho Dr
Las Vegas, NV
(800)422-6966

# Scenic Airlines

- Seating and windows customized to allow perfect picture taking opportunities
- Amazing views of Hoover Dam, Lake Mead, the Colorado River and the Grand Canyon
- Multi-lingual narrations

1265 Airport Rd
Boulder City, NV
(702)835-8484

# Bounce U

- Check out our website for schedule & details
- Great for parties
- The ultimate party and play experience
- Open & cosmic bounce, programs and camps

1000 Stephanie Pl
Henderson, NV
(702)735-5867

# Scenic Airlines

- Seating and windows customized to allow perfect picture taking opportunities
- Amazing views of Hoover Dam, Lake Mead, the Colorado River and the Grand Canyon
- Multi-lingual narrations

1265 Airport Rd
Boulder City, NV
(702)835-8484

# Adventure Indoor Playground

- Walk Ins and Memberships.
- For 6 Months to 7 Years Old
- Private Parties Available.

5693 S Jones Blvd Ste 114
Las Vegas, NV
(702)522-7133

## UP TO $9 VALUE

www.jumpersjungle.com

**Enjoy one FREE ADMISSION when a second ADMISSION of equal or greater value is purchased - maximum discount $9.**

Weekends excluded.

**Promotion valid now thru 12/30/2017**
See reverse side for additional conditions or restrictions.

**D62**

## $25 OFF

www.jumpersjungle.com

**Enjoy $25 OFF a MULTI PASS CARD - maximum discount $25.**

Weekends excluded.

**Promotion valid now thru 12/30/2017**
See reverse side for additional conditions or restrictions.

**D63**

## UP TO $25 VALUE

www.VegasIndoorSkydiving.com

**Enjoy $25 off a SINGLE FLIGHT.**

Both offers can be combined.

**Promotion valid now thru 12/30/2017**
See reverse side for additional conditions or restrictions.

**D64**

## UP TO $5 VALUE

www.VegasIndoorSkydiving.com

**Enjoy $5 off any VIDEO SERVICE.**

Both offers can be combined.

**Promotion valid now thru 12/30/2017**
See reverse side for additional conditions or restrictions.

**D65**

## UP TO $15 VALUE

www.createhenderson.com

**Enjoy one FREE ADMISSION when a second ADMISSION of equal or greater value is purchased - maximum discount $15.**

**Promotion valid now thru 12/30/2017**
See reverse side for additional conditions or restrictions.

**D66**

## UP TO $25 VALUE

www.racingexperiencelv.com

**Enjoy one FREE RACE when a second RACE of equal or greater value is purchased - maximum discount $25.**

**Promotion valid now thru 12/30/2017**
See reverse side for additional conditions or restrictions.

**D67**

# Jumper's Jungle

- We are an Indoor Jumpspace & Partyspace Family Fun Center!
- Perfect for Events and Parties.
- Always check our Calendar for Open Play and Special Events.
- Party Packages Available.
- Open Daily.

4005 W Reno Ave
Las Vegas, NV
(702)463-5867

4220 W Craig Rd
North Las Vegas, NV
(702)463-5867

# Jumper's Jungle

- We are an Indoor Jumpspace & Partyspace Family Fun Center!
- Perfect for Events and Parties.
- Always check our Calendar for Open Play and Special Events.
- Party Packages Available.
- Open Daily.

4005 W Reno Ave
Las Vegas, NV
(702)463-5867

4220 W Craig Rd
North Las Vegas, NV
(702)463-5867

This promotional offer is not valid on any other discount/promotion or on defined holidays. See Rules of Use for more details. Offer valid at all participating locations. Excludes tax, tip, alcohol, and some sale items.    0000000170G

# Vegas Indoor Skydiving

200 Convention Center Dr Ste A
(Half a block off the strip, just north of the Encore Hotel and Casino)
Las Vegas, NV
(702)731-4768

# Vegas Indoor Skydiving

200 Convention Center Dr Ste A
(Half a block off the strip, just north of the Encore Hotel and Casino)
Las Vegas, NV
(702)731-4768

This promotional offer is not valid on any other discount/promotion or on defined holidays. See Rules of Use for more details. Offer valid at all participating locations. Excludes tax, tip, alcohol, and some sale items.    0000000R0FF

# Gene Woods Racing Experience

- 12pm – 11pm Fri & Sat
- 4pm – 11pm Sun - Thurs
- Fastest Go Karts in Nevada with amazing view of the Las Vegas Strip.
- Arcade.
- Longest and widest track.
- We provide everything you need.

121 E Sunset Rd
Las Vegas, NV
(702)489-1830

# Create

- Craft studio and indoor playground
- Updated Weekly Schedule on our website
- Camps & classes available
- Crafts for kids & adults!

1570 W Horizon Ridge Pkwy Ste 170
Henderson, NV
(702)897-9977

## UP TO $13 VALUE

www.impact-archery.com

**Enjoy one FREE ADMISSION when a second ADMISSION of equal or greater value is purchased - maximum discount $13.**

**Promotion valid now thru 12/30/2017**
See reverse side for additional conditions or restrictions.      **D68**

---

## BUY ONE GET ONE

www.grandcanyoncoaches.com

**Enjoy one FREE SOUTH RIM BUS TOUR when a second SOUTH RIM BUS TOUR of equal or greater value is purchased.**
Must call direct and mention code ENTERTAINMENT. Discount based off of full retail price per person. Tracking Code:ENTERTAINMENT. Additional fuel surcharge may be collected at check-in. Limit 6 per coupon.

**Tracking Code: ENTERTAINMENT**

**Promotion valid now thru 12/30/2017**
See reverse side for additional conditions or restrictions.      **D69**

---

## BUY ONE GET ONE

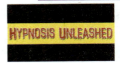

www.hypnosisunleashed.com

**Enjoy one complimentary TICKET when a second TICKET of equal or greater value is purchased.**

**Promotion valid now thru 12/30/2017**
See reverse side for additional conditions or restrictions.      **D70**

---

## BUY ONE GET ONE

www.LVLT.org

**Enjoy one FREE TICKET when a second TICKET of equal or greater value is purchased.**
Reservations suggested 48 hours in advance. Valid on regular priced tickets only.

**Promotion valid now thru 12/30/2017**
See reverse side for additional conditions or restrictions.      **D71**

---

## UP TO $10 VALUE

INDOOR PLAYGROUND
www.fidgetslv.com

**Enjoy one FREE ADMISSION when a second ADMISSION of equal or greater value is purchased - maximum discount $10.**

**Promotion valid now thru 12/30/2017**
See reverse side for additional conditions or restrictions.      **D72**

---

## BUY ONE GET ONE

www.sangennarofeast.com

**Enjoy one FREE TICKET when a second TICKET of equal or greater value is purchased.**

**Promotion valid now thru 12/30/2017**
See reverse side for additional conditions or restrictions.      **D73**

# Grand Canyon Coaches

- Roundtrip motorcoach tour from Las Vegas to Grand Canyon South Rim with views of the Southwest Desert
- Brief stop on the O'Callaghan-Tillman Bridge for photo opportunities of Hoover Dam
- Multiple stops at the South Rim with Scenic overlooks (Meal included)
- Tour Duration: Approx. 14 hours (not including hotel transfers)

1265 Airport Rd
Boulder City, NV
(702)577-9056

# Impact Archery

- Accessories & More.
- Lessons & Leagues.
- General Admission includes one hour of shooting time with equipment and basic instruction.
- Shooting Events.
- Bow Maintenance.
- Indoor Shooting Lanes.

6323 Dean Martin Dr
Las Vegas, NV
(702)701-7766

# Las Vegas Little Theatre

- Call (702) 362-7996 for information

3920 Schiff Dr
Las Vegas, NV
(702)362-7996

# Hypnosis Unleashed

- 21 & over
- 7 nights a week at 9pm
- Adult comedy hypnosis starring Terry Stokes & Michael Johns

3663 Las Vegas Blvd S
(in the Harmon Theater on the corner of Harmon & Las Vegas Blvd S)
Las Vegas, NV
(702)836-0830

# San Gennaro Feast

- SAN GENNARO FEAST ITALIAN FOOD AND MUSIC FESTIVAL
- Dates September 13-18th 2016
- Please go to website for additional dates
- More rides & games with Helm & Sons Amusements
- Great Nonstop Live Entertainment! and much more

628 West Craig Rd
Las Vegas, NV
(702)227-0295

# Fidgets Indoor Playground

- Open Playtime
- Classes & Events.
- Birthday Parties
- Photography

7835 S Rainbow Blvd Ste 15
Las Vegas, NV
(702)597-1117

## UP TO $67 VALUE

www.vtheaterboxoffice.com

**Enjoy one FREE TICKET when a second TICKET of equal or greater value is purchased - maximum discount $67.**

**Promotion valid now thru 12/30/2017**
See reverse side for additional conditions or restrictions.      **D74**

---

## BUY ONE GET ONE

*MARC SAVARD*
COMEDY HYPNOSIS

www.MarcSavard.com

**Enjoy one FREE TICKET when a second TICKET of equal or greater value is purchased.**

**Promotion valid now thru 12/30/2017**
See reverse side for additional conditions or restrictions.      **D75**

---

## BUY ONE GET ONE

www.jeffcivillico.com

**Enjoy one complimentary TICKET when a second TICKET is purchased.**
Reserverd seats only.

**Promotion valid now thru 12/30/2017**
See reverse side for additional conditions or restrictions.      **D76**

---

## BUY ONE GET ONE

www.varietytheater.com

**Enjoy one complimentary TICKET when a second TICKET of equal or greater value is purchased.**
Redeem at Saxe Theater box office only. Not valid on holidays and holiday weekends.

**Promotion valid now thru 12/30/2017**
See reverse side for additional conditions or restrictions.      **D77**

---

## BUY ONE GET ONE

www.varietytheater.com

**Enjoy one complimentary TICKET when a second TICKET of equal or greater value is purchased.**
Redeem at V Theater box office only. Not valid on holidays and holiday weekends.

**Promotion valid now thru 12/30/2017**
See reverse side for additional conditions or restrictions.      **D78**

---

## BUY ONE GET ONE

www.nathanburton.com

**Enjoy one complimentary TICKET when a second TICKET of equal or greater value is purchased.**
Reserved seats only.

**Promotion valid now thru 12/30/2017**
See reverse side for additional conditions or restrictions.      **D79**

## Marc Savard Comedy Hypnosis

• Sun - Thur at 10pm
• An Energized Mix of Comedy, Hypnosis, and Chaos
• Ages 18 and over
• Awarded the 2008 Star Award as Best Hypnotist by S.H.O.W
• Dark Friday
• See the Show or Be the Show!

3663 Las Vegas Blvd S
(In V Theater at Miracle Mile Shops inside Planet Hollywood Hotel & Casino)
Las Vegas, NV
(702)374-1906

## All Shook Up

• Get "all shook up" with a tribute show to the King of Rock ' n' Roll, Elvis Presley
• Nightly at 6pm

3663 Las Vegas Blvd S
(Located in V Theater in Planet Hollywood Resort in Miracle Mile Shops)
Las Vegas, NV
(702)260-7200

## Vegas The Show

• Must purchase an adult VIP ticket
• Relive the best moments of dynamic singers, dancers, and unforgettable personalities to ever step foot on the world-famous Strip
• We recreate the greatest moments in Vegas' history and tell the story of the most influential and exciting entertainers who made Vegas...Vegas!
• For showtimes call 702-260-7200

3663 Las Vegas Blvd S
(Planet Hollywood Resort in Miracle Miles Shop)
Las Vegas, NV
(702)260-7200

## Jeff Civillico Comedy in Action

• Great fun show for ALL ages!
• Performing daily at 2pm excluding Tuesdays and Fridays
• Jeff Civillico is an entertainment dynamo with a clean comedy show that blends physical humor, stunts, and juggling with friendly audience interaction and insane amounts of energy

3645 Las Vegas Blvd S
Las Vegas, NV
(702)473-0193

## Nathan Burton Comedy Magic

• Great for the whole family!
• Nathan's stunning magic show incorporates dazzling showgirls, whimsical illusions, and that boyhood charming personality, which makes this fun & action packed magic show a perfect mix of sheer comedic illusion for people of all ages
• Performing six days a week Tuesday - Sunday

35555 Las Vegas Blvd S
Las Vegas, NV
(800)715-9219

## BeatleShow

• Voted "Best Beatles show across the universe!"
• Come see Paul, John, George and Ringo perform their greatest hits
• For showtimes call 702-932-1818
• Recreates the music and excitement of a real Beatles concert live on stage
• Must purchase adult VIP show ticket

3663 Las Vegas Blvd S
(Planet Hollywood Resort in Miracle Mile Shops)
Las Vegas, NV
(702)932-1818

# Mac King Show

- Fun for the entire family
- This show captures the true essence of both comedy and magic!
- Witness his clever goldfish tricks
- Tuesday, Wednesday, Thursday, Friday, Saturday at 1pm & 3pm

3475 Las Vegas Blvd S
(In main showroom at Harrah's Las Vegas)
Las Vegas, NV
(702)693-6143

# Las Vegas Live Comedy Club

- Las Vegas Live Comedy Club brings together some of the best comics for a show that's sure to leave you in stitches
- Nightly at 9pm.

3663 Las Vegas Blvd S
(located in V Theater in Planet Hollywood Resort in Miracle Mile Shops)
Las Vegas, NV
(702)260-7200

# V - The Ultimate Variety Show

- For showtimes call 702-932-1818
- Must purchase adult VIP show ticket
- Comedy, magic, aerial acrobatics, dancing and modern-day Vaudeville acts
- V has something for everyone
- Voted "Best Show in Vegas!"

3663 Las Vegas Blvd S
(Planet Hollywood Resort in Miracle Mile Shops)
Las Vegas, NV
(702)932-1818

# Tuff-N-Uff

- Helped launch MMA careers of pros such as: Ronda Rousey, Jon Fitch & Ryan Couture
- Proving ground for amateur fighters providing an unparalleled outlet for up & coming fighters
- Founded in 1994
- We strive to help the younger generation of fighters pursue their dreams of becoming professional MMA athletes through the development of individual athletic skills, work ethic, discipline, sportsmanship, self-respect & pride

9811 W Charleston Blvd Suite 2643
Las Vegas, NV
(888)965-8833

# Recycled Percussion

- Great for the whole family!
- Recycled Percussion uses buckets, power tools and anything else they can get their drumsticks on to create their unique style of junk rock.

3663 Las Vegas Blvd S
(Planet Hollywood Resort in Miracle Miles Shop)
Las Vegas, NV
(702)260-7200

# Comedy Pet Theater

- At 4pm except Sunday & Monday.
- From dogs jumping rope to cats pushing strollers, this show is ideal for kids and kids-at-heart.
- Picture the cutest pet trick you can imagine. You'll see it here!

3663 Las Vegas Blvd S
(V Theater inside Miracle Mile Shops of Planet Hollywood Resort & Casino)
Las Vegas, NV
(702)260-7200

## UP TO **$12** VALUE

www.communitylink.koz.com

**Enjoy one complimentary TICKET when a second TICKET of equal or greater value is purchased - maximum discount $12.**

**Promotion valid now thru 12/30/2017**
See reverse side for additional conditions or restrictions.    **D86**

---

## UP TO **$63** VALUE

www.VTheaterBoxOffice.com

**Enjoy one FREE TICKET when a second TICKET of equal or greater value is purchased - maximum discount $63.**

**Promotion valid now thru 12/30/2017**
See reverse side for additional conditions or restrictions.    **D87**

---

## UP TO **$10** VALUE

**Enjoy one complimentary DAY PASS when a second DAY PASS of equal or greater value is purchased - maximum discount $10.**

**Promotion valid now thru 12/30/2017**
See reverse side for additional conditions or restrictions.    **D88**

---

## UP TO **$12** VALUE

www.monsterminigolf.com

**Enjoy one FREE ROUND of MINIATURE GOLF when a second FREE ROUND of MINIATURE GOLF of equal or greater value is purchased - maximum discount $12.**

**Promotion valid now thru 12/30/2017**
See reverse side for additional conditions or restrictions.    **D89**

---

## UP TO **$8** VALUE

www.allfamilyfuncenter.com

**Enjoy one FREE ADMISSION when a second ADMISSION of equal or greater value is purchased - maximum discount $8.**

**Promotion valid now thru 12/30/2017**
See reverse side for additional conditions or restrictions.    **D90**

---

## BUY ONE GET ONE

**Receive ONE COMPLIMENTARY RESERVED LEVEL TICKET when a SECOND RESERVED LEVEL TICKET is purchased.**
Offer valid Sunday through Thursday home games at Cashman Field only. Not valid on fireworks or post-game concerts home games. 51s Management Reserve all rights. Offer expires June 30, 2017.

**Promotion valid now thru 6/30/2017**
See reverse side for additional conditions or restrictions.    **D91**

# Hitzville The Show

- Jin-Jin Reeves and a cast of other talented entertainers revisit some of the greatest Motown hits of all time.
- Dark Sun.
- Performing Mon. - Sat. at 5:30pm

3663 Las Vegas Blvd S
(located in V Theater in Planet Hollywood Resort in Miracle Mile Shops)
Las Vegas, NV
(702)260-7200

# Theatre In The Valley

- Call for reservations & our schedule
- Community theatre in Henderson featuring 4 plays per season

10 W Pacific Ave
Henderson, NV
(702)558-7275

500 Harris St
(at the Valley View Recreation Ctr.)
Henderson, NV
(702)558-7275

# KISS by Monster Mini Golf

- Gift shop.
- Arcade games.
- Indoor glow in the dark KISS themed mini golf.
- Wedding chapel.
- Party room.

4503 PARADISE RD
(Across from Hard Rock Hotel)
Las Vegas, NV
(702)558-6256

# Kids' Club

- Birthday parties & Playgroups
- Day Plays & Monthly Memberships
- Ages 18 months to 8 years old
- Tumblings & Youth Exercise Classes
- 8,000 sqft indoor playground

5831 W Craig Rd Ste 103
Las Vegas, NV
(702)272-2114

# Las Vegas 51s

- $1.00 Beer Thursdays
- New York Mets Triple-A Affiliate
- $1.00 Menu Mondays
- Firework Shows
- Giveaway Nights

850 Las Vegas Blvd N
(Cashman Field)
Las Vegas, NV
(702)943-7204

# All Family Fun Center

- 3D Mini Golf
- Arcade
- Laser Tag
- Party Packages Available

3315 E Russell Rd Ste 4k
(E Russell & Pecos)
Las Vegas, NV
(702)834-7033

## UP TO $10 VALUE

www.balloonswithatwist.com

### Enjoy $10 OFF ANY PARTY BOOKING.
Not Valid with any other discounts or promotions.

**Promotion valid now thru 12/30/2017**
See reverse side for additional conditions or restrictions.  **D92**

---

## SAVE

www.balloonswithatwist.com

### FREE MAGIC SHOW with a 2 Hour Party Booking.
Not Valid with any other discounts or promotions.

**Promotion valid now thru 12/30/2017**
See reverse side for additional conditions or restrictions.  **D93**

---

## UP TO $75 VALUE

www.redrockfencingcenter.com

### Enjoy 50% off the regular price of THREE LESSONS - maximum discount $75.
Valid for Introductory Classes. Call to Schedule an Appointment. Call to Schedule an Appointment. See website for schedules.

**Promotion valid now thru 12/30/2017**
See reverse side for additional conditions or restrictions.  **D94**

---

## UP TO $15 VALUE

www.beecreativeceramics.com

### Enjoy one FREE POTTERY ITEM when a second POTTERY ITEM of equal or greater value is purchased - maximum discount $15.

**Promotion valid now thru 12/30/2017**
See reverse side for additional conditions or restrictions.  **D95**

---

## BUY ONE GET ONE

www.redrockclimbingcenter.com

### Enjoy one FREE LEARN TO CLIMB SERIES when a second LEARN TO CLIMB SERIES of equal or greater value is purchased.
On Availability basis.

**Promotion valid now thru 12/30/2017**
See reverse side for additional conditions or restrictions.  **D96**

---

## BUY ONE GET ONE

www.livegameescape.com

### Enjoy one FREE ADMISSION when a second ADMISSION of equal or greater value is purchased.

**Promotion valid now thru 12/30/2017**
See reverse side for additional conditions or restrictions.  **D97**

# Balloons with a Twist

- Caricature artists
- Air brush face painting
- Balloon decorations
- Pony rides
- Face painters
- Bounce house
- WE COME TO YOU!!
- Clowns
- Magicians
- Photographs
- Costumed characters
- Also ask about...
- Interactive games
- DJs
- Food carts

9811 W Charleston Blvd Ste 2443
Las Vegas, NV
(702)242-8861

# Balloons with a Twist

- Caricature artists
- Air brush face painting
- Balloon decorations
- Pony rides
- Face painters
- Bounce house
- WE COME TO YOU!!
- Clowns
- Magicians
- Photographs
- Costumed characters
- Also ask about...
- Interactive games
- DJs
- Food carts

9811 W Charleston Blvd Ste 2443
Las Vegas, NV
(702)242-8861

# Bee Creative Ceramics

- Large selections of greenware & bisque color & supplies.
- Sun. 10 a.m.-5 p.m.
- Great for all types of party.
- No paint fee - everything all inclusive!
- Paint your own ceramics.
- Fri. & Sat. 10 a.m.-9 p.m.
- Mon.-Thurs. 10 a.m.-8 p.m.

6375 S Pecos
Ste. 112
Las Vegas, NV
(702)998-2545

# Red Rock Fencing Center

5075 Cameron St
Las Vegas, NV
(702)222-1901

# Live Game Escape

- Expand your imaginations with various stimulating brain challenges
- Perfect place to host corporate team trainings, one-of a-kind birthday parties, or other special events
- Four different exciting story escape rooms for your adventure
- First live room escape experience opened in Las Vegas

3300 S Jones Blvd Ste 201
Las Vegas, NV
(702)237-4164

# Red Rock Climbing Center

- Gym membership included.
- Ages 12 & up.
- Call for availability.
- Learn to Climb Series is a 4 week program.
- Free harness and shoe rental.

8201 W CHARLESTON BLVD STE 150
Las Vegas, NV
(702)254-5604

## Fast Lap Indoor Kart Racing

- Just Minutes from the Strip.
- Our Karts were inspired by the 2006 CIK Outdoor World Champions Sodi-Kart.
- Open Daily at 11:00 a.m.
- Karts are equipped with Honda 200cc engines which can reach speeds up to 50 mph!
- We pride ourself on maintaining consistent and equal racing machines for your competitive enjoyment.

3215 Corridor Dr
Mira Loma, CA
(951)681-3601

4288 Polaris Ave
Las Vegas, NV
(702)736-8113

This promotional offer is not valid on any other discount/promotion or on defined holidays. See Rules of Use for more details. Offer valid at all participating locations. Excludes tax, tip, alcohol, and some sale items.          148266

---

## Nevada Climbing Centers

- Fitness Equipment Available
- Over 7,500 sq. ft. of climbing surface
- Party & Events
- Kids Summer Camp

3065 E Patrick Ln Ste 4
Las Vegas, NV
(702)898-8192

This promotional offer is not valid on any other discount/promotion or on defined holidays. See Rules of Use for more details. Offer valid at all participating locations. Excludes tax, tip, alcohol, and some sale items.          0000000XA0I

---

## Fast Lap Indoor Kart Racing

- Just Minutes from the Strip.
- Our Karts were inspired by the 2006 CIK Outdoor World Champions Sodi-Kart.
- Open Daily at 11:00 a.m.
- Karts are equipped with Honda 200cc engines which can reach speeds up to 50 mph!
- We pride ourself on maintaining consistent and equal racing machines for your competitive enjoyment.

3215 Corridor Dr
Mira Loma, CA
(951)681-3601

4288 Polaris Ave
Las Vegas, NV
(702)736-8113

This promotional offer is not valid on any other discount/promotion or on defined holidays. See Rules of Use for more details. Offer valid at all participating locations. Excludes tax, tip, alcohol, and some sale items.          148266

---

## U Bottle It

- Classes include:
- Provide your own or buy our bottles & closures
- Use of equipment and storage needed to make your wine or beer
- Two to four convenient classes set around your schedule for up to 6 people
- Beer extract or wine ingredient kits not included

2230 W Horizon Ridge Pkwy Ste 150
Henderson, NV
(702)565-5040

This promotional offer is not valid on any other discount/promotion or on defined holidays. See Rules of Use for more details. Offer valid at all participating locations. Excludes tax, tip, alcohol, and some sale items.          35658

---

## Fast Lap Indoor Kart Racing

- Just Minutes from the Strip.
- Our Karts were inspired by the 2006 CIK Outdoor World Champions Sodi-Kart.
- Open Daily at 11:00 a.m.
- Karts are equipped with Honda 200cc engines which can reach speeds up to 50 mph!
- We pride ourself on maintaining consistent and equal racing machines for your competitive enjoyment.

3215 Corridor Dr
Mira Loma, CA
(951)681-3601

4288 Polaris Ave
Las Vegas, NV
(702)736-8113

This promotional offer is not valid on any other discount/promotion or on defined holidays. See Rules of Use for more details. Offer valid at all participating locations. Excludes tax, tip, alcohol, and some sale items.          148266

---

## Las Vegas Premier Paintball

- All Day Package includes: entry, air, marker, mask, hopper & tank
- Great for parties and corporate events
- Outdoor paintball with 3 playing fields for different levels of play

1400 N Rampart Blvd
Las Vegas, NV
(702)574-2066

This promotional offer is not valid on any other discount/promotion or on defined holidays. See Rules of Use for more details. Offer valid at all participating locations. Excludes tax, tip, alcohol, and some sale items.          000000014Z0

## UP TO $180 VALUE

www.grandcanyontourandtravel.com

**Enjoy one complimentary GRAND CANYON SOUTH RIM BUS TOUR when a second GRAND CANYON SOUTH RIM BUS TOUR of equal or greater value is purchased - maximum discount $180.**

**Code: Entertainment**

**Promotion valid now thru 12/30/2017**
See reverse side for additional conditions or restrictions.     **D104**

## BUY ONE GET ONE

**Enjoy one complimentary ADMISSION when a second ADMISSION of equal or greater value is purchased.**

Tickets available at UNLV Performing Arts Office. Call for information at 451-6672 or 895-3801. On Availability basis.

**Promotion valid now thru 12/30/2017**
See reverse side for additional conditions or restrictions.     **D105**

## UP TO $60 VALUE

www.hooverdamtourcompany.com

**Enjoy one complimentary HOOVER DAM EXPRESS TOUR when a second HOOVER DAM EXPRESS TOUR of equal or greater value is purchased - maximum discount $60.**

**Code: Entertainment**

**Promotion valid now thru 12/30/2017**
See reverse side for additional conditions or restrictions.     **D106**

## BUY ONE GET ONE

 **NATIONAL ATOMIC TESTING MUSEUM**

www.NationalAtomicTestingMuseum.org

**Enjoy one FREE $14 GENERAL ADMISSION when a second $14 GENERAL ADMISSION is purchased.**

Not Valid with any other discounts or promotions. Area 51 Exhibit Excluded.

**SKU#: 1204**

**Promotion valid now thru 12/30/2017**
See reverse side for additional conditions or restrictions.     **D107**

## UP TO $20 VALUE

www.knotts.com

**Enjoy $20 off REGULAR ADMISSION (ages 12+) .**

Valid any day Knott's Berry Farm is open to the public & regular tickets are on sale. Present this coupon at any Knott's Berry Farm ticket window. Limit six (6) discounts per coupon. Cannot be combined with any other offers or discounts. Hours, prices, promotions & attraction availability are subject to change without notice. Coupon is not valid for special ticket events, Halloween Haunt* or park buyouts.

**Promotion valid now thru 12/30/2017**
See reverse side for additional conditions or restrictions.     **D108**

## UP TO $6 VALUE

www.soakcityoc.com

**Enjoy $6 off REGULAR WATER PARK ADMISSION.**

Valid any day Knott's Soak City Water Park is open to the public & regular tickets are on sale. Present this coupon at any Knott's Soak City Water Park ticket booth. Cannot be combined with any other offers or discounts. Coupon is not valid for any special ticket events or park buyouts. Limit six (6) discounts per coupon. Hours, prices, promotions & attraction availability are subject to change without notice.

**Promotion valid now thru 12/30/2017**
See reverse side for additional conditions or restrictions.     **D109**

# Southern Nevada Musical Arts Society

- Dr. Douglas R. Peterson music director
- Tickets available at UNLV Performing Arts Office or call 895-3801
- Magnificent choral-orchestra
- For a season brochure & information call 451-6672
- Nevada's oldest & most distinguished musical society

3950 Springhill Ave
Las Vegas, NV
(702)451-6672

# Grand Canyon Tour & Travel

- Approximate return to Las Vegas is 8:45 p.m
- Hotel to Hotel Pick-up and Drop-off (Pick-up is approximately at 6:30 a.m.)
- Lunch
- Grand Canyon rim tour with 5 stops
- Deluxe Motor Coach

795 E Tropicana Ave
Las Vegas, NV
(800)422-6966

# National Atomic Testing Museum

- Experience an atomic explosion in the Ground Zero Theater.
- Follow the Nevada Test Site's progression from the first tests to present day.
- Interact with dozens of exhibits, and witness history at five different movie venues.

755 E Flamingo Rd
Las Vegas, NV
(702)794-5150

# Hoover Dam Tour Company

- Mini Las Vegas, Henderson, and Boulder City narrated tour
- Top of the line deluxe motor coach
- Photo opportunities of Lake Mead, Colorado River & Black Canyon with 2 hours at the dam
- Documentary movie en route
- Stop at Ethel M Chocolate Factory (free samples)

795 E Tropicana Ave
Las Vegas, NV
(888)512-0075

15040567

8039 Beach Blvd
Buena Park, CA
(714)220-5200

1 5 0 4 0 2 9 3

8039 Beach Blvd
Buena Park, CA
(714)220-5200

## SAVE

### SIENA
GOLF CLUB

www.sienagolfclub.com

**Enjoy one complimentary GREEN FEE when 3 GREEN FEES of equal or greater value are purchased - maximum discount $189.**

**Promotion valid now thru 12/30/2017**
See reverse side for additional conditions or restrictions.          D110

## SAVE

www.thearroyogolfclub.com

**Enjoy one complimentary GREEN FEE when 3 GREEN FEES of equal or greater value are purchased - maximum discount $189.**

**Promotion valid now thru 12/30/2017**
See reverse side for additional conditions or restrictions.          D111

## SAVE

www.golfbouldercity.com

**Enjoy one complimentary GREEN FEE when 3 GREEN FEES of equal or greater value are purchased - maximum discount $160.**

Reservations Required. Not Valid with any other discounts or promotions.

**Promotion valid now thru 12/30/2017**
See reverse side for additional conditions or restrictions.          D112

## UP TO $8 VALUE

www.golfbouldercity.com

**Enjoy one complimentary BUCKET OF BALLS when a second BUCKET OF BALLS of equal or greater value is purchased - maximum discount $8.**

Not Valid with any other discounts or promotions.

**Promotion valid now thru 12/30/2017**
See reverse side for additional conditions or restrictions.          D113

## SAVE

www.golfbouldercity.com

**Enjoy one complimentary GREEN FEE when 3 GREEN FEES of equal or greater value are purchased - maximum discount $62.**

Reservations Required. Not Valid with any other discounts or promotions.

**Promotion valid now thru 12/30/2017**
See reverse side for additional conditions or restrictions.          D114

## UP TO $5 VALUE

www.golfbouldercity.com

**Enjoy one complimentary BUCKET OF BALLS when a second BUCKET OF BALLS of equal or greater value is purchased - maximum discount $5.**

Not Valid with any other discounts or promotions.

**Promotion valid now thru 12/30/2017**
See reverse side for additional conditions or restrictions.          D115

# Arroyo Golf Club

- The Arroyo Arnold Palmer Course, located at Red Rock Country Club, is open to public play and is located in the Master Planned Community of Summerlin in Las Vegas.
- The Arroyo golf course ribbons seamlessly through the rugged terrain and is nestled between the spectacular landscapes of Red Rock Canyon.

2250c Red Springs Dr
(Sahara Ave. near the 215)
Las Vegas, NV
(702)258-2300

# Siena Golf Club

- Surrounded by the towering Spring Mountains, Siena Golf Club features gently rolling fairways and artful bunkering – plus dazzling views of the Las Vegas skyline.
- Enjoy the waterfalls, Italian inspired buildings, and fine dining, but come for some of the best golf in Vegas!

10575 Siena Monte Ave
Las Vegas, NV
(702)341-9200

# Boulder Creek Golf Club

- 6 Sets of tees
- Generous fairway landing areas
- Greenside contours, bunkers & water features will keep every golfer honest
- A 27 hole Mark Rathert Jewel, Boulder Creek is a challenging, beautiful golf course that, stretches to 7,400 yards... & it's just minutes away from Vegas on the way to Hoover Dam

1501 Veterans Memorial Dr
Boulder City, NV
(702)294-6534

# Boulder Creek Golf Club

- 6 Sets of tees
- Generous fairway landing areas
- Greenside contours, bunkers & water features will keep every golfer honest
- A 27 hole Mark Rathert Jewel, Boulder Creek is a challenging, beautiful golf course that, stretches to 7,400 yards... & it's just minutes away from Vegas on the way to Hoover Dam

1501 Veterans Memorial Dr
Boulder City, NV
(702)294-6534

# Boulder City Golf Course

- Billy Casper & David Rainville designed this scenic, par 72 course
- Hundreds of trees, large receptive greens & open fairways
- Boulder City Golf Course plays at just over 6,500 yards, it is a lush course that treats you like an old friend that hasn't forgotten that golf should be played for fun... & you can walk!

1 Clubhouse Dr
Boulder City, NV
(702)293-9236

# Boulder City Golf Course

- Billy Casper & David Rainville designed this scenic, par 72 course
- Hundreds of trees, large receptive greens & open fairways
- Boulder City Golf Course plays at just over 6,500 yards, it is a lush course that treats you like an old friend that hasn't forgotten that golf should be played for fun... & you can walk!

1 Clubhouse Dr
Boulder City, NV
(702)293-9236

**UP TO $20 VALUE**

**VEGAS HOT**
*yoga & pilates*
www.vegashot.com

**Enjoy the regular price of any LESSONS at 50% off the regular price - maximum discount $20.**

**Promotion valid now thru 12/30/2017**
See reverse side for additional conditions or restrictions.     **D116**

**UP TO $50 VALUE**

**thebodybar(re).**

www.thebodybarre.com

**Enjoy one FREE ONE WEEK OF CLASSES when a second ONE WEEK OF CLASSES of equal or greater value is purchased - maximum discount $50.**

New Clients only.

**Promotion valid now thru 12/30/2017**
See reverse side for additional conditions or restrictions.     **D117**

**UP TO $12 VALUE**

**Namaste** yoga studio

www.namasteyogalasvegas.com

**Enjoy one FREE CLASS when a second CLASS of equal or greater value is purchased - maximum discount $12.**

**Promotion valid now thru 12/30/2017**
See reverse side for additional conditions or restrictions.     **D118**

**UP TO $69 VALUE**

www.fitbodyvegas.com

**Enjoy 50% off the regular price of one MONTH OF CLASSES - maximum discount $69.**

**Promotion valid now thru 12/30/2017**
See reverse side for additional conditions or restrictions.     **D119**

**BUY ONE GET ONE**

*Art of Pilates®*

www.artofpilates.com

**Enjoy one FREE REFORMER CLASSES when second REFORMER CLASSES of equal or greater value is purchased.**

New Clients only.

**Promotion valid now thru 12/30/2017**
See reverse side for additional conditions or restrictions.     **D120**

**UP TO $20 VALUE**

www.climbrefuge.com

**Enjoy one FREE ADMISSION when a second ADMISSION of equal or greater value is purchased - maximum discount $20.**

**Promotion valid now thru 12/30/2017**
See reverse side for additional conditions or restrictions.     **D121**

# thebodybar(re)

- Combination of Pilates, Yoga & Cardio using Ballet Barre.
- Check our website for class schedule.
- All levels welcome.
- Small class size up to 12 people.

2530 SAINT ROSE PKWY STE 150
Henderson, NV
(702)362-2773

# Vegas Hot! Yoga & Pilates

- Call to schedule a tour. One time use only.
- Classes held in heated 7,000-sq.-ft. studio for deeper stretching & detoxification
- www.vegashot.com

5875 S Rainbow Blvd
Las Vegas, NV
(702)257-8171

# Fit Body Boot Camp

- 30 minute sessions.
- Burn twice the fat in half the time!
- Check out our website for class schedule.

7293 W Sahara Ave Suite 1
Las Vegas, NV
(702)750-2956

# Namaste Yoga Studio

- Check website for class schedule.
- Massage.
- Piloxing & Zumba.
- Yoga.
- Fitness Classes.

7240 W Azure Dr Ste 115
Las Vegas, NV
(702)683-1872

# The Refuge Climbing & Fitness

- Over 11,000 sq. ft. of some of the best indoor climbing in the country
- Kids Activities
- Yoga, Bouldering, and Fitness Classes
- Birthday Parties & Corporate Events

6283 S Valley View Blvd Ste C
Las Vegas, NV
(702)383-0175

# Art of Pilates

- Private Pilate Sessions.
- All Fitness Levels Welcome.
- Trainer over 25 years of experience.

6346 S Pecos Rd
(S Pecos & Sunset)
Las Vegas, NV
(702)436-9004

## SPECIAL PRICE

**BODYHEAT**
HOT PILATES & YOGA
www.bodyheatyoga.com

**Enjoy one FREE WEEK OF FREE YOGA.**
New Customers only. Locals only.

**Promotion valid now thru 12/30/2017**
See reverse side for additional conditions or restrictions.　**D122**

## BUY ONE GET ONE

www.cf702.com

**Enjoy one FREE WEEK OF CROSSFIT EXCELERATE BOOT CAMP when a second WEEK OF CROSSFIT EXCELERATE BOOT CAMPof equal or greater value is purchased.**
New Clients only.

**Promotion valid now thru 12/30/2017**
See reverse side for additional conditions or restrictions.　**D123**

## BUY ONE GET ONE

www.hotpilateslasvegas.com

**Enjoy one FREE LESSON when a second LESSON of equal or greater value is purchased.**
New Clients only.

**Promotion valid now thru 12/30/2017**
See reverse side for additional conditions or restrictions.　**D124**

## UP TO $50 VALUE

www.summerlincrossfit.com

**Enjoy one FREE ONE WEEK OF CLASSES when a second ONE WEEK OF CLASSES of equal or greater value is purchased - maximum discount $50.**

New Clients only.

**Promotion valid now thru 12/30/2017**
See reverse side for additional conditions or restrictions.　**D125**

## UP TO $63 VALUE

www.soulfirestudios.com

**Enjoy one FREE ONE MONTH OF CLASSES when a second ONE MONTH OF CLASSES of equal or greater value is purchased - maximum discount $63.**

**Promotion valid now thru 12/30/2017**
See reverse side for additional conditions or restrictions.　**D126**

## UP TO $150 VALUE

www.thepitvegas.com

**Enjoy one FREE ONE MONTH OF MARTIAL ARTS CLASSES when a second ONE MONTH OF MARTIAL ARTS CLASSES of equal or greater value is purchased - maximum discount $150.**
New customers only.

**Promotion valid now thru 12/30/2017**
See reverse side for additional conditions or restrictions.　**D127**

# Crossfit 702

- High-intensity interval training program for "excelerated" fat loss.
- This is 1-hour of nonstop conditioning for anyone who wants to lose fat, tone muscle, gain flexibility and increase cardio.

7520 W WASHINGTON AVE STE 180
Las Vegas, NV
(702)462-6212

# BodyHeat Hot Pilates & Yoga

- Body Sculpt.
- Boot Camp.
- Hot Pilates.
- Hot Yoga.

8876 S Eastern Ave Ste 106
(Eastern & Pebble)
Las Vegas, NV
(702)432-0028

# Summerlin Crossfit

- Personal Training.
- Small class size up to 10 people.
- All levels welcome.
- TRX.
- Crossfit.
- Check our website for class schedule.

3700 S Hualapai Way Ste 104
(S Hualapai & Twain)
Las Vegas, NV
(702)240-7523

# Inferno Hot Pilates

- Piloxing.
- Hot Pilates.
- Bikini Bottom.
- Zumba.
- TRX Suspension.
- Power Sculpt.
- Kettlebell.

5752 S FORT APACHE RD STE 155
Las Vegas, NV
(702)262-5557

# The Pit Vegas

- Check out our website for class schedule
- Mixed martial arts, karate, kickboxing, & fitness
- We are a full service martial arts school catering to men, women, & children of all ages & athletic abilities

930 Wigwam Pkwy
Henderson, NV
(702)900-2728

# Soulfire Studios

- Check out website for class schedule
- Story Dance Camps
- Performance Arts Workshop
- Classes for age 20 months to adult
- Check our website for class schedule

8540 W Lake Mead Blvd Ste 110
Las Vegas, NV
(702)207-7685

**UP TO $60 VALUE**

www.hollywoodkidsacademy.com

**Enjoy one complimentary ONE MOTH CLASS, upon payment of same of equal or greater value - maximum discount $60.**

New clients only. For dance or vocal classes only.

**Promotion valid now thru 12/30/2017**
See reverse side for additional conditions or restrictions.    **D128**

---

**BUY ONE GET ONE**

www.hollywoodkidsacademy.com

**Enjoy one complimentary TICKET when a second TICKET of equal or greater value is purchased.**

**Promotion valid now thru 12/30/2017**
See reverse side for additional conditions or restrictions.    **D129**

---

**UP TO $200 VALUE**

www.diamonddancestudio.com

**Enjoy one FREE ONE CLASS PACKAGE when a second ONE CLASS PACKAGE of equal or greater value is purchased - maximum discount $200.**

New Customers only.

**Promotion valid now thru 12/30/2017**
See reverse side for additional conditions or restrictions.    **D130**

---

**UP TO $40 VALUE**

www.PamelaAnnSchoolofDance.com

**Enjoy one FREE ONE MONTH OF DANCE LESSONS when a second MONTH OF DANCE LESSONS of equal or greater value is purchased - maximum discount $40.**
New Customers only. Valid for one hour classes only.Excludes Private, Pilates & Musical Theater.

**Promotion valid now thru 12/30/2017**
See reverse side for additional conditions or restrictions.    **D131**

---

**SAVE**

www.SummerlinDance.com

**Enjoy one FREE MONTH OF DANCE CLASSES AND REGISTRATION with purchase of a second MONTH OF DANCE CLASSES - maximum discount $55.**
New students only.

**Promotion valid now thru 12/30/2017**
See reverse side for additional conditions or restrictions.    **D132**

---

**UP TO $15 VALUE**

**Enjoy 50% off the regular price of a CLASS - maximum discount $15.**

**Promotion valid now thru 12/30/2017**
See reverse side for additional conditions or restrictions.    **D133**

# Hollywood Kids Theater

• Check out our website for show dates and times!

| | | |
|---|---|---|
| 10870 S Eastern Ave Ste 101 Henderson, NV (702)633-5500 | 4161 N Rancho Dr Ste 140 Las Vegas, NV (702)633-5500 | 6500 E Sahara Ave Las Vegas, NV (702)633-5500 |

# Hollywood Kids Academy

• Where dreams come true!
• We offer dancing, singing & acting classes
• For children ages 3 - 9

| | | |
|---|---|---|
| 10870 S Eastern Ave Ste 101 Henderson, NV (702)633-5500 | 4161 N Rancho Dr Ste 140 Las Vegas, NV (702)633-5500 | 6500 E Sahara Ave Las Vegas, NV (702)633-5500 |

# Pamela Ann School of Dance

• "Where Dancing Is Still Fun"
• Zumba, Yoga, and Pilates.
• Over 20 years of experience.
• Ballet, Jazz, Hip-Hop, Tap, Break dancing, and Lyrical.
• Mommy & Me classes.
• Ages 18 months to Adult.

55 S Gibson Rd Ste 113
(off the 215 & Gibson)
Henderson, NV
(702)629-3322

# Diamond Dance Studio

• Check our website for class schedule
• Private lessons available
• Classes for ages 2 & up in Tap, Jazz, Ballet, Contemporary, Lyrical, Musical Theater, Hip Hop & Tumbling
• We have a competition team that competes throughout the year

3 Sunset Way Suite A17
Henderson, NV
(702)326-4265

# Polecats Aerial Fitness

• Memberships & Private Lessons Available
• Yoga
• Aerial Silks
• Pole Fitness
• Lyra/Aerial Hoop
• Pilates
• Check out our class schedule on our Facebook

7920 S Rainbow Blvd Ste 105
(S Rainbow & Windmill)
Las Vegas, NV
(702)998-9044

# Studio One's Summerlin Dance Academy

• Ranked #1 dance studio in Nevada and Top 25 in the US by the Federation of Dance Competitions
• Check our our website for class schedule
• From Hip Hop to Contemporary, Tap to Jazz, and many others, classes are offered for beginning students to the advanced & competitive levels

| | | |
|---|---|---|
| 1535 W Warm Springs Rd Ste 100 Henderson, NV (702)202-9561 | 1181 S Buffalo Dr Ste 130 Las Vegas, NV (702)838-5131 | 6070 S Rainbow Blvd Ste 8 Las Vegas, NV (702)897-5095 |

# Local Retail & Services Index

# Get More

## Get thousands more discounts to use at home or when traveling.

Download the mobile app now, included with this membership.
Search for "Entertainment® Coupons" in your app store.

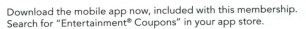

**Get these offers, and thousands more, on the mobile app!**
Search for **"Entertainment® Coupons"** in your app store to download.

# Use Your Phone To Save®

## Download the Entertainment® Mobile App
## **Included** with This Membership

**SHOW YOUR
PHONE TO SAVE**
Simply show your mobile
coupon to the merchant
to receive your discount.

**SAVE ACROSS
THE NATION**
Save at thousands of
locations at home and
when you travel.

**FIND WHAT'S
NEAR YOU**
Geolocators allow you to
find great discounts near
you, wherever you go.

**MERCHANT INFO**
View locations, offers,
redemption information,
phone numbers, and more.

**EASILY BROWSE**
View offers by location,
category, distance from
you, and redemption type.
Find the perfect offer!

Search for "Entertainment® Coupons" in your app store, or visit
**www.entertainment.com/mobile** for more information.

## Jockey

Valid at All Participating Locations.

www.entertainment.com

# $10 OFF

### $10 OFF a purchase of
### $60 or more.
Offer cannot be combined with any
other coupons. Excludes all Jockey bras.

**JOCKEY.**

Associate enter code: 000009097438

www.jockey.com

**Promotion valid now thru 12/31/2017**
See reverse side for additional conditions or restrictions.

**E1**

---

## Jockey

Valid at All Participating Locations.

www.entertainment.com

# $15 OFF

### $15 OFF a purchase of
### $75 or more.
Offer cannot be combined with any
other coupons. Excludes all Jockey bras.

**JOCKEY.**

Associate enter code: 000009097445

www.jockey.com

**Promotion valid now thru 12/31/2017**
See reverse side for additional conditions or restrictions.

**E2**

---

## Jockey

Valid at All Participating Locations.

entertainment
www.entertainment.com

# $20 OFF

### $20 OFF a purchase of
### $100 or more.
Offer cannot be combined with any
other coupons. Excludes all Jockey bras.

**JOCKEY.**

Associate enter code: 000009097452

www.jockey.com

**Promotion valid now thru 12/31/2017**
See reverse side for additional conditions or restrictions.

**E3**

0  00009 09743  8

Valid at All Participating Locations.

49783647

This promotional offer is not valid on any other discount/promotion or on defined holidays. See Rules of Use for more details. Offer valid at all participating locations. Excludes tax, tip, alcohol, and some sale items.

0  00009 09744  5

Valid at All Participating Locations.

49783672

This promotional offer is not valid on any other discount/promotion or on defined holidays. See Rules of Use for more details. Offer valid at all participating locations. Excludes tax, tip, alcohol, and some sale items.

0  00009 09745  2

Valid at All Participating Locations.

49783675

This promotional offer is not valid on any other discount/promotion or on defined holidays. See Rules of Use for more details. Offer valid at all participating locations. Excludes tax, tip, alcohol, and some sale items.

# $10 VALUE

heartland.jiffylube.com

**Enjoy $10 off the regular price of any ROTELLA®
T5 SYNTHETIC BLEND OR ROTELLA® T6 FULL
SYNTHETIC OIL CHANGE.**

Coupon required. No appointment necessary. Not valid on conventional oil, Value
Oil Change Plus*, or with any other offer or discount for the same service. Extra
charge for 4X4s. Jiffy Lube* , the Jiffy Lube design mark and Jiffy Lube Signature
Service* are registered trademarks of Jiffy Lube International, Inc.* . © 2016 Jiffy
Lube International, Inc.All rights reserved. ©SOPUS products. All rights reserved.

**Code: MG88M2**

**Promotion valid now thru 12/30/2017**
See reverse side for additional conditions or restrictions.          **E4**

---

# $25 VALUE

heartland.jiffylube.com

**Enjoy $25 off the regular price of any
FUEL SYSTEM CLEANING SERVICE.**

Coupon required. No appointment necessary. Not valid with any other
offer or discount for the same service. Offer not valid on PLUS services. Jiffy
Lube* , the Jiffy Lube design mark and Jiffy Lube Signature Service* are
registered trademarks of Jiffy Lube International, Inc.* . © 2016 Jiffy Lube
International, Inc.All rights reserved. ©SOPUS products. All rights reserved.

**Code: TB6DQ2**

**Promotion valid now thru 12/30/2017**
See reverse side for additional conditions or restrictions.          **E5**

---

# $25 VALUE

heartland.jiffylube.com

**Enjoy $25 off the regular price of any
SERPENTINE BELT SERVICE.**

Coupon required. No appointment necessary. Not valid with any other
offer or discount for the same service. Offer not valid on PLUS services. Jiffy
Lube* , the Jiffy Lube design mark and Jiffy Lube Signature Service* are
registered trademarks of Jiffy Lube International, Inc.* . © 2016 Jiffy Lube
International, Inc.All rights reserved. ©SOPUS products. All rights reserved.

**Code: G7Y8U2**

**Promotion valid now thru 12/30/2017**
See reverse side for additional conditions or restrictions.          **E6**

---

# $25 VALUE

heartland.jiffylube.com

**Enjoy $25 off the regular price of any
RADIATOR ANTIFREEZE/COOLANT SERVICE.**

Coupon required. No appointment necessary. Not valid with any other offer or
discount for the same service. Offer not valid on PLUS services. Jiffy Lube* , the
Jiffy Lube design mark and Jiffy Lube Signature Service* are registered
trademarks of Jiffy Lube International, Inc.* . © 2016 Jiffy Lube International,
Inc.All rights reserved. ©SOPUS products. All rights reserved.

**Code: WGNAE2**

**Promotion valid now thru 12/30/2017**
See reverse side for additional conditions or restrictions.          **E7**

---

# $30 VALUE

heartland.jiffylube.com

**Enjoy $30 off the regular price of any AIR
CONDITIONING SERVICE.**

Coupon required. No appointment necessary. Not valid with any other
offer or discount for the same service. Offer not valid on PLUS services. Jiffy
Lube* , the Jiffy Lube design mark and Jiffy Lube Signature Service* are
registered trademarks of Jiffy Lube International, Inc.* . © 2016 Jiffy Lube
International, Inc.All rights reserved. ©SOPUS products. All rights reserved.

**Code: E97MM2**

**Promotion valid now thru 12/30/2017**
See reverse side for additional conditions or restrictions.          **E8**

---

# $10 VALUE

heartland.jiffylube.com

**Enjoy $10 off the regular price of any
PENNZOIL HIGH MILEAGE VEHICLE®,
GOLD™, SYNTHETIC BLEND, PLATINUM® WITH
PUREPLUS™ TECHNOLOGY, OR ULTRA PLATINUM®
WITH PUREPLUS™ TECHNOLOGY OIL CHANGE.**

Coupon required. No appt necessary. Not valid on conventional oil, Value Oil Change Plus*,
or with any other offer or discount for the same service. Extra charge for 4X4s. Jiffy Lube* , the
Jiffy Lube design mark & Jiffy Lube Signature Service* are registered trademarks of Jiffy
Lube International, Inc.* . © 2016 Jiffy Lube International, Inc.All rights reserved. ©SOPUS
products.

**Code: DGJAS2**

**Promotion valid now thru 12/30/2017**
See reverse side for additional conditions or restrictions.          **E9**

# Jiffy Lube

• No appointment necessary
• Visit our website for participating service centers & details

Visit heartland.jiffylube.com for participating locations and service descriptions.

This promotional offer is not valid on any other discount/promotion or on defined holidays. See Rules of Use for more details. Offer valid at all participating locations. Excludes tax, tip, alcohol, and some sale items.     0000000QYZF

# Jiffy Lube

• No appointment necessary
• Visit our website for participating service centers & details

Visit heartland.jiffylube.com for participating locations and service descriptions.

This promotional offer is not valid on any other discount/promotion or on defined holidays. See Rules of Use for more details. Offer valid at all participating locations. Excludes tax, tip, alcohol, and some sale items.     0000000QYYY

# Jiffy Lube

• No appointment necessary
• Visit our website for participating service centers & details

Visit heartland.jiffylube.com for participating locations and service descriptions.

This promotional offer is not valid on any other discount/promotion or on defined holidays. See Rules of Use for more details. Offer valid at all participating locations. Excludes tax, tip, alcohol, and some sale items.     0000000QYZ4

# Jiffy Lube

• No appointment necessary
• Visit our website for participating service centers & details

Visit heartland.jiffylube.com for participating locations and service descriptions.

This promotional offer is not valid on any other discount/promotion or on defined holidays. See Rules of Use for more details. Offer valid at all participating locations. Excludes tax, tip, alcohol, and some sale items.     0000000QYZI

# Jiffy Lube

• No appointment necessary
• Visit our website for participating service centers & details

Visit heartland.jiffylube.com for participating locations and service descriptions.

0000000QY4J

# Jiffy Lube

• No appointment necessary
• Visit our website for participating service centers & details

Visit heartland.jiffylube.com for participating locations and service descriptions.

This promotional offer is not valid on any other discount/promotion or on defined holidays. See Rules of Use for more details. Offer valid at all participating locations. Excludes tax, tip, alcohol, and some sale items.     0000000QYZA

**TERMITE / PEST CONTROL**
www.delconpestcontrol.com

### Enjoy $15 off ONE TIME TREATMENT - maximum discount $15.
New clients only.

**Promotion valid now thru 12/30/2017**
See reverse side for additional conditions or restrictions.    E10

---

**TERMITE / PEST CONTROL**
www.delconpestcontrol.com

### Enjoy $30 off COMPLETE PIGEON CONTROL - maximum discount $30.
Includes eradicate Pigeons, wash roof, remove nests, spiking & screening. New clients only. Some restrictions apply.

**Promotion valid now thru 12/30/2017**
See reverse side for additional conditions or restrictions.    E11

---

**TERMITE / PEST CONTROL**
www.delconpestcontrol.com

### Enjoy $25 off any BEE SERVICE - maximum discount $25.
New clients only.

**Promotion valid now thru 12/30/2017**
See reverse side for additional conditions or restrictions.    E12

---

**TERMITE / PEST CONTROL**
www.delconpestcontrol.com

### Enjoy 50% off INITIAL SERVICE.
With one year agreement. New clients only.

**Promotion valid now thru 12/30/2017**
See reverse side for additional conditions or restrictions.    E13

---

pestcontrol702.com

### Enjoy an INITIAL SERVICE for $39.
With a one year agreement.

**Promotion valid now thru 12/30/2017**
See reverse side for additional conditions or restrictions.    E14

---

pestcontrol702.com

### Enjoy 25% off NIGHT-TIME BLACK LIGHT SCORPION TREATMENT.

**Promotion valid now thru 12/30/2017**
See reverse side for additional conditions or restrictions.    E15

# Delcon Termite & Pest Control

- Over 30 Years of Experience.
- Local Family Owned.
- Same Day Service.
- Safe for Children & Pets.
- Residential & Commercial.

Servicing Las Vegas, Henderson, Summerlin & Mesquite. (702)656-0455.

# Delcon Termite & Pest Control

- Over 30 Years of Experience.
- Local Family Owned.
- Same Day Service.
- Safe for Children & Pets.
- Residential & Commercial.

Servicing Las Vegas, Henderson, Summerlin & Mesquite. (702)656-0455.

# Delcon Termite & Pest Control

- Over 30 Years of Experience.
- Local Family Owned.
- Same Day Service.
- Safe for Children & Pets.
- Residential & Commercial.

Servicing Las Vegas, Henderson, Summerlin & Mesquite. (702)656-0455.

# Delcon Termite & Pest Control

- Over 30 Years of Experience.
- Local Family Owned.
- Same Day Service.
- Safe for Children & Pets.
- Residential & Commercial.

Servicing Las Vegas, Henderson, Summerlin & Mesquite. (702)656-0455.

# Innovative Pest Management

- Prompt Same Day Service
- Very Affordable Rates
- Safe for Children & Pets
- Residential & Commercial

Please call us at (702)522-8300.

# Innovative Pest Management

- Prompt Same Day Service
- Very Affordable Rates
- Safe for Children & Pets
- Residential & Commercial

Please call us at (702)522-8300.

## UP TO $10 VALUE

www.lakescleaners.com

**Enjoy 50% off the regular price of any DRY CLEANING ORDER - maximum discount $10.**

**Promotion valid now thru 12/30/2017**
See reverse side for additional conditions or restrictions.          **E16**

## UP TO $10 VALUE

**Village East Cleaners**

www.villageeastcleaners.com

**Enjoy 50% off the regular price of any DRY CLEANING ORDER - maximum discount $10.**
Household items and Alterations excluded. Leather, suede, furs, drapes, wedding gowns, laundry & storage excluded.

**Promotion valid now thru 12/30/2017**
See reverse side for additional conditions or restrictions.          **E17**

---

## UP TO $10 VALUE

www.lakescleaners.com

**Enjoy 50% off the regular price of any DRY CLEANING ORDER - maximum discount $10.**

**Promotion valid now thru 12/30/2017**
See reverse side for additional conditions or restrictions.          **E18**

## UP TO $10 VALUE

**Village East Cleaners**

www.villageeastcleaners.com

**Enjoy 50% off the regular price of any DRY CLEANING ORDER - maximum discount $10.**
Household items and Alterations excluded. Leather, suede, furs, drapes, wedding gowns, laundry & storage excluded.

**Promotion valid now thru 12/30/2017**
See reverse side for additional conditions or restrictions.          **E19**

---

## UP TO 50% OFF

www.cleanbaycleaners.com

**Enjoy any DRY CLEANING ORDER at 50% off the regular price.**
New Customers only.

**Promotion valid now thru 12/30/2017**
See reverse side for additional conditions or restrictions.          **E20**

## UP TO $10 VALUE

**Village East Cleaners**

www.villageeastcleaners.com

**Enjoy 50% off the regular price of any DRY CLEANING ORDER - maximum discount $10.**
Household items and Alterations excluded. Leather, suede, furs, drapes, wedding gowns, laundry & storage excluded.

**Promotion valid now thru 12/30/2017**
See reverse side for additional conditions or restrictions.          **E21**

# Village East Cleaners & Alterations Center

- Member of the association of wedding gown specialties
- Sun 10am- 3pm
- Drive-thru on Horizon Ridge location
- Mon - Sat 7am -7pm
- Established 1978
- $25 off wedding gown preservation
- Village East Cleaners is the 'Greener' Dry Cleaner

11041 S Eastern Ave
(Eastern & Sunridge Heights)
Henderson, NV
(702)933-2110

1760 W Horizon Ridge Pkwy
(Horizon Ridge & Valle Verde)
Henderson, NV
(702)897-0098

# Lakes Cleaners & Laundry

- Pick Up & Delivery
- Same day cleaning - In by 9am and Out by 2pm
- We recycle hangers!
- Sat 9am - 2pm
- Mon - Fri 6am - 6pm
- Drive thru

8657 W Sahara Ave
(E of Citibank on W Sahara)
Las Vegas, NV
(702)363-4800

# Village East Cleaners & Alterations Center

- Member of the association of wedding gown specialties
- Sun 10am- 3pm
- Drive-thru on Horizon Ridge location
- Mon - Sat 7am -7pm
- Established 1978
- $25 off wedding gown preservation
- Village East Cleaners is the 'Greener' Dry Cleaner

11041 S Eastern Ave
(Eastern & Sunridge Heights)
Henderson, NV
(702)933-2110

1760 W Horizon Ridge Pkwy
(Horizon Ridge & Valle Verde)
Henderson, NV
(702)897-0098

# Lakes Cleaners & Laundry

- Pick Up & Delivery
- Same day cleaning - In by 9am and Out by 2pm
- We recycle hangers!
- Sat 9am - 2pm
- Mon - Fri 6am - 6pm
- Drive thru

8657 W Sahara Ave
(E of Citibank on W Sahara)
Las Vegas, NV
(702)363-4800

# Village East Cleaners & Alterations Center

- Member of the association of wedding gown specialties
- Sun 10am- 3pm
- Drive-thru on Horizon Ridge location
- Mon - Sat 7am -7pm
- Established 1978
- $25 off wedding gown preservation
- Village East Cleaners is the 'Greener' Dry Cleaner

11041 S Eastern Ave
(Eastern & Sunridge Heights)
Henderson, NV
(702)933-2110

1760 W Horizon Ridge Pkwy
(Horizon Ridge & Valle Verde)
Henderson, NV
(702)897-0098

# Cleanbay Cleaners

- You Live, We Clean, Green
- Laundry Service, Tailorinig & Recycle Programs
- Free Pick Up & Delivery

278 E Lake Mead Pkwy
Ste A
Henderson, NV
(702)558-0364

310 E Warm Springs
Rd Ste C
Las Vegas, NV
(702)260-9955

# 50% OFF

## THE TAX & WEALTH GROUP

**Enjoy 50% off INDIVIDUAL INCOME TAX PREPARATION (includes all schedules & state tax if needed).**
New clients only.

**Promotion valid now thru 12/30/2017**
See reverse side for additional conditions or restrictions.       E22

---

# UP TO $3 VALUE

**Enjoy $3 off a SELF WASH & BLOW DRY (regularly $15).**

**Promotion valid now thru 12/30/2017**
See reverse side for additional conditions or restrictions.       E23

---

# UP TO $5 VALUE

## Edible
### ARRANGEMENTS
EdibleArrangements.com

**Enjoy $5 off any ORDER of $25 or more.**
Valid on select products at locations listed. Cannot be combined with any other offers. Offer code must be mentioned when placing order. Local orders only. One discount per customer per visit.

**Code: ENTB2014**

**Promotion valid now thru 12/30/2017**
See reverse side for additional conditions or restrictions.       E24

---

# UP TO 10% OFF

**Enjoy 10% off any RETAIL PURCHASE.**
Exclude sale items.

**Promotion valid now thru 12/30/2017**
See reverse side for additional conditions or restrictions.       E25

---

# SAVE

## Edible
### ARRANGEMENTS
EdibleArrangements.com

**Enjoy a FREE 8 DIPPED BANANAS in any arrangement - maximum discount $12.**
Valid on select products at locations listed. Cannot be combined with any other offers. Offer code must be mentioned when placing order. Local orders only. One discount per customer per visit.

**Code: ENTB2014**

**Promotion valid now thru 12/30/2017**
See reverse side for additional conditions or restrictions.       E26

---

# UP TO $5 VALUE

**Enjoy $5 off a SELF WASH & BLOW DRY (regularly $15).**

**Promotion valid now thru 12/30/2017**
See reverse side for additional conditions or restrictions.       E27

# The Soggy Dog

- Closed Mondays.
- Health & wellness center for your pets.
- We provide towels, aprons, shampoo, blow dryers, brushes & grooming table.
- Waist high tub with warm water.
- You wash your dog, we clean the mess!
- Pet foods, toys, treats, collars, supplements, shampoos.

1450 W Horizon Ridge Pkwy Ste C202
(Just off I-215 Exit Stephanie; S. in Foothills Plaza)
Henderson, NV
(702)452-3647

---

# The Tax & Wealth Group

- Securities offered through Questar Capital Corporation, Member FINRA/SIPC
- Individual & business tax returns
- We welcome out of state residence & file all 50 states
- Services include stocks, bonds, mutual funds, retirement planning and annuities
- We specialize in rental & investment income taxes
- The Tax & Wealth Group , Inc is independent of Questar Capital Corp

7469 W Lake Mead Blvd Ste 140
Las Vegas, NV
(702)202-0755

---

# The Soggy Dog

- Closed Mondays.
- Health & wellness center for your pets.
- We provide towels, aprons, shampoo, blow dryers, brushes & grooming table.
- Waist high tub with warm water.
- You wash your dog, we clean the mess!
- Pet foods, toys, treats, collars, supplements, shampoos.

1450 W Horizon Ridge Pkwy Ste C202
(Just off I-215 Exit Stephanie; S. in Foothills Plaza)
Henderson, NV
(702)452-3647

---

# Edible Arrangements

- Corporate accounts welcome.
- Pick Up & Delivery available.
- Fresh Fruit Bouquets for All Occasions.

Henderson
213 N Stephanie St
Ste A
(702)434-8334

Las Vegas
1291 S Decatur Blvd
Ste 140
(702)822-4469

3754 E Flamingo Rd
(702)433-2491

6454 Sky Pointe Dr
Ste 160
(702)453-7848

7260 W Lake Mead
Blvd Ste 3
(702)243-1866

8174 Las Vegas Blvd
S Ste 106
(702)263-1474

8520 W Desert Inn
Rd Ste E4
(702)256-3331

---

# The Soggy Dog

- Closed Mondays.
- Health & wellness center for your pets.
- We provide towels, aprons, shampoo, blow dryers, brushes & grooming table.
- Waist high tub with warm water.
- You wash your dog, we clean the mess!
- Pet foods, toys, treats, collars, supplements, shampoos.

1450 W Horizon Ridge Pkwy Ste C202
(Just off I-215 Exit Stephanie; S. in Foothills Plaza)
Henderson, NV
(702)452-3647

---

# Edible Arrangements

- Corporate accounts welcome.
- Pick Up & Delivery available.
- Fresh Fruit Bouquets for All Occasions.

Henderson
213 N Stephanie St
Ste A
(702)434-8334

Las Vegas
1291 S Decatur Blvd
Ste 140
(702)822-4469

3754 E Flamingo Rd
(702)433-2491

6454 Sky Pointe Dr
Ste 160
(702)453-7848

7260 W Lake Mead
Blvd Ste 3
(702)243-1866

8174 Las Vegas Blvd
S Ste 106
(702)263-1474

8520 W Desert Inn
Rd Ste E4
(702)256-3331

**UP TO $25 VALUE**

# SUPERIOR TINTING

www.superiorautoglasstinting.com

**Enjoy 20% off the regular price of any FULL-SIZED VEHICLE TINTING SERVICE - maximum discount $25.**

Specials Excluded.

**Promotion valid now thru 12/30/2017**
See reverse side for additional conditions or restrictions.          E28

---

## 10% OFF

**Enjoy 10% off any EPOXY FLOOR equal to or greater than 400 sq.ft.**

**Promotion valid now thru 12/30/2017**
See reverse side for additional conditions or restrictions.          E29

---

## $25 OFF

www.precisiontune.com

**$25 Off Brake Service.**

Coupon Code: EB. Valid at participating locations only. Not valid with any other offers. Discount off regular price. Other restrictions may apply.

**Coupon Code: EB**

**Promotion valid now thru 12/30/2017**
See reverse side for additional conditions or restrictions.          E30

---

## $5 OFF

www.precisiontune.com

**$5 Off Any Premium Oil Change Service.**

Coupon Code: EB. Not valid with any other offers. Discount off regular price. Other restrictions may apply. Valid at participating locations only.

**Coupon Code: EB**

**Promotion valid now thru 12/30/2017**
See reverse side for additional conditions or restrictions.          E31

---

**UP TO $10 VALUE**

www.brakemasterslv.com

**Enjoy $10 off the regular price of an OIL CHANGE.**

**Promotion valid now thru 12/30/2017**
See reverse side for additional conditions or restrictions.          E32

---

**UP TO $50 VALUE**

www.brakemasterslv.com

**Enjoy 20% off the regular price of any AUTO SERVICE - maximum discount $50.**

**Promotion valid now thru 12/30/2017**
See reverse side for additional conditions or restrictions.          E33

# All Things Garage

- Garage Flooring Coatings
- Custom Cabinetry
- Ceiling Storage Solutions
- Heavy Duty Wall Shelving

3065 North Rancho Drive, Suite 180
Las Vegas, NV
(702)525-2501

# Superior Tinting

- Headlamp polishing
- Rock chip repair
- Auto tinting
- Quality service since 1967
- Windshield replacement

2695 S Decatur Blvd Ste 200
Las Vegas, NV
(702)877-3222

# Precision Tune

- 1-800-GET-TUNE

Valid at All Participating Locations.

# Precision Tune

- 1-800-GET-TUNE

Valid at All Participating Locations.

# Brake Masters

- An Honest Brake since 1983.
- Lifetime Brakes.
- Fleet Service Available.
- Shuttle Service.
- A/C Service & Repair.
- Express Oil & Filter.
- Extended Warranties Accepted.
- Radiator, Batteries, Transmission Fluid Exchange, Alignments, and Much More.

3540 E Tropicana Ave Ste 100
Las Vegas, NV
(702)454-7100

# Brake Masters

- A/C Service & Repair.
- Shuttle Service.
- An Honest Brake since 1983.
- Lifetime Brakes.
- Radiator, Batteries, Transmission Fluid Exchange, Alignments, and Much More.
- Fleet Service Available.
- Express Oil & Filter.
- Extended Warranties Accepted.

| 1910 N Rock Springs Dr Las Vegas, NV (702)454-0006 | 8080 S Eastern Ave Las Vegas, NV (702)454-0003 | 4620 W Craig Rd N Las Vegas, NV (702)454-0500 |

UP TO **10%** OFF

www.movingcompanynorthlasvegas.com

**Enjoy 10% off the TOTAL BILL.**

**Promotion valid now thru 12/30/2017**
See reverse side for additional conditions or restrictions. **E34**

UP TO **$50** VALUE

www.movingcompanynorthlasvegas.com

**Enjoy 20% off the TOTAL BILL -
maximum discount $50.**

**Promotion valid now thru 12/30/2017**
See reverse side for additional conditions or restrictions. **E35**

UP TO **$30** VALUE

www.southwestbikes.com

**Enjoy 20% off the TOTAL
PURCHASE - maximum discount
$30.**
Sale Items Excluded.

**Promotion valid now thru 12/30/2017**
See reverse side for additional conditions or restrictions. **E36**

UP TO **50%** OFF

www.BubblesAutoSpa.net

**Enjoy 50% off ULTIMATE WASH.**
Must redeem coupon in office. Must redeem coupon in office.

**Promotion valid now thru 12/30/2017**
See reverse side for additional conditions or restrictions. **E37**

UP TO **$15** VALUE

www.potteryshopstudio.com

**Enjoy one FREE POTTERY ITEM
when a second POTTERY ITEM of
equal or greater value is purchased
- maximum discount $15.**

**Promotion valid now thru 12/30/2017**
See reverse side for additional conditions or restrictions. **E38**

UP TO **$5** VALUE

www.childrensorchard.com

**Enjoy $5 off a minimum purchase
of $20.**

**Promotion valid now thru 12/30/2017**
See reverse side for additional conditions or restrictions. **E39**

# Denali Moving

- Competitive Pricing
- 7 Days A Week
- Courteous & Professional
- Local & Long Distance Moving
- All Necessary Padding & Equipment Provided
- Licensed. Bonded. Insured.
- Residential & Commercial
- Storage Units Available

201 Commerce Park Ct
North Las Vegas, NV
(702)369-1070

# Denali Moving

- Competitive Pricing
- 7 Days A Week
- Courteous & Professional
- Local & Long Distance Moving
- All Necessary Padding & Equipment Provided
- Licensed. Bonded. Insured.
- Residential & Commercial
- Storage Units Available

201 Commerce Park Ct
North Las Vegas, NV
(702)369-1070

This promotional offer is not valid on any other discount/promotion or on defined holidays. See Rules of Use for more details. Offer valid at all participating locations. Excludes tax, tip, alcohol, and some sale items.  00000020KVM

# Bubbles AutoSpa

- 8 vacuum bays
- Free hot dogs, tacos and shaved ice treats from 10am to 5pm
- Full service detailing
- New, state of the art automotive touchless laserwash
- Spot carpet cleaner
- 6 newly equipped self service wash bays

2535 S Torrey Pines Dr
(S Torrey Pines & Sahara)
Las Vegas, NV
(702)489-7990

# Southwest Bikes

- Fri & Sat 10am- 7pm
- Mon - Thur 10am - 6pm
- Knowledgeable staff & certified mechanics
- Full line of bikes - road, mountain, cross bikes, cruisers & BMX
- Bike fit, parts, accessories, apparel and service
- Sun 12pm -5pm
- Join our cycling club!
- Bike rentals available

7260 W Azure Dr Ste 110
Las Vegas, NV
(702)227-RIDE

# Children'S Orchard

- Find a Treasure.
- Save a Fortune.

7035 W Ann Rd Ste 140
Las Vegas, NV
(702)839-1991

# The Pottery Shop

- Home parties
- Parties available
- Open 7 days
- No appointment necessary
- School fundraisers
- Kids camp
- Classroom workshops
- Pieces range from $8 to $70
- Weekly specials
- Story time

6623 LAS VEGAS BLVD S UNIT 140
(In Town Square)
LAS VEGAS, NV
(702)699-5600

# National Retail & Services

It's easy to save on these great brands and more!

Find a complete listing of this section's merchants on the back of this page.

 MEN'S WEARHOUSE

**Find 100s more offers:**
www.entertainment.com/shop & on the mobile app

NATIONAL RETAIL & SERVICES

# National Retail & Services Index

This is a listing of our National merchants.
For Local Retail & Services listings, see the index for section E.

the magic of
## macy's
.com

**UP TO 20% OFF**

the magic of
### macy's
.com

## TAKE AN EXTRA 20% OFF*

A single purchase of select regular, sale & clearance clothing & accessories (extra 10% off select sale & clearance home items, shoes, coats, suits, dresses, lingerie, swim for her, men's suit separates & sport coats & jewelry; select sale & clearance watches; select regular-priced items).

*Exclusions apply; see reverse.

**Promotion valid now thru 12/31/2017**
See reverse side for additional conditions or restrictions.

F1

**UP TO 20% OFF**

the magic of
### macy's
.com

## TAKE AN EXTRA 20% OFF*

A single purchase of select regular, sale & clearance clothing & accessories (extra 10% off select sale & clearance home items, shoes, coats, suits, dresses, lingerie, swim for her, men's suit separates & sport coats & jewelry; select sale & clearance watches; select regular-priced items).

*Exclusions apply; see reverse.

**Promotion valid now thru 12/31/2017**
See reverse side for additional conditions or restrictions.

F2

0000000000130390613

Excludes **ALL**: bridal salons, cosmetics/fragrances, Deals of the Day, Doorbusters/web busters, electrics/electronics, Everyday Values (EDV), furniture/mattresses, Last Act, Macy's Backstage, rugs, specials, super buys, Breville, bridge & designer sportswear, Coach, Dyson, Eileen Fisher, Fitbit, Frye, Hanky Panky, Jack Spade, Kate Spade, KitchenAid Pro Line, Le Creuset, Levi's, Locker Room By Lids, Marc Jacobs, Michele watches, Natori, Sam Edelman, Samsung watches, Shun, Stuart Weitzman, The North Face, Theory, Tumi, Vitamix, Wacoal, Wolford, Wüsthof, athletic clothing, shoes & accessories; designer jewelry/watches, gift cards, gourmet foods, jewelry trunk shows, payment on credit accounts, previous purchases, restaurants, services, special orders, special purchases, tech watches, wine, macys.com; **ALL REGULAR-PRICED**: Breitling, designer handbags/shoes; CeCe by Cynthia Steffe, Dooney & Bourke, Emporio Armani, French Connection for her, Ghurka, designer Impulse brands, Juicy, Karen Kane, Lacoste, Lalique, Lauren/Polo/Ralph Lauren/Denim & Supply, Lladro, Michael Aram, MICHAEL Michael Kors/Michael Kors, NYDJ, premium denim brands, products offered by vendors who operate leased departments in any of our stores including: Burberry, Gucci, Longchamp, Louis Vuitton, select licensed depts., Sperry, Spanx, sterling flatware, Swarovski, Vera Wang, Vince Camuto for her, watches, Waterford, all china/crystal/silver. Cannot be combined with any savings pass/coupon, extra discount or credit offer, except opening a new Macy's account. Extra savings % applied to reduced prices.

This promotional offer is not valid with any other discount/promotion. See Rules of Use or visit www.entertainment.com/rulesofuse.          49783581

0000000000130390613

Excludes **ALL**: bridal salons, cosmetics/fragrances, Deals of the Day, Doorbusters/web busters, electrics/electronics, Everyday Values (EDV), furniture/mattresses, Last Act, Macy's Backstage, rugs, specials, super buys, Breville, bridge & designer sportswear, Coach, Dyson, Eileen Fisher, Fitbit, Frye, Hanky Panky, Jack Spade, Kate Spade, KitchenAid Pro Line, Le Creuset, Levi's, Locker Room By Lids, Marc Jacobs, Michele watches, Natori, Sam Edelman, Samsung watches, Shun, Stuart Weitzman, The North Face, Theory, Tumi, Vitamix, Wacoal, Wolford, Wüsthof, athletic clothing, shoes & accessories; designer jewelry/watches, gift cards, gourmet foods, jewelry trunk shows, payment on credit accounts, previous purchases, restaurants, services, special orders, special purchases, tech watches, wine, macys.com; **ALL REGULAR-PRICED**: Breitling, designer handbags/shoes; CeCe by Cynthia Steffe, Dooney & Bourke, Emporio Armani, French Connection for her, Ghurka, designer Impulse brands, Juicy, Karen Kane, Lacoste, Lalique, Lauren/Polo/Ralph Lauren/Denim & Supply, Lladro, Michael Aram, MICHAEL Michael Kors/Michael Kors, NYDJ, premium denim brands, products offered by vendors who operate leased departments in any of our stores including: Burberry, Gucci, Longchamp, Louis Vuitton, select licensed depts., Sperry, Spanx, sterling flatware, Swarovski, Vera Wang, Vince Camuto for her, watches, Waterford, all china/crystal/silver. Cannot be combined with any savings pass/coupon, extra discount or credit offer, except opening a new Macy's account. Extra savings % applied to reduced prices.

This promotional offer is not valid with any other discount/promotion. See Rules of Use or visit www.entertainment.com/rulesofuse.          49783581

NATIONAL RETAIL & SERVICES

**$5 VALUE**

# sears®

## $5 off an in-store qualifying purchase of $50 or more.

Excludes Consumer Electronics and Lawn and Garden. Additional exclusions apply. See reverse for details.

F3

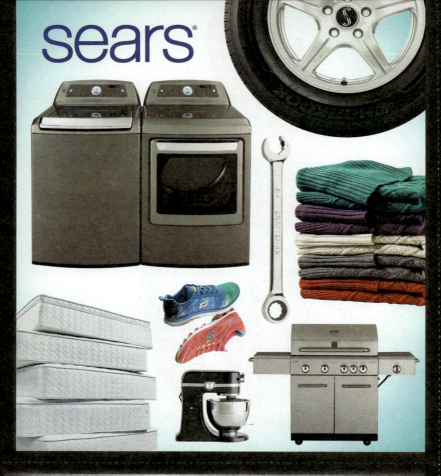

R5800039429$500

Join. Shop. Save.

## NATIONAL MEMBERSHIP PROGRAMS

**SPECIAL OFFER**

## Purchase a NEW Costco Membership and Receive a Special Offer.

Visit Entdeals.com/costcomembership for details.

**Promotion valid now thru 12/31/2017**
See reverse side for additional conditions or restrictions.

F4

# 20%OFF

ONE OF OUR
HUNDREDS
OF THOUSANDS
OF ITEMS.

**Coupon** *offer on back*

## BED BATH & BEYOND®

© 2017 Bed Bath & Beyond Inc and its subsidiaries

**NATIONAL RETAIL & SERVICES**

---

**20% OFF**

## BED BATH & BEYOND®

**20% OFF Any Single Item.**

# The Best Brands. Huge Selection. Great Value.

Call **1-800-GO BEYOND**® for locations coast to coast.

# We accept Manufacturers' Coupons

**Now Accepting Medicare OTC, Medicaid OTC and AARP Benefits**
**Use Your American Express, Visa, Mastercard, Discover or Pay Near Me!**
SNAP/EBT accepted in most stores. Visit familydollar.com/PayNearMe for more information.

# FAMILY DOLLAR®

# SMART WAYS TO SAVE!

 **WOW!**

Over 2,000 Items for **$1**!

 **EVEN LOWER PRICES!**

We've Lowered Prices on the Products You Use Most!

Get Low Prices, Every Day!

Buy Our Brands and Save, 100% Guaranteed!

Visit **familydollar.com** to find a store near you!

**Multiple Ways to Connect With Us & SAVE!**

NATIONAL RETAIL & SERVICES

Life, STYLED

1658136 4MW_vi

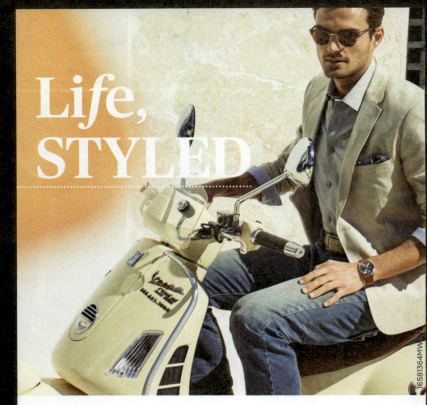

# Life, STYLED

## MEN'S WEARHOUSE®

MENSWEARHOUSE.COM

RISE TO THE OCCASION

i6581364MW

AEML 1010101

Take 40% off the regular price of retail items. Excludes shoes, clearance, Outlet products, Exceptional Value items and custom clothing. Coupon must be surrendered at the time of purchase. Valid in-store only. Discount is not combinable with other promotional offers or discounts. Valid at all Participating Locations.

the

# DRESSBAR

at
dressbarn

*the destination
for the
dress obsessed*

**DRESSES**
*starting at*
**$42!**

## 20% OFF

*est.1962*

# dressbarn

## 20% OFF entire regular priced purchase.

**Coupon code: 3519**

**Promotion valid 7/1/2016 thru 12/31/2017**
See reverse side for additional conditions or restrictions.

F9

# christopher & banks® | cj banks®

| MISSY | PETITE | WOMEN |
|-------|--------|-------|
| 4-16 | 4P-16P | 14W-24W |

*We love making every woman look and feel her best, with pieces that suit her personal style.*

christopherandbanks.com | join our community

## 30% OFF

# christopher & banks® | cj banks®

| MISSY | PETITE | WOMEN |
|-------|--------|-------|
| 4-16 | 4P-16P | 14W-24W |

## 30% off one full price item.

**Promo Code: 43258**

**Promotion valid 7/1/2016 thru 12/31/2017**
See reverse side for additional conditions or restrictions.

# christopher & banks® | cj banks®

### MISSY    PETITE    WOMEN
4-16      4P-16P      14W-24W

*We love making every woman look and feel her*
*best, with pieces that suit her personal style.*

christopherandbanks.com | join our community

43258

**NATIONAL RETAIL & SERVICES**

# CATHERINES
## PLUS SIZES

Specializing in
Sizes 16W – 34W
and 0X – 5X.

For a store near you,
call 1 (800) 971-4973 or
visit us at catherines.com.

# CATHERINES®
## PLUS SIZES

Discover Catherines and find a whole new world of fashion in sizes 16W-34W and 0X-5X, including petites.

Fresh updates, irresistible outfits, statement pieces and unexpected finds ... designed exclusively for you.

We're the brand you trust to always fit you beautifully.

16-0431A1 WK 49 © 2016 Catherines

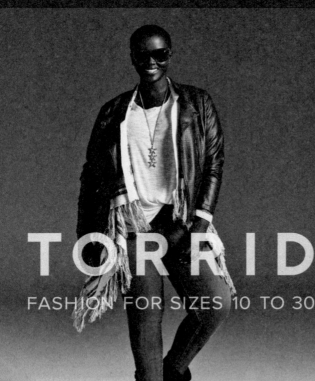

FASHION FOR SIZES 10 TO 30

TORRID.COM

$15 VALUE

# TORRID

FASHION FOR SIZES 10 TO 30

## $15 OFF
## YOUR NEXT PURCHASE OF $75 OR MORE

www.torrid.com/ent2017

**Promotion valid now thru 12/31/2017**
See reverse side for additional conditions or restrictions.

F13

# TORRID

## FASHION FOR SIZES 10 TO 30

TORRID.COM

# TORRID

## FASHION FOR SIZES 10 TO 30

1 99999 00549 0

*Receive $15 off a purchase of $75 or more. Original single-use coupon must be presented and surrendered at time of purchase. Limit one coupon per customer. Not valid on prior purchases, payment on credit card, and qualifying items do not include clearance merchandise, gift cards, taxes and shipping. Valid on Torrid branded products only and excludes third-party brands. Other exclusions may apply. May not be combined with any other offer, promotion or discount. Void if altered, copied, transferred, sold, purchased or where prohibited, taxed or restricted by law. Not redeemable for cash. Torrid is not responsible for lost or stolen coupons. Returns and exchanges subject to Torrid return policy. Dollar value of returned merchandise will be calculated based on the percentage discount. May not be used in conjunction with the Hot Topic employee discount. Valid for use online. To redeem online, you must go to http://www.torrid.com/ENT2017. Valid for online and in store purchases at U.S. Torrid stores thru December 31, 2017.

**To redeem online, you must go to www.torrid.com/ENT2017**

This promotional offer is not valid with any other discount/promotion. See Rules of Use or visit www.entertainment.com/rulesofuse.          0000000PK12

$20 VALUE

# Soma
YOUR NEW BRA DESTINATION™
SIZES 32A–44G

## $20 OFF your purchase of $100 or more

**Promotion valid now thru 12/31/2017**
See reverse side for additional conditions or restrictions.

F14

$20 VALUE

# Soma
YOUR NEW BRA DESTINATION™
SIZES 32A–44G

## $20 OFF your purchase of $100 or more

**Promotion valid now thru 12/31/2017**
See reverse side for additional conditions or restrictions.

F15

YOUR NEW BRA DESTINATION™
SIZES 32A–44G

94856

Present coupon at time of purchase. Offer valid in Soma boutiques (including outlets) only. Not valid by phone or soma.com. Qualifying amount and offer valid on Soma branded product only. Not valid on purchase of gift cards, previously purchased merchandise, taxes or shipping. One time use only. May not be combined with other coupons, offers or events, except Love Soma Rewards certificates. If you return a portion of your purchase, an applicable portion of your original discount will be forfeited. One coupon per transaction. Coupon may not be sold, auctioned, transferred or reproduced. No cash value. Valid on specified dates only.

**Visit Soma.com to experience our beautiful and sensual lingerie, loungewear and beauty.**

YOUR NEW BRA DESTINATION™
SIZES 32A–44G

94856

Present coupon at time of purchase. Offer valid in Soma boutiques (including outlets) only. Not valid by phone or soma.com. Qualifying amount and offer valid on Soma branded product only. Not valid on purchase of gift cards, previously purchased merchandise, taxes or shipping. One time use only. May not be combined with other coupons, offers or events, except Love Soma Rewards certificates. If you return a portion of your purchase, an applicable portion of your original discount will be forfeited. One coupon per transaction. Coupon may not be sold, auctioned, transferred or reproduced. No cash value. Valid on specified dates only.

**Visit Soma.com to experience our beautiful and sensual lingerie, loungewear and beauty.**

This promotional offer is not valid with any other discount/promotion. See Rules of Use or visit www.entertainment.com/rulesofuse.        49781900

# *Aéropostale*

**AEROPOSTALE.COM**

**50020358**

**50020366**

# rue21®

## $10 off EVERY $30 purchase.

**Promotion valid 7/1/2016 thru 12/31/2017**
See reverse side for additional conditions or restrictions.

F19

## *charming* charlie

## $10 OFF your purchase of $50.

**Promotion valid 8/1/2016 thru 12/31/2017**
See reverse side for additional conditions or restrictions.

F20

## *charming* charlie

## $10 OFF your purchase of $50.

**Promotion valid 8/1/2016 thru 12/31/2017**
See reverse side for additional conditions or restrictions.

F21

NATIONAL RETAIL & SERVICES

050384

Valid July 1, 2016–December 31, 2017 in store. Amount of deduction will be given at the point of sale pre-tax and net of discounts. Limit one coupon per customer. Coupon must be turned in at time of purchase. Not valid with any other coupons. No cash value. Excludes 40% off or more and buy one get one free items. Some price points lower than 40% off excluded. Only original coupons will be accepted. Duplicate copies not accepted. Not valid on gift cards or previous purchases. Not valid for associate use.

700100010243

Minimum $50 purchase required. Offer valid at Charming Charlie stores only. Offer is valid towards full price and clearance merchandise and in-store merchandise promotions. Limit one coupon per transaction. Not valid nor combinable with any other coupons or offers with the exception of Charm Club Rewards and Birthday Rewards. Must present and surrender coupon in store. Only one redemption per customer. Void if reproduced and where prohibited. Not valid on gift cards, returns, exchanges or previous purchases. Coupon is not transferable or refundable and is not valid on price adjustments. If minimum purchase is required, amount is before tax. Offers subject to change without notice. Charming Charlie associates are not eligible to redeem offer. Offer valid from 8/1/16 thru 12/31/17.

700100010243

Minimum $50 purchase required. Offer valid at Charming Charlie stores only. Offer is valid towards full price and clearance merchandise and in-store merchandise promotions. Limit one coupon per transaction. Not valid nor combinable with any other coupons or offers with the exception of Charm Club Rewards and Birthday Rewards. Must present and surrender coupon in store. Only one redemption per customer. Void if reproduced and where prohibited. Not valid on gift cards, returns, exchanges or previous purchases. Coupon is not transferable or refundable and is not valid on price adjustments. If minimum purchase is required, amount is before tax. Offers subject to change without notice. Charming Charlie associates are not eligible to redeem offer. Offer valid from 8/1/16 thru 12/31/17.

This promotional offer is not valid with any other discount/promotion. See Rules of Use or visit www.entertainment.com/rulesofuse.          49782923

NATIONAL RETAIL & SERVICES

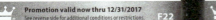

OVER **90 MILLION** EARS PIERCED WOLDWIDE
**YOUR EAR PIERCING SPECIALISTS**

# claire's
GETTING READY IS HALF THE FUN!

OVER **90 MILLION** EARS PIERCED WOLDWIDE

**YOUR EAR PIERCING SPECIALISTS**

**claire's**

GETTING READY IS HALF THE FUN!

"IT'S NOT JUST A BETTER DEAL.
**IT'S AMERICA'S BEST.**" SM

**AMERICA'S BEST**
CONTACTS & EYEGLASSES

AmericasBest.com | 1-800-TWO-PAIR

## $5 off a purchase of $30 or more

**Coupon Code 251520934**

 **Promotion valid 7/1/16 thru 10/31/2016**
See reverse side for additional conditions or restrictions. **F29**

## $5 off a purchase of $30 or more

**Coupon Code 251520942**

 **Promotion valid 11/1/16 thru 2/28/2017**
See reverse side for additional conditions or restrictions. **F30**

## $5 off a purchase of $30 or more

**Coupon Code 251520950**

 **Promotion valid 3/1/17 thru 7/31/2017**
See reverse side for additional conditions or restrictions. **F31**

## $5 off a purchase of $30 or more

**Coupon Code 251520968**

 **Promotion valid 8/1/17 thru 12/31/2017**
See reverse side for additional conditions or restrictions. **F32**

$5 off a purchase of $30 or more. LIMIT ONE COUPON PER CUSTOMER. Present this coupon in-store. Offer may be used only once. Coupon not transferable and cannot be combined with any other coupon discounts. Coupon valid in U.S. only and is not redeemable at Shopko® locations, Payless.com, and where otherwise restricted, prohibited or taxed. Offer excludes gift cards and is not valid on prior purchases. Void if copied, altered, transferred, purchased or sold; codes may not be posted or obtained on Internet. Cash value is 1/50 cent.

**Coupon Code 251520942**
**Valid 11/1/2016 through 2/28/2017.**

This promotional offer is not valid with any other discount/promotion. See Rules of Use or visit www.entertainment.com/rulesofuse.    49781032

---

$5 off a purchase of $30 or more. LIMIT ONE COUPON PER CUSTOMER. Present this coupon in-store. Offer may be used only once. Coupon not transferable and cannot be combined with any other coupon discounts. Coupon valid in U.S. only and is not redeemable at Shopko® locations, Payless.com, and where otherwise restricted, prohibited or taxed. Offer excludes gift cards and is not valid on prior purchases. Void if copied, altered, transferred, purchased or sold; codes may not be posted or obtained on Internet. Cash value is 1/50 cent.

**Coupon Code 251520934**
**Valid 7/1/2016 through 10/31/2016.**

This promotional offer is not valid with any other discount/promotion. See Rules of Use or visit www.entertainment.com/rulesofuse.    49781029

---

$5 off a purchase of $30 or more. LIMIT ONE COUPON PER CUSTOMER. Present this coupon in-store. Offer may be used only once. Coupon not transferable and cannot be combined with any other coupon discounts. Coupon valid in U.S. only and is not redeemable at Shopko® locations, Payless.com, and where otherwise restricted, prohibited or taxed. Offer excludes gift cards and is not valid on prior purchases. Void if copied, altered, transferred, purchased or sold; codes may not be posted or obtained on Internet. Cash value is 1/50 cent.

**Coupon Code 251520968**
**Valid 8/1/2017 through 12/31/2017.**

This promotional offer is not valid with any other discount/promotion. See Rules of Use or visit www.entertainment.com/rulesofuse.    49781041

---

$5 off a purchase of $30 or more. LIMIT ONE COUPON PER CUSTOMER. Present this coupon in-store. Offer may be used only once. Coupon not transferable and cannot be combined with any other coupon discounts. Coupon valid in U.S. only and is not redeemable at Shopko® locations, Payless.com, and where otherwise restricted, prohibited or taxed. Offer excludes gift cards and is not valid on prior purchases. Void if copied, altered, transferred, purchased or sold; codes may not be posted or obtained on Internet. Cash value is 1/50 cent.

**Coupon Code 251520950**
**Valid 3/1/2017 through 7/31/2017.**

This promotional offer is not valid with any other discount/promotion. See Rules of Use or visit www.entertainment.com/rulesofuse.    49781038

# REAL
## value
### for the whole family

REAL SHOES. REAL PEOPLE. REAL LIFE.

$**10** VALUE

## $10 OFF the purchase of $65 or more.

**Coupon Code: 55673**

**Promotion valid now thru 12/31/2017**
See reverse side for additional conditions or restrictions.

F33

# REAL *style*

**Rack Room Shoes** is the trusted family footwear retailer of choice. We feature the newest, on-trend styles of name brand shoes & accessories, plus timeless favorites. At Rack Room Shoes, it's about offering you the shoes to carry you through the ordinary, extraordinary events of your life.

## Just some of our favorite brands:

plus so many more!

VISIT US AT *rackroomshoes.com*

55673

Offer Valid through 12/31/2017 at Rack Room Shoes store locations.

Offer not valid online. Limit one coupon per transaction. COUPON MAY ONLY BE USED ONCE AND MAY NOT BE MODIFIED, COPIED OR UPLOADED. Must present coupon at time of purchase, cannot be combined with other coupons or used for the purchase of Gift Card(s) and is not redeemable for cash. Offer excluded on certain styles and brands, including but not limited to: Adidas, Asics, Birkenstock, Converse, Keds, Merrell, Rainbow, Reebok, Rockport, Saucony, Sperry, Teva, Tommy Hilfiger Kids', Timberland Pro, plus all Nike styles. Discount is taken before taxes. CAN BE COMBINED WITH EARNED QUALIFYING REWARDS DOLLARS BUT NOT OTHER REWARDS COUPON OFFERS.

See store associate for details.

# JCPenney | portraits

## YOUR FAMILY DESERVES THE BEST PHOTOGRAPHY

PROFESSIONAL PHOTOS PRICED JUST RIGHT

## JCPenney | portraits

Present at session. $9.99 session fee per subject, FREE with portrait membership. One FREE 8x10 traditional sheet per family, per day. Traditional sheets are unenhanced 10x13 or smaller. Digital album includes all high-resolution images photographed in your session with a copyright license to use and modify the images. Bordered products and other specialty designs created in studio are not included in the digital album. Traditional sheets and digital album are not discounted further. Percent off not valid on digital images, CDs, media bundle, featured product, portrait memberships, services or merchandise. Not valid on reorders, online orders, outdoor photography, previous purchases or with other offers. Void if copied, scanned, altered, transferred, purchased, sold or prohibited by law. No cash value. Valid through 12/31/17 PC1810907.

This promotional offer is not valid with any other discount/promotion. See Rules of Use or visit www.entertainment.com/rulesofuse.      49780985

◎ PORTRAIT STUDIO

# little smiles. big savings.
### professional photography at a price you will love.

schedule a session and find studio locations at targetportraits.com

NATIONAL RETAIL & SERVICES

---

## ◎ PORTRAIT STUDIO

**50% off your photo purchase and receive 1 free 8x10 traditional sheet ($3.99 for additional traditional sheets). Additionally qualify for a special price of $99.99 for a digital album.**

---

## ◎ PORTRAIT STUDIO

**50% off your photo purchase and receive 1 free 8x10 traditional sheet ($3.99 for additional traditional sheets). Additionally qualify for a special price of $99.99 for a digital album.**

NATIONAL RETAIL & SERVICES

◎ **PORTRAIT STUDIO**

Present at session. $9.99 session fee per subject, FREE with portrait membership. One FREE 8x10 traditional sheet per family, per day. Traditional sheets are unenhanced 10x13 or smaller. Digital album includes all high-resolution images photographed in your session with a copyright license to use and modify the images. Bordered products and other specialty designs created in studio are not included in the digital album. Traditional sheets and digital album are not discounted further. Percent off not valid on digital images, CDs, media bundle, featured product, portrait memberships, services or merchandise. Not valid on reorders, online orders, previous purchases or with other offers. Void if copied, scanned, altered, transferred, purchased, sold or prohibited by law. No cash value.
Valid through 12/31/17. PC27248.

This promotional offer is not valid with any other discount/promotion.
See Rules of Use or visit www.entertainment.com/rulesofuse.          49780990

over
# 45,000
## items
let us help you choose!

nursery · car seats · safety · activity · feeding · bath · clothing · toys · diaper bags · health · strollers

**over 100 locations** nationwide!

**buy buy BABY**®
Everything for newborns to toddlers.®

---

♛®

$**5** VALUE

# $5 OFF of $25 or more.

**buy buy BABY**®
Everything for newborns to toddlers.℠

F38

**buy buy BABY®**
Everything for newborns to toddlers.®

# baby registry

REGISTER FOR YOUR LITTLE
BUNDLE AND GET A BUNDLE℠

**Free Goody Bag**
Available In-Store

**Free Personal Shops**
with an Expert
Registry Consultant

**Completion Discount**

**Friends Referral Rewards**

**Free Registry**
Announcement Cards

**Online Registry Tools**

**Hassle-Free Returns**

## Visit us at buybuybaby.com for store locations.

**CONNECT WITH US**
receive COUPONS AND OFFERS
learn about NEW DEALS AND VALUES FIRST
get SOLUTIONS AND INSPIRATION

first time subscribers get
**20% off**
one single item offer
for use on a
future purchase

 **EMAIL**
Text your email address
to **42229** or sign up at:
buybuybaby.com/
rdentertainment.asp

 **TEXT**
Text **OFFER** to **42229**
Message and data rates may apply. Mobile internet
access required. Up to 8 msg/month. Text **STOP** to
42229 to cancel. http://www.buybuybaby.com/tcp
for Terms, Conditions, and Privacy.

||||||| BARCODE |||||||
3685194000000017365

Valid in store only. Copies not accepted. Limit one coupon, Savings Certificate, special offer or discount per item; cannot be combined with a price match. Coupon valid for one use only; electronic copies of physical coupons are treated as one coupon. Any return of purchase will reduce your savings proportionately. The costs of shipping, taxes or gift cards are not counted toward any minimum purchase required, and coupon cannot be applied to such items. Not valid for wholesale purchases; Company reserves the right to limit quantities. Valid only in the U.S. Offer excludes: A Pea in the Pod®, Baby Brezza®, Baby Jogger™, Babyletto™, Babymel™, Baby's Dream Furniture, BABYZEN™, BÉABA®, Bloom®, Bugaboo, Bumbleride™, clek®, CYBEX, DaVinci™, Dyson, Ergobaby®, Foundations®, franklin & ben™, HALO® Bassinest™, Inglesina®, Maxi-Cosi®, Million Dollar Baby Classic™, Motherhood Maternity®, Mountain Buggy®, Nursery Works™, Oeuf, Orbit Baby®, Peg Pérego, Petunia Pickle Bottom®, Phil & Teds®, Quinny®, Romero Britto™, Stokke®, storksak®, Svan®, Thule®, Under Armour®, UPPAbaby®, Vera Bradley®, diapers, wipes, formula, baby food, or portrait studio services. Additional online items excluded; see www.buybuybaby.com/exclusions0616

### 40% OFF

## 40% OFF any one regular price item.

---

### $50 VALUE

**$50 CASH with Paid Tax Return if redeemed Jan.–Feb. 15, 2017 (Promo Code: ENTCIF), or $50 OFF Tax Preparation valid Feb. 16– April 7, 2017 (Promo Code: ENT50L).**

For a Liberty Tax Service location call 866-871-1040 or visit LibertyTax.com.

---

### $5 VALUE

## $5 OFF a purchase of $25 or more*.

NATIONAL RETAIL & SERVICES

Not valid on: As Seen on TV, Silhouette and Cricut brands; Polaroid products; Custom special order products, services and package pricing; Rainbow Loom products, 3Doodler 3D Printing Pen and accessories, sewing machines, Heidi Swapp Minc machine, Starlight ornaments, 4' and taller Christmas trees, books, magazines, CD/DVDs, gift cards and debit card products; beverages; Buy More, Save More offers; sale, clearance or buy and get items; Everday Value; online purchases; class, event, birthday party, shipping, delivery or installation fees. Limit one coupon per product. Limit one coupon of each type per transaction per day. Original coupon must be surrendered at purchase. Not applicable to prior purchases. Limited to stock on hand. Void where prohibited. Exclusions subject to change. See store associate for details. Coupon valid 7/1/2016–12/31/2017.

With paid tax preparation. Valid at participating locations. Cannot be combined with other offers or used toward past services. One coupon per customer and per return. Void where prohibited by law.

For a Liberty Tax Service location call 866-871-1040 or visit LibertyTax.com.

DP103040

**\*Exclusions:**
Coupon valid at store named on back of mailer for one transaction only. Not valid on sale, discounted and clearance priced merchandise, rental, in-store services, Ace gift cards, city stickers, garbage tags and lawn/trash bags, lumber and building materials, fuel, previously purchased merchandise, Weber® branded products, Stihl® branded products, power tools, power equipment, YETI® branded products, water heaters, grills, EdenPURE® heaters, and other items that each participating store may designate, or in conjunction with any other coupon, excluding Rewards. Any purchase minimum is calculated before applying Reward redemption and before tax. Coupon may not be sold or transferred. Void if photocopied or duplicated. No cash value. Coupon cannot be replaced if merchandise is returned. **Additional exclusions may apply. See store for details.**

**Valid at Participating Ace Hardware Stores.**

**NATIONAL RETAIL & SERVICES**

**71265483**

Limit 1 coupon per customer per day. Save 20% on any 1 item purchased.

*Cannot be used with other discount, coupon or any of the following items or brands: Inside Track Club membership, extended service plan, gift card, open box item, 3 day parking lot sale item, compressors, floor jacks, saw mills, storage cabinets, chests or carts, trailers, trenchers, welders, Admiral, Badland, CoverPro, Daytona, Diablo, Franklin, Hercules, Holt, Jupiter, Predator, Stik-Tek, StormCat, Union, Vanguard, Viking. Not valid on prior purchases. Non-transferable. Original coupon must be presented.

Valid through 12/31/17.

**71268010**

Limit 1 coupon per customer per day. Save 20% on any 1 item purchased.

*Cannot be used with other discount, coupon or any of the following items or brands: Inside Track Club membership, extended service plan, gift card, open box item, 3 day parking lot sale item, compressors, floor jacks, saw mills, storage cabinets, chests or carts, trailers, trenchers, welders, Admiral, Badland, CoverPro, Daytona, Diablo, Franklin, Hercules, Holt, Jupiter, Predator, Stik-Tek, StormCat, Union, Vanguard, Viking. Not valid on prior purchases. Non-transferable. Original coupon must be presented.

Valid through 12/31/17.

**71259694**

**ONE 1" x 25 FT. TAPE MEASURE (ITEM 69031/69030) WITH ANY PURCHASE.**

**LIMIT 1** - Cannot be used with other discount, coupon or prior purchase. Coupon good at our stores, HarborFreight.com or by calling 800-423-2567. Offer good while supplies last. Shipping & Handling charges may apply if not picked up in-store. Nontransferable. Original coupon must be presented. Valid through 12/31/17. Limit one FREE GIFT coupon per customer per day.

**$10 VALUE**

## $10 OFF $50 or More Purchase.

Sign up for your PaintPerks™ benefits for everyday savings, decorating ideas, how-to tips, and more to help make your painting project perfect. Register at swpaintperks.com or at your neighborhood Sherwin-Williams paint store.

**Promotion valid 7/1/2016 thru 12/31/2017**
See reverse side for additional conditions or restrictions.

F45

**$15 VALUE**

## $15 OFF $75 or More Purchase.

Sign up for your PaintPerks™ benefits for everyday savings, decorating ideas, how-to tips, and more to help make your painting project perfect. Register at swpaintperks.com or at your neighborhood Sherwin-Williams paint store.

**Promotion valid 7/1/2016 thru 12/31/2017**
See reverse side for additional conditions or restrictions.

F46

**15% OFF**

## 15% OFF Regular Priced Items.

Sign up for your PaintPerks™ benefits for everyday savings, decorating ideas, how-to tips, and more to help make your painting project perfect. Register at swpaintperks.com or at your neighborhood Sherwin-Williams paint store.

**Promotion valid 7/1/2016 thru 12/31/2017**
See reverse side for additional conditions or restrictions.

F47

NATIONAL RETAIL & SERVICES

5 35777 28544 7

Valid on retail sales of retail products only. Minimum purchase of $50 in a single transaction, before sales tax and after all discounts have been applied. Savings is applied to qualifying items purchased on a prorated basis; any refunds will be given in the prorated amount, which will reduce your savings. May be combined with a percent-off coupon or sale event. Multiple dollars-off coupons will not be honored. Must surrender coupon at time of redemption. Cash value: 1/100 of 1¢. Offer excludes previous purchases and purchases of gift cards and Paint Shield™ Microbicidal Paint. Other exclusions may apply, see store for details. Void if transferred, purchased, sold, altered, duplicated, or where prohibited by law. Valid at Sherwin-Williams and Sherwin-Williams operated retail paint stores only. We reserve the right to accept, refuse, or limit the use of any coupon. Offer valid 7/1/16-12/31/17. ©2016 The Sherwin-Williams Company.

**Valid at Sherwin-Williams and Sherwin-Williams operated retail paint stores only.**

This promotional offer is not valid with any other discount/promotion. See Rules of Use or visit www.entertainment.com/rulesofuse.    49781001

5 35777 28545 4

Valid on retail sales of retail products only. Minimum purchase of $75 in a single transaction, before sales tax and after all discounts have been applied. Savings is applied to qualifying items purchased on a prorated basis; any refunds will be given in the prorated amount, which will reduce your savings. May be combined with a percent-off coupon or sale event. Multiple dollars-off coupons will not be honored. Must surrender coupon at time of redemption. Cash value: 1/100 of 1¢. Offer excludes previous purchases and purchases of gift cards and Paint Shield™ Microbicidal Paint. Other exclusions may apply, see store for details. Void if transferred, purchased, sold, altered, duplicated, or where prohibited by law. Valid at Sherwin-Williams and Sherwin-Williams operated retail paint stores only. We reserve the right to accept, refuse, or limit the use of any coupon. Offer valid 7/1/16-12/31/17. ©2016 The Sherwin-Williams Company.

**Valid at Sherwin-Williams and Sherwin-Williams operated retail paint stores only.**

This promotional offer is not valid with any other discount/promotion. See Rules of Use or visit www.entertainment.com/rulesofuse.    49781011

5 35777 28546 1

Valid on retail sales of retail products only. Discount taken off of our list price. Sale pricing or other offers that result in greater savings will supersede this offer. Must surrender coupon at time of redemption. Cash value: 1/100 of 1¢. Offer excludes previous purchases, and purchases of gift cards, Paint Shield™ Microbicidal Paint, Multi-Purpose primers, HGTV HOME™ by Sherwin-Williams Paint brands, Minwax® Wood Finish quarts, ladders, spray equipment and accessories. Other exclusions may apply, see store for details. Void if transferred, purchased, sold, altered, duplicated, or where prohibited by law. Valid at Sherwin-Williams and Sherwin-Williams operated retail paint stores only. We reserve the right to accept, refuse, or limit the use of any coupon. Offer valid 7/1/16-12/31/17. ©2016 The Sherwin-Williams Company.

**Valid at Sherwin-Williams and Sherwin-Williams operated retail paint stores only.**

This promotional offer is not valid with any other discount/promotion. See Rules of Use or visit www.entertainment.com/rulesofuse.    49781007

**Office DEPOT. OfficeMax®**

# GEAR UP FOR SAVINGS

Supplies • Technology • Furniture • Print Services

---

**Office DEPOT.**
**OfficeMax®**

**$10 OFF your qualifying purchase of $50 or more.**

---

**Office DEPOT.**
**OfficeMax®**

**$10 OFF your qualifying purchase of $50 or more.**

# GIVEBACK to schools

**Office DEPOT. OfficeMax**

Your chosen school will receive 5% back in credit for FREE supplies when you make a qualifying purchase at Office Depot® or OfficeMax®. **Don't know your school's ID? Ask at checkout.**

**Visit officedepot.com/givebts to learn more**

Give Back to Schools Program: Pre-K-12th grade only. Not available in Puerto Rico or the U.S. Virgin Islands. 5% of qualifying purchases made during each program period will be offered quarterly as an Office Depot® OfficeMax® Merchandise Certificate to the participating school designated by each customer (up to a total of $10 million). Products that do not qualify are: technology and consumer electronic products and accessories; media and software that is not education or reference related; furniture and furniture accessories; ink and toner; gift and prepaid cards; postage stamps; purchases from Copy & Print Depot™ and OfficeMax Services Center; and purchases made to contract business accounts. Credits are not available to schools with less than $10 in tallied credits. Unaccepted/declined credits are void. Visit officedepot.com/givebts for details.

## 93201995

**Valid in-store only.** Minimum purchase required after discounts and before tax. Must present this original coupon (reproductions not valid) to cashier at time of purchase. Cannot be combined with Store Purchasing, Procurement or Retail Connect Cards. Cannot be used as an account payment. **Not valid for purchases:** 1) made in Office Depot or OfficeMax convenience/clearance/closing stores; 2) of gift or prepaid cards; 3) of any technology or consumer electronic products and accessories or media and software products; 4) of sale-priced case paper; 5) of performance protection/MaxAssurance® plans and Essentials kits; 6) of postage or mailing/shipping services; 7) of value business cards; 8) of HP ink or toner; 9) of Epson ink; 10) of Tech Depot Services or third party services; 11) of premiums/free gifts with purchase; or 12) of appliances. Coupon is good for one-time use only, is not transferable, is not for resale or auction and cannot be combined with other offers or promotions. No cash back. Void where prohibited. We reserve the right to limit quantities sold to each customer. **Limit 1 coupon per household/business.**

**Coupon valid 9/1/2016-12/31/2017.**

This promotional offer is not valid with any other discount/promotion. See Rules of Use or visit www.entertainment.com/rulesofuse    49782050

## 93201995

**Valid in-store only.** Minimum purchase required after discounts and before tax. Must present this original coupon (reproductions not valid) to cashier at time of purchase. Cannot be combined with Store Purchasing, Procurement or Retail Connect Cards. Cannot be used as an account payment. **Not valid for purchases:** 1) made in Office Depot or OfficeMax convenience/clearance/closing stores; 2) of gift or prepaid cards; 3) of any technology or consumer electronic products and accessories or media and software products; 4) of sale-priced case paper; 5) of performance protection/MaxAssurance® plans and Essentials kits; 6) of postage or mailing/shipping services; 7) of value business cards; 8) of HP ink or toner; 9) of Epson ink; 10) of Tech Depot Services or third party services; 11) of premiums/free gifts with purchase; or 12) of appliances. Coupon is good for one-time use only, is not transferable, is not for resale or auction and cannot be combined with other offers or promotions. No cash back. Void where prohibited. We reserve the right to limit quantities sold to each customer. **Limit 1 coupon per household/business.**

**Coupon valid 9/1/2016-12/31/2017.**

This promotional offer is not valid with any other discount/promotion. See Rules of Use or visit www.entertainment.com/rulesofuse    49782050

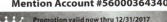

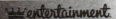

## $19.99 Oil Change with 4-Tire Rotation and Brake Inspection.

www.monro.com

**Promotion valid now thru 12/31/2017**
See reverse side for additional conditions or restrictions.

F56

---

## FREE Flat Repair.

www.monro.com

**Promotion valid now thru 12/31/2017**
See reverse side for additional conditions or restrictions.

F57

---

## FREE Tire Rotation.

www.monro.com

**Promotion valid now thru 12/31/2017**
See reverse side for additional conditions or restrictions.

F58

NATIONAL RETAIL & SERVICES

Includes up to 5 quarts of conventional oil, chassis lube (where applicable) and vehicle inspection. Free tire rotation has no cash value. See store for complete details. With this coupon. Most vehicles. Not valid with other offers. Additional charges may apply. A 9.99% charge will be added to the retail list price of all service work, not on tires, not to exceed $39, and represents shop supply and equipment costs and profits (does not apply in New York).

**Valid at All Participating Locations.**

Bring in your flat and we will patch and remount it for free. Commercial and heavy duty trucks excluded. Limit one per customer and or vehicle. See store for details.

**Valid at All Participating Locations.**

Commercial and heavy duty trucks excluded.

**Valid at All Participating Locations.**

**JIFFY LUBE® HAS OVER 2,000 LOCATIONS TO SERVICE YOUR AUTOMOTIVE NEEDS.**

Visit jiffylube.com or scan the QR code to find a Jiffy Lube® near you.

### $5 OFF your next Jiffy Lube Signature Service® oil change.

Coupon Code: EZC2J2

 Promotion valid now thru 12/31/2017
See reverse side for additional conditions or restrictions.  F59

### 10% OFF Ancillary Services.

Coupon Code: 6V48Q2

 Promotion valid now thru 12/31/2017
See reverse side for additional conditions or restrictions.  F60

# sears®
## AUTO CENTER

**SPECIAL OFFER**

### $17.99 oil change (reg. $29.99) or $12 OFF any synthetic oil change.

**sears®**
**AUTO CENTER**

**Coupon #41761**

**Promotion valid 7/1/2016 thru 12/31/2017**
See reverse side for additional conditions or restrictions.                    F61

**SPECIAL OFFER**

### $17.99 oil change (reg. $29.99) or $12 OFF any synthetic oil change.

**sears®**
**AUTO CENTER**

**Coupon #41761**

**Promotion valid 7/1/2016 thru 12/31/2017**
See reverse side for additional conditions or restrictions.                    F62

NATIONAL RETAIL & SERVICES

**sears**®

AUTO CENTER

---

**sears**®

AUTO CENTER

Includes up to 5 quarts of conventional oil and $3.49 oil filter. $4.00 shop fee applies except in CA, IL, MN, and PR. Premium oil filter are additional cost. Not available in all stores. Most vehicles. One coupon per purchase. Void where prohibited by law. Cash value 1/20¢. May not be combined with any other coupon or associate discount. See stores for details.

© 2016 Sears Brands, LLC. Exp 12/31/17. Coupon #41761.

---

**sears**®

AUTO CENTER

Includes up to 5 quarts of conventional oil and $3.49 oil filter. $4.00 shop fee applies except in CA, IL, MN, and PR. Premium oil filter are additional cost. Not available in all stores. Most vehicles. One coupon per purchase. Void where prohibited by law. Cash value 1/20¢. May not be combined with any other coupon or associate discount. See stores for details.

© 2016 Sears Brands, LLC. Exp 12/31/17. Coupon #41761.

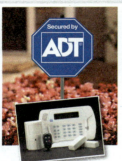

*Celebrate life's most important moments with*
Artisan designed, handcrafted
flowers and gifts from FTD.

## Save 20% on all flowers and gifts

Visit **www.ftd.com/ent17save20** or call **1-800-SEND-FTD**
and mention promo code 35524.

 ®

**20% OFF**

## 20% OFF all
## Flowers and Gifts*.

Shop now www.ftd.com/ent17save20
or call 1-800-SEND-FTD and mention
promo code 35524.

49781837

*Celebrate life's most important moments with*

# Artisan designed, handcrafted flowers and gifts from FTD.

## Save $15 on all flowers and gifts

Visit **www.ftd.com/ent17save15** or call **1-800-SEND-FTD** and mention promo code **35526.**

$15 OFF

## $15 OFF all Flowers and Gifts*.

Shop now www.ftd.com/ent17save15 or call 1-800-SEND-FTD and mention promo code 35526.

49781840

**Promotion valid now thru 12/31/2017**
This promotional offer is not valid with any other discount/promotion. See Rules of Use or visit www.entertainment.com/rulesofuse

F65

*Since 1934*

# Harry & David®

America's First Choice for
Gifting, Entertaining, and Everyday Delights

*Since 1934*

**Harry & David®**

MEDFORD, OREGON
USA

## 20% OFF
### your Harry & David product purchase of $75 or more online.

Order online at
www.harryanddavid.com/ebook20

**Promotion valid now thru 12/31/2017**
See reverse side for additional conditions or restrictions.

*Since 1934*

**Harry & David®**

MEDFORD, OREGON
USA

## 10% OFF your product purchase online or in stores.

**Promotion valid now thru 12/31/2017**
See reverse side for additional conditions or restrictions.

F68

America's First Choice for
Gifting, Entertaining, and Everyday Delights

## Dipped. Decorated. Delicious.

Gourmet gifts from $19.99 +s/h

### 20% OFF Any Product, Any Time*

*20% off discount will appear upon checkout. Minimum product purchase of $29.00. Discounts do not apply to gift cards or certificates, same-day delivery, shipping and handling, taxes or third-party hosted products (e.g., wine), and cannot be combined with other offers or discounts. Discounts not valid on bulk or corporate purchases of 10 units or more.

Go to www.Berries.com/book20 or call (877) 329-7271 and mention "Entertainment® Book."

0000000QK41

*Shari's Berries.*

**Promotion valid now thru 12/31/2017**                                                F69
This promotional offer is not valid with any other discount/promotion. See Rules of Use or visit www.entertainment.com/rulesofuse.

---

## Personalize your most *thoughtful gifts*

embroidered · laser-engraved · custom icons · hand-painted · sandblasted · hand-carved

**PERFECTLY PERSONALIZED**

### 25% OFF Any Product, Any Time*

*25% off discount will appear upon checkout. Minimum product purchase of $29.00. Discounts do not apply to gift cards or certificates, shipping and handling, personalization fees or taxes, and cannot be combined with other offers or discounts.

Go to www.PersonalCreations.com/book25off or call (866) 705-0600 and mention "Entertainment® Book."

## personal**creations**

0000000QK3L

**Promotion valid now thru 12/31/2017**                                                F70
This promotional offer is not valid with any other discount/promotion. See Rules of Use or visit www.entertainment.com/rulesofuse.

---

## EVERY FLAVOR IS *Unforgettable*

Thank you... Happy birthday...
It's the thought that counts.

### 20% OFF Any Product, Any Time*

*20% off discount will appear upon checkout. Minimum product purchase of $29.00. Discounts do not apply to gift cards or certificates, same-day delivery, shipping and handling, taxes or third-party hosted products (e.g., wine), and cannot be combined with other offers or discounts. Discounts not valid on bulk or corporate purchases of 10 units or more.

Go to www.CherryMoonFarms.com/book20 or call (888) 242-2902 and mention "Entertainment® Book."

## CHERRY MOON FARMS®

0000000QK33

**Promotion valid now thru 12/31/2017**                                                F71
This promotional offer is not valid with any other discount/promotion. See Rules of Use or visit www.entertainment.com/rulesofuse.

# Save BIG on our top web deals.

# New Movies & Games for less

 Flip this over for even more ways to save.

**Rent 1 DVD, Get 1 Free for the First Night.**

Promo Code: 9GHLGWER95

 Promo valid 9/1/2016 thru 12/31/2016
See reverse side for additional conditions or restrictions. F79

**$1.25 off the first night of a DVD rental.**

Promo Code: DFJKL7834F

 Promo valid 1/1/2017 thru 4/30/2017
See reverse side for additional conditions or restrictions. F80

**$2.00 off the first night of a Game rental.**

Promo Code: WK47BF83BW

 Promo valid 5/1/2017 thru 8/31/2017
See reverse side for additional conditions or restrictions. F81

**$1.50 off the first night of a Blu-Ray Disc® rental.**

Promo Code: PE8SB36AKT

 Promo valid 9/1/2017 thru 12/31/2017
See reverse side for additional conditions or restrictions. F82

# play pass

0 — PTS — 100

# Join Redbox Play Pass

to start earning points towards free
1-night rentals. Get a FREE 1-night DVD
rental when you sign up.

## redbox.com/rewards

redbox
NEW RELEASE
movies & games

Promo code for free 1-day DVD rental will be emailed within 48 hours of joining.
Subject to additional terms. Void where prohibited.

Promo code expires 4/30/2017 11:59 p.m. CT. Limit: 1 code per transaction, regardless of # of rentals. 1 time use only. Code valid online, on the official Redbox mobile app or at the box in the amount of the discount stated off of the first day's rental fee for a DVD, Blu-ray Disc® or video game. Not valid for prior rentals. Your payment card (necessary for any rental) will be charged the full daily rental rate for any additional items, plus applicable tax (except for jurisdictions that do not require sales tax to be charged or collected) for the first rental day, if applicable, and will be charged the full daily rental fee for all items plus applicable tax (except for jurisdictions that do not require sales tax to be charged or collected) for each day you don't return your rental by 9:00 pm local time (at the box) after first rental night. Void where prohibited by law. Code must not be copied, sold or otherwise offered. Any other use constitutes fraud. Can't be combined with other offers. Not redeemable for cash. Subject to cancellation or change at any time.

This promotional offer is not valid with any other discount/promotion.
See Rules of Use or visit www.entertainment.com/rulesofuse. 49782676

Promo code expires 12/31/2016 11:59 p.m. CT. Discount applies to the item of equal or lesser value. Limit: 1 code per transaction, regardless of # of rentals. 1 time use only. Code valid online, on the official Redbox mobile app or at the box in the amount of the discount stated off of the first day's rental fee for a DVD. Not valid for prior rentals. Your payment card (necessary for any rental) will be charged the full daily rental rate for any additional items, plus applicable tax (except for jurisdictions that do not require sales tax to be charged or collected) for the first rental day, if applicable, and will be charged the full daily rental fee for all items plus applicable tax (except for jurisdictions that do not require sales tax to be charged or collected) for each day you don't return your rental by 9:00 pm local time (at the box) after first rental day. Void where prohibited by law. Code must not be copied, sold or otherwise offered. Any other use constitutes fraud. Can't be combined with other offers. Not redeemable for cash. Subject to cancellation or change at any time.

This promotional offer is not valid with any other discount/promotion.
See Rules of Use or visit www.entertainment.com/rulesofuse. 49782675

Promo code expires 12/31/2017 11:59 p.m. CT. Limit: 1 code per transaction, regardless of # of rentals. 1 time use only. Code valid online, on the official Redbox mobile app or at the box in the amount of the discount stated off of the first day's rental fee for a DVD, Blu-ray Disc® or video game. Not valid for prior rentals. Your payment card (necessary for any rental) will be charged the full daily rental rate for any additional items, plus applicable tax except for jurisdictions that do not require sales tax to be charged or collected) for the first rental day, if applicable, and will be charged the full daily rental fee for all items plus applicable tax (except for jurisdictions that do not require sales tax to be charged or collected) for each day you don't return your rental by 9:00 pm local time (at the box) after first rental night. Void where prohibited by law. Code must not be copied, sold or otherwise offered. Any other use constitutes fraud. Can't be combined with other offers. Not redeemable for cash. Subject to cancellation or change at any time.

This promotional offer is not valid with any other discount/promotion.
See Rules of Use or visit www.entertainment.com/rulesofuse. 49782682

Promo code expires 8/31/2017 11:59 p.m. CT. Limit: 1 code per transaction, regardless of # of rentals. 1 time use only. Code valid online, on the official Redbox mobile app or at the box in the amount of the discount stated off of the first day's rental fee for a DVD, Blu-ray Disc® or video game. Not valid for prior rentals. Your payment card (necessary for any rental) will be charged the full daily rental rate for any additional items, plus applicable tax (except for jurisdictions that do not require sales tax to be charged or collected) for the first rental day, if applicable, and will be charged the full daily rental fee for all items plus applicable tax (except for jurisdictions that do not require sales tax to be charged or collected) for each day you don't return your rental by 9:00 pm local time (at the box) after first rental night. Void where prohibited by law. Code must not be copied, sold or otherwise offered. Any other use constitutes fraud. Can't be combined with other offers. Not redeemable for cash. Subject to cancellation or change at any time.

This promotional offer is not valid with any other discount/promotion.
See Rules of Use or visit www.entertainment.com/rulesofuse. 49782679

## Some Cards Are Just Tastier.

*An Applebee's® Gift Card gives you tons of tasty options you won't find anywhere else. Start with our new Appetizers, Pub Plates and Sampler Platters, which give you and your crew unprecedented choices and sampling options. Or go with one of our original All-In Burgers®, featuring flavorful toppings seared directly into fresh ground beef. If you are looking for something packed with "better for you" ingredients, choose favorites like the Cedar Grilled Lemon Chicken or Pepper-Crusted Sirloin & Whole Grains from our delicious under 600 calories menu to ensure you are getting a balanced combination of nutrition and flavor.*

*Applebee's—where premium ingredients and preparation take bar and grill classics to a new level.*

*Applebee's gift cards are always easy to order, are available in either plastic or digital formats, and can be used at 2,000 U.S. and Canada locations.*

*For tasteful gift-giving at its best, visit www.applebees.com/gift-cards to learn more.*

Applebee's® trademarks and logos are used with permission of Applebee's Restaurants LLC ("Applebee's") and such marks constitute registered trademarks or service marks of Applebee's. Applebee's is not affiliated with HSP EPI Acquisition, LLC d/b/a Entertainment® and is not a sponsor or co-sponsor of this program. Applebee's is not responsible for delivery of any gift cards promised, earned, purchased or otherwise offered through this program. Please see the Applebee's gift card or visit www.applebees.com for additional terms and conditions, which are subject to change at the sole discretion of Applebee's or its affiliates.

Visit **www.entdeals.com/Applebees** to take advantage of this deal.

## Some of the best memories are made at the breakfast table.

*Breakfast is the food that warms your soul and brings a smile to your face. And we believe it should be enjoyed any time of day. For more than 57 years, at more than 1,650 locations, millions of guests have been making memories at IHOP®. Whatever the occasion, wherever you are, create a memory with an IHOP gift card. Always easy to order, IHOP gift cards are convenient, flexible and available in either plastic or digital formats. Plus, there are no fees or expiration dates.*

*So treat yourself and make a great memory at IHOP.*

*Visit www.ihop.com to learn more.*

IHOP® trademarks and logos are used with permission of IHOP Restaurants LLC ("IHOP") and such marks constitute registered trademarks or service marks of IHOP. IHOP is not affiliated with HSP EPI Acquisition, LLC d/b/a Entertainment® and is not a sponsor or co-sponsor of this program. IHOP is not responsible for delivery of any gift cards promised, earned, purchased or otherwise offered through this program. Please see the IHOP gift card or visit www.ihop.com for additional terms and conditions, which are subject to change at the sole discretion of IHOP or its affiliates.

Visit **www.entdeals.com/IHOP** to take advantage of this deal.

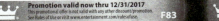

# **New** Benefit for Members

## Get discounts on gift cards.

**Save 5%** when you buy gift cards for restaurants, shopping and more.

**Learn more at:** entertainment.com/giftcards

# Save BIG on our top web deals!

## Saving is Easy
1. Visit any website listed below to access that retailer's online deals.
2. If a promo code is listed, enter it at checkout.

### SPECIAL OFFERS
For a special promotion every week, come see what savings await you.

Visit **www.entdeals.com/Target2017**

**F86**

### PURCHASE A NEW COSTCO MEMBERSHIP AND RECEIVE A SPECIAL OFFER.
Visit **Entdeals.com/costcomembership** for details.

**F87**

### 20% OFF PLUS FREE SHIPPING AND FREE EXCHANGES.
To redeem, visit **www.shoebuy.com/ent17**

**F88**

### 20% OFF YOUR ENTIRE ORDER AT ONLINESHOES.COM
Some restrictions apply. See site for complete list of exclusions.

Please visit
**www.OnlineShoes.com/entertainment**

**F89**

**NATIONAL RETAIL ONLINE**

### Access hundreds more web deals:
www.entertainment.com/shop & on the mobile app

**Promotion valid now thru 12/31/2017, unless noted otherwise.**

# Save BIG on our top web deals!

## Saving is Easy

1. Visit any website listed below to access that retailer's online deals.
2. If a promo code is listed, enter it at checkout.

**NATIONAL RETAIL ONLINE**

# Save BIG on our top web deals!

### *Saving is Easy*
1. Visit any website listed below to access that retailer's online deals.
2. If a promo code is listed, enter it at checkout.

The Best in Custom Blinds and Window Coverings

## 30% OFF* SELECTED SIGNATURE SERIES® WINDOW TREATMENTS BY BUDGET BLINDS.

Schedule your FREE In-Home Consultation at **www.BudgetBlinds4U.com** or call 866-208-5275.

*Not valid with any other offers, discounts or coupons. Valid for a limited time only. Offer good at initial time of estimate only. At participating franchises only. Ask for details. Each franchise independently owned and operated.

**F94**

## ENJOY 20% OFF ANY SINGLE ITEM PURCHASE.

Cannot be used with other discount, coupon or any of the following items or brands: Inside Track Club membership, extended service plan, gift card, open box item, 3 day parking lot sale item, compressors, floor jacks, saw mills, storage cabinets, chests or carts, trailers, trenchers, welders, Admiral, Badland, CoverPro, Daytona, Diablo, Franklin, Hercules, Holt, Jupiter, Predator, Stik-Tek, StormCat, Union, Vanguard, Viking. Not valid on prior purchases. Non-transferable. Valid through 12/31/17.

Valid at **HarborFreight.com**. Use coupon code 71265483 at checkout.

**F95**

## SWISS DIAMOND IS PLEASED TO OFFER A 15% OFF DISCOUNT.

Swiss Diamond cookware is the #1 nonstick cookware! Made in Switzerland, it has a cast aluminum body (guaranteed never to warp) with a patented nonstick coating reinforced with real diamonds for a lifetime of easy clean-up and even heat distribution. It allows cooking without fat and oil, is dishwasher safe and resistant to damage from metal utensils. Carrying a full line of cookware, including fry pans, skillets, sauté pans, sauce pots, stock pots and many specialty cookware, Swiss Diamond cookware comes with a limited lifetime warranty!

All orders placed on **SwissDiamond.com** are eligible. Simply enter **SG-ENT-15** at checkout.

**F96**

## $1 FOR FIRST MONTH'S RENT* PLUS UP TO 15% OFF MONTHLY RENT**

*Offered only on selected units. Subject to availability. Other restrictions, taxes and fees apply. Applies to first month's rent only.

**Online pricing available only for online reservations and rentals. Up to 15% promotion applies to monthly rent only. COUPON NOT REDEEMABLE AT LOCATIONS. MUST USE THE PHONE NUMBER OR WEBSITE ADDRESS TO RESERVE IN ORDER TO GET THIS DEAL. Promotions good for new customers only. Not available on transfers or additional spaces.

Visit **SaveatPublicStorage.com**

**F97**

**NATIONAL RETAIL ONLINE**

## Access hundreds more web deals:
www.entertainment.com/shop & on the mobile app

**Promotion valid now thru 12/31/2017, unless noted otherwise.**

This promotional offer is not valid with any other discount/promotion. See Rules of Use or visit **www.entertainment.com/rulesofuse**.

# HEALTHY LIVING
# Rewards®

♛entertainment

**Specially selected discounts that can support you in your health and wellness goals!**

- Athletic shoes and sporting goods
- Fitness centers
- Nutrition and weight loss
- Exercise equipment
- Medical IDs and personal safety
- Health maintenance

**$10 OFF**

# TAKE $10 OFF YOUR PURCHASE OF $50 OR MORE.

**Promotion valid 08/01/2016 thru 1/31/2017**
See reverse side for additional conditions or restrictions.

F98

**$15 OFF**

# TAKE $15 OFF YOUR PURCHASE OF $75 OR MORE.

**Promotion valid 2/1/2017 thru 7/31/2017**
See reverse side for additional conditions or restrictions.

F99

**HEALTHY LIVING REWARDS®**

**$20 OFF**

# TAKE $20 OFF YOUR PURCHASE OF $100 OR MORE.

**Promotion valid 8/1/2017 thru 12/31/2017**
See reverse side for additional conditions or restrictions.

F100

**P00026112**

\* Limit one coupon per customer. **Valid on in-store purchases only.** Must be used in one transaction. Minimum purchase of $50, excludes tax and shipping charges. Cannot be combined with any other offers, team discounts or used for gift cards, licenses or previously purchased merchandise. Not redeemable for cash, gift cards or store credit. No reproductions or rain checks accepted. Returns or exchanges where a ScoreCard Reward or other discount was applied may result in an adjusted refund amount. Excludes clearance items. Clearance items have .X3 or .X7 endings. Some exclusions apply.  See store and DICKS.com/Exclusions for details.

**Valid 8/1/2016 through 1/31/2017.**

**P00026113**

\* Limit one coupon per customer. **Valid on in-store purchases only.** Must be used in one transaction. Minimum purchase of $75, excludes tax and shipping charges. Cannot be combined with any other offers, team discounts or used for gift cards, licenses or previously purchased merchandise. Not redeemable for cash, gift cards or store credit. No reproductions or rain checks accepted. Returns or exchanges where a ScoreCard Reward or other discount was applied may result in an adjusted refund amount. Excludes clearance items. Clearance items have .X3 or .X7 endings. Some exclusions apply.  See store and DICKS.com/Exclusions for details.

**Valid 2/1/2017 through 7/31/2017.**

**P00026114**

\* Limit one coupon per customer. **Valid on in-store purchases only.** Must be used in one transaction. Minimum purchase of $100, excludes tax and shipping charges. Cannot be combined with any other offers, team discounts or used for gift cards, licenses or previously purchased merchandise. Not redeemable for cash, gift cards or store credit. No reproductions or rain checks accepted. Returns or exchanges where a ScoreCard Reward or other discount was applied may result in an adjusted refund amount. Excludes clearance items. Clearance items have .X3 or .X7 endings. Some exclusions apply.  See store and DICKS.com/Exclusions for details.

**Valid 8/1/2017 through 12/31/2017.**

HEALTHY LIVING REWARDS®

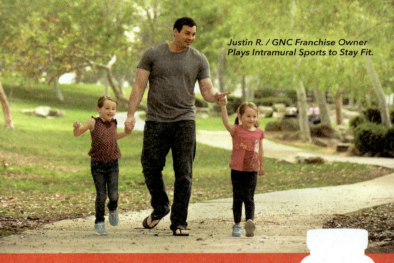

# HOW DO YOU START FEELING HEALTHIER?

## JUST ASK. WE MAKE IT SIMPLE.

*Justin R. / GNC Franchise Owner
Plays Intramural Sports to Stay Fit.*

**You've got questions. We've got answers.**
Stop by your local GNC or visit us at GNC.com/JustAsk

**GNC**
LIVE WELL

### $10 OFF
Any Purchase of $50 or More

**In-Store Coupon #29355**

**GNC**
LIVE WELL

### 20% OFF
Your Total Purchase

**In-Store Coupon #29354**

# HOW DO WE GUARANTEE SATISFACTION?

## JUST ASK. WE MAKE IT SIMPLE.

If you're not 100% satisfied, neither are we. If something's not right for you, bring it back and we'll refund your money.^

^Must bring product back within 30 days with a valid sales receipt and photo ID. In the absence of a sales receipt, an exchange will be offered on GNC brand products based on the lowest price within the last 60 days. No exchange or refund will be offered on non-GNC brand products without a receipt. Excludes GNC gift cards, Gold Cards, shipping, handling and other charges. See associate for details.

**GNC LIVE WELL**

**GNC LIVE WELL**

**$10** VALUE

# FAMOUS footwear.

## Take $10 OFF any in-store purchase of $50 or more.

Visit www.famousfootwear.com/entertainment16
for your special online offer.

**Promotion valid 7/1/2016 thru 12/31/2017**
See reverse side for additional conditions or restrictions.

F103

---

## 10% OFF

ROAD**RUNNER** SPORTS
World's Largest Running & Walking Store.

## Enjoy 10% OFF your next purchase with Road Runner Sports.

Road Runner Sports is the world's largest running & walking store, where you'll find
ALL the best athletic shoes, clothing, accessories and gear at your very best prices!

Available in-store and online. (See reverse for details.)

### Promo Code: C6X10031

**Promotion valid now thru 12/31/2017**
See reverse side for additional conditions or restrictions.

F104

---

## SPECIAL OFFER

*Curves*®

## Join Curves today and get 50% OFF the enrollment fee!

**Promotion valid now thru 12/31/2017**
See reverse side for additional conditions or restrictions.

F105

HEALTHY LIVING REWARDS®

9 10100 28600 9

Valid 07/01/2016-12/31/2017. Coupon may be used only once in Famous Footwear or Famous Footwear Outlet stores. Not valid online. Not valid on select Nike styles, select Converse styles, select Sperry, for cash or cash equivalent, on purchase of gift cards or on previously purchased merchandise. Other exclusions may apply, ask store associate for details. Offer may not be combined with any other coupons (other than Rewards certificates). Photocopies or reproductions of coupons will not be accepted. Items purchased with certificates, coupons or special promotions will result in adjusted refund or exchange amount. Limit 21 pairs of shoes. One transaction per person.

7 1 5 0 5 0 0 1 6 1

Delight in 10% off on your favorite running shoes, apparel and gear! Excludes select adidas, saucony, asics and nike styles, other exclusions apply. Valid in-store only. Visit roadrunnersports.com/retail to find your neighborhood store.

To redeem online, you must go to **entdeals.com/roadrunnersports**

Use promo code: **C6X10031** at checkout.

Valid at all participating locations.

Enrollment fee and monthly fees vary by location. Offer expires 12/31/17 and requires joining same day as first visit for a minimum 12-month recurring billing contract. Valid for new Curves members only. Not valid with any other offer or discount. Valid at participating location only. Classes and Jillian Michaels workouts scheduled by location and only offered at participating locations. No cash value.

© 2016 Curves International, Inc.

# HEALTHY LIVING Rewards

👑 entertainment

## Saving is Easy

1. Visit any website listed below to access that retailer's online deals.
2. If a promo code is listed, enter it at checkout.

### 10% OFF YOUR PURCHASE*

Offer available at **entdeals.com/puritanspride**

*Discount will automatically apply to cart; minimum order threshold does not include tax or shipping; valid on Puritan's Pride® brand products only; limit one (1) per customer; cannot be combined with any additional coupon or 3rd party cash back offers; certain products, including clearance section items, may be excluded. All products subject to availability. To expedite orders, we may substitute a smaller bottle if ordered quantity is out of stock. Terms and conditions subject to change. Internet distribution or resale strictly prohibited. We reserve the right, at our sole discretion, to refuse or cancel any order for any reason. For your convenience, you will not be charged until your payment method is authorized, the order information is verified for accuracy and your order is shipped.

**F106**

### TRY US FREE FOR A MONTH (PLUS THE COST OF FOOD)

Month of free consultations valid with trial membership or program enrollment. Cost of food ($15-$23/day and $17-$26CAN) and shipping not included with offer. Offer valid at participating centers and Jenny Craig Anywhere, not valid at jennycraig.com. New members only, program enrollment or trial membership required. No cash value. Not valid with any other offers or discounts. One offer per person. Offer expires 12/31/17. Restrictions apply. Adjustment code: J12.

Visit **www.jennycraig.com/entertainment** to get your free coupon. Then call 1-800-Jenny20 to be connected to your closest Jenny Craig center.

**F107**

### FREE 30-DAY TRIAL MEMBERSHIP + A FITNESS ASSESSMENT — A $160 VALUE.

Includes 30 Day trial Membership — $40 value; Free fitness assessment — $100 value; Global access key card — $20 value; offer only available online by going to **www.snapfitness.com/partnerships**. Excludes, onetime global access, shipping and handling fee.

**F108**

### 25% OFF YOUR NEXT ORDER!

Personal Chef To Go offers healthy, delicious meals in reasonable portions and at affordable prices. We have meals for large families to busy singles and everyone in-between. We even offer vegetarian and other food sensitivity options.

Limit one offer per coupon holder. Cannot be combined with other offers.

Visit **www.personalcheftogo.com** and enter code **Heathy25** at checkout.

**F109**

HEALTHY LIVING REWARDS®

## Access hundreds more web deals:

www.entertainment.com/shop & on the mobile app

**Promotion valid now thru 12/31/2017, unless noted otherwise.**

This promotional offer is not valid with any other discount/promotion. See Rules of Use or visit www.entertainment.com/rulesofuse.

# HEALTHY LIVING **Rewards**

♕ *entertainment*

## *Saving is Easy*

1. Visit any website listed below to access that retailer's online deals.
2. If a promo code is listed, enter it at checkout.

---

Gym Quality Equipment for every**BODY**!

### 5% OFF YOUR ONLINE PURCHASE.

Yowza Fitness makes the process of buying advanced fitness equipment easy. We invite you to check out our innovative line of the highest rated ellipticals and treadmills on the market today. Gym Quality Equipment for every**BODY**!

Valid at **www.yowzafitness.com** and use **Coupon Code: YOWZA5**. Coupon will be applied at checkout. Coupon cannot be combined with any other offer or free gift at time of purchase. See site for details. **F110**

---

### 10% OFF AB DOLLY.

Tone and tighten ALL your abdominal muscles with the fast, fun and effective ABDolly! Works in ANY range of motion and in ANY direction to target those hard to reach areas. Perfect for all ages and fitness levels.

Visit **www.abdolly.com/rewards** for your special offer. Expires 12/31/2017. See site for details. Discount applied at checkout. **F111**

---

### 10% OFF ALL GAZELLE MODELS.

Glide into amazing shape! The Gazelle Glider, featuring Tony Little, America's personal trainer, combines cardio, muscle toning and stretching to deliver a quick and effective low-impact total body workout! A fitness favorite for over 20 years.

Visit **www.gazelleglider.com/rewards** for your special offer. Expires 12/31/2017. See site for details. Discount applied at checkout. **F112**

---

### 15% OFF TOTAL GYM FIT.

Build strength and blast away fat in just 10–20 minutes a day! A trusted leader in home fitness for over 40 years, Total Gym, used by countless athletes and celebs, like Chuck Norris and Christie Brinkley, includes everything you need to get in the BEST shape of your life!

Visit **www.totalgymdirect.com/rewards** for your special offer. Expires 12/31/2017. See site for details. Discount applied at checkout. **F113**

---

## Access hundreds more web deals:

www.entertainment.com/shop & on the mobile app

**Promotion valid now thru 12/31/2017, unless noted otherwise.**

This promotional offer is not valid with any other discount/promotion. See Rules of Use or visit **www.entertainment.com/rulesofuse**

*HEALTHY LIVING REWARDS®*

# HEALTHY LIVING Rewards

👑 entertainment

## Saving is Easy

1. Visit any website listed below to access that retailer's online deals.
2. If a promo code is listed, enter it at checkout.

### 15% OFF ANY HEALTH & WELLNESS PRODUCTS.

Entertainment Readers, $42.50 can get you a set of poles and start you walking. Burns up to 50% more calories than traditional walking. Aligns the body and lets you walk taller and lighter, as your spine stacks, shoulders open, chest lifts and core engages. Reduces stress to knees, hips and back up to 30%. Visit balancewalking.com to see a complete list of benefits that will be delivered to your body, by just adding poles to your walk.

Use **Coupon Code: ENT** to get 15% off any health and wellness products at **balancewalking.com**. Have fun working 90% of your muscles while decreasing your perceived rate of exertion. It's an Easy Exercise For Everyone.

**F114**

### ENJOY 10% OFF + FREE SHIPPING ON YOUR NEXT ORDER WITH ROAD RUNNER SPORTS.

Delight in 10% off on your Favorite Running Shoes, Apparel and Gear + Free Shipping! Use Offer Code C6X10031. Excludes select adidas, saucony, asics and nike styles, other exclusions apply.

Offer available at **entdeals.com/roadrunnersports**
Offer Code: **C6X10031**

**F115**

### 20% OFF YOUR ENTIRE ONLINE PURCHASE.

Looking to stay active? Shop a range of sports identification and safety products to keep you not only confident but motivated! Be Safe. Be Seen.

See **www.4id.com** for details.
Use **Promo Code: 4idLED** at checkout.

**F116**

### 20% OFF YOUR ENTIRE ONLINE PURCHASE.

Visit **www.hopepaige.com** and use **Promo Code: HopePaige20** at checkout.

**F117**

**HEALTHY LIVING REWARDS®**

## Access hundreds more web deals:

www.entertainment.com/shop & on the mobile app

**Promotion valid now thru 12/31/2017, unless noted otherwise.**

This promotional offer is not valid with any other discount/promotion. See Rules of Use or visit **www.entertainment.com/rulesofuse**.

# HEALTHY LIVING Rewards

👑 entertainment

## Saving is Easy

1. Visit any website listed below to access that retailer's online deals.
2. If a promo code is listed, enter it at checkout.

---

# HEALTHY LIVING Rewards

👑 entertainment

## Saving is Easy

1. Visit any website listed below to access that retailer's online deals.
2. If a promo code is listed, enter it at checkout.

### 15% OFF ANY HEALTH & WELLNESS PRODUCTS.

Entertainment Readers, $42.50 can get you a set of poles and start you walking. Burns up to 50% more calories than traditional walking. Aligns the body and lets you walk taller and lighter, as your spine stacks, shoulders open, chest lifts and core engages. Reduces stress to knees, hips and back up to 30%. Visit balancewalking.com to see a complete list of benefits that will be delivered to your body, by just adding poles to your walk.

Use **Coupon Code: ENT** to get 15% off any health and wellness products at **balancewalking.com**. Have fun working 90% of your muscles while decreasing your perceived rate of exertion. It's an Easy Exercise For Everyone.

**F114**

World's Largest Running & Walking Store.

### ENJOY 10% OFF + FREE SHIPPING ON YOUR NEXT ORDER WITH ROAD RUNNER SPORTS.

Delight in 10% off on your Favorite Running Shoes, Apparel and Gear + Free Shipping! Use Offer Code C6X10031. Excludes select adidas, saucony, asics and nike styles, other exclusions apply.

Offer available at **entdeals.com/roadrunnersports**
Offer Code: **C6X10031**

**F115**

### 20% OFF YOUR ENTIRE ONLINE PURCHASE.

Looking to stay active? Shop a range of sports identification and safety products to keep you not only confident but motivated! Be Safe. Be Seen.

See **www.4id.com** for details.
Use **Promo Code: 4idLED** at checkout.

**F116**

Medical ID Marketplace

### 20% OFF YOUR ENTIRE ONLINE PURCHASE.

Visit **www.hopepaige.com** and use **Promo Code: HopePaige20** at checkout.

**F117**

HEALTHY LIVING REWARDS®

## Access hundreds more web deals:

www.entertainment.com/shop & on the mobile app

**Promotion valid now thru 12/31/2017, unless noted otherwise.**

This promotional offer is not valid with any other discount/promotion. See Rules of Use or visit **www.entertainment.com/rulesofuse**.

# HEALTHY LIVING **Rewards**

👑 *entertainment*

## *Saving is Easy*

1. Visit any website listed below to access that retailer's online deals.
2. If a promo code is listed, enter it at checkout.

**HEALTHY LIVING REWARDS®**

# National Travel & Hotels

## Going on a Trip? Book with Entertainment®!

Find a complete listing of this section's merchants on the back of this page.

**Find 100s more offers:**
www.entertainment.com/travel & on the mobile app

# Take Your Entertainment® Membership Along When You Travel

Visit member.entertainment.com when you book your next adventure to save big and do more for less.

**Car Rentals · Hotels · Top Destinations**
**Condos & Resorts · Vacation Packages · Cruises**

## Drive Away with Savings — with Our Car Rental Deals

## Experience Great Savings at Top Destinations

Use **Entertainment® on Vacation** to get member-only deals and discounts exclusive to 12 popular destinations. Enjoy savings on airfare, car rentals, hotels, dining, attractions & more!

| | | | |
|---|---|---|---|
| Atlanta | Boston | Chicago | Denver |
| Las Vegas | Los Angeles | Orlando | Phoenix |
| San Diego | San Francisco | Seattle | Southern Florida |

# Save on Your Hotel Stay — We Have the Best Deals!

## Book by Brand & Save

America's Best Value Inn — Up to 10% off

Aston — Up to 20% off

Comfort Inn — Up to 10% off

Days Inn — Up to 20% off

Holiday Inn — 10-30% off

and so many more!

## Save with Our Partner Booking Sites

Snazzy Traveler — Up to 75% off

Booking.com — Up to 50% off

Entertainment® Hotel Bucks — Up to 40% off

Getaroom.com — Up to 20% Off online Rates
Plus $25-$35 Off

hotels.com — 10% off already discounted hotels

Visit member.entertainment.com for a complete listing

# National Travel & Hotels Index

NATIONAL TRAVEL & HOTELS

![entertainment](crown logo) ***entertainment***®

# ON VACATION

## TOP 12 DESTINATIONS

**Specially selected discounts exclusive to these cities!**

See the following pages when planning your trip to:

# Experience Atlanta

## PLAN YOUR TRIP

**Save up to $20 OFF our Service Fees on Flights.**
1-888-204-1645 and use promo code ONE2017.
www.OneTravel.com

**Up to 35% OFF base rates.**
1-800-245-8572 and use AWD# B790093.
www.avis.com/epatlanta

**Entertainment® members save 5% OFF base rates on rentals in the U.S. and Canada.**
1-800-PAYLESS and use promo code A067700.
www.paylesscar.com/entertainment

## WHILE YOU'RE THERE — Find the local savings

featured attractions

FIND IT ON THE APP!

**Atlanta History Center** — Buy One, Get One Admission

**Atlanta Movie Tours** — Buy One, Get One Admission

**Stone Mountain Golf Club** — 50% off Standard Rate for 2–4 Players

**Georgia Symphony Orchestra** — Buy One, Get One Admission

Please see each individual offer for additional conditions and restrictions. Merchants and offers are subject to change.

## entertainment.
## ON VACATION

## FEATURED HOTELS:

Book online at **www.entertainment.com/IHG16**. For reservations call **(877) 580-2943**.

**Holiday Inn** - **Centennial Park (Atlanta Downtown)**
101 Andrew J. Young International Blvd., Atlanta

**Holiday Inn Express & Suites** - **Atlanta Buckhead**
800 Sidney Marcus Blvd., Atlanta

**Staybridge Suites** - **Atlanta Perimeter Center**
4601 Ridgeview Rd., Atlanta

**Hotel Indigo**
683 Peachtree St. NE, Atlanta

**InterContinental** - **Atlanta Buckhead**
3315 Peachtree Rd. NE, Atlanta

**Crowne Plaza** - **Airport**
1325 Virginia Ave., Atlanta

below on your mobile app while you're in Atlanta, plus 100s more!

**Barcelona Wine Bar** — 2 Free Tapas

**The Smoke Ring** — 25% off the Total Bill – up to $25

**The 57th Fighter Group Restaurant** — 20% off the Total Bill – up to $25

**Harry & Sons** — $10 off

# Experience Boston & New England

## PLAN YOUR TRIP

**Save up to $20 OFF our Service Fees on Flights.**
1-888-204-1645 and use promo code ONE2017.
www.OneTravel.com

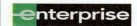

**Save on Everyday Low Rates!**
**Reference Customer # ENBKDC7**

Book now at enterprise.com/ent17
or call 1-888-446-9952.

## WHILE YOU'RE THERE — Find the local savings

featured attractions

FIND IT ON THE APP!

**Franklin Park Zoo** — Complimentary Children's Museum

**Isabella Stewart Gardner Museum** — Buy One, Get One Admission

**Stone Zoo** — Complimentary Children's Admission

**Wheelock Family Theatre** — Buy One, Get One Admission

Please see each individual offer for additional conditions and restrictions. Merchants and offers are subject to change.

## FEATURED HOTELS:

Book online at **www.entertainment.com/IHG16**. For reservations call **(877) 580-2943**.

**Holiday Inn Express & Suites** - Boston Garden
280 Friend St., Boston, MA 02114

**InterContinental**
510 Atlantic Ave., Boston, MA 02210

**Holiday Inn Express & Suites**
250 Monsignor O'Brien Hwy., Cambridge

**Crowne Plaza**
320 Washington St., Newton

**Hotel Indigo** - Newton Riverside
399 Grove St., Newton

**Holiday Inn** - Boston Bunker Hill Area
30 Washington St., Somerville

below on your mobile app while you're in Boston, plus 100s more!

**Da Vinci Ristorante** — $10 off $30

**Muqueca Restaurant** — Buy One, Get One Entree

**Bravo Restaurant** — 25% off the Total Bill – up to $50

**Fenmore American Bistro** — 25% off the Total Bill – up to $50

# Experience Chicago

## PLAN YOUR TRIP

 **Save up to $20 OFF our Service Fees on Flights.**
1-888-645-9758 and use promo code COA2017.
www.CheapOAir.com

 **Up to 35% OFF base rates.**
1-800-245-8572 and use AWD# B790082.
www.avis.com/epchicago

 **Up to 30% OFF base rates.**
1-888-724-6212 and use offer code (BCD) X44063.
www.budget.com/epchicago

## WHILE YOU'RE THERE — Find the local savings

featured attractions

FIND IT ON THE APP!

**Chicago Water Sport Rentals** — 50% off any Two Hour Rental

**Spirit of Chicago**
— $50 off Dinner Cruise Ticket with Purchase of a Second Dinner Cruise Ticket

**Seadog Cruises** — Buy One, Get One Architectural River Tour

**Amazing Chicago's Funhouse Maze (Navy Pier)** — Buy One, Get One Admission

Please see each individual offer for additional conditions and restrictions. Merchants and offers are subject to change.

## FEATURED HOTELS:

To make your reservation, book online at **www.wyndhamhotelgroup.com/ent** or call **(877) 670-7088** and use **ID# 1000000181**.

### WYNDHAM
HOTEL GROUP

**Wyndham Garden Elk Grove Village/O'Hare**
2550 Landmeier Rd., Elk Grove Village

**Hawthorn Suites by Wyndham Chicago Schaumburg**
1200 Bank Dr., Schaumburg

**Wingate by Wyndham Tinley Park**
18421 N. Creek Dr., Tinley Park

**Wyndham Grand Chicago Riverfront**
71 E. Wacker Dr., Chicago

**Days Inn Chicago**
644 W. Diversey Pkwy., Chicago

**Wyndham Glenview Suites Chicago North**
1400 N. Milwaukee Ave., Glenview

below on your mobile app while you're in Chicago, plus 100s more!

**featured dining**

**FIND IT ON THE APP!**

**Tutto Italiano Ristorante** — Buy One, Get One Entrée – up to $15

**The Indian Garden** — Buy One, Get One Entrée – up to $15

**Rainforest Cafe** — $5 off Any Purchase

**Hershey's Chicago Bake Shoppe**
— Buy One, Get One Menu Item – up to $5

# Experience Denver

## PLAN YOUR TRIP

**Save up to $20 OFF our Service Fees on Flights.**
1-888-204-1645 and use promo code ONE2017.
www.OneTravel.com

**Save on Everyday Low Rates.**
Reference Customer # ENBKDM7. Book now at
enterprise.com/ent17 or call 1-888-446-9952.

**$15 OFF**
Reference Customer # 7016629 and Coupon Code
AD2826JAA. Book now at alamo.com/offer/ent17
or call 1-800-237-0984.

## WHILE YOU'RE THERE — Find the local savings

featured attractions

FIND IT ON THE APP!

**Pirates Cove Family Fun Aquatic Center** — Buy One, Get One Admission

**Denver Botanic Gardens** — Buy One, Get One Admission

**The Wildlife Experience** — Buy One, Get One Admission

**The Children's Museum of Denver** — Buy One, Get One Admission

Please see each individual offer for additional conditions and restrictions. Merchants and offers are subject to change.

ON VACATION

## FEATURED HOTELS:

Book online at www.entertainment.com/choicehotels or call (800) 533-2100
and mention Special Rate ID: 00803210.

HOTELS®

**The Golden Hotel** - **An Ascend Collection Hotel**
800 11th St., Golden

**Quality Inn & Suites** - **Denver International Airport**
6890 Tower Road, Denver

**Comfort Inn**
10200 W. I-70 Frontage Rd. S., Wheatridge

**Comfort Inn** - **Denver East**
4380 Peoria Street, Denver

**Comfort Suites** - **Denver Tech Center**
7384 S. Clinton St., Englewood

**Cambria Hotel and Suites**
16001 E. 40th St., Aurora

below on your mobile app while you're in Denver, plus 100s more!

featured dining

FIND IT ON THE APP!

**The Delectable Egg** — Buy One, Get One Entrée – up to $9

**Sam's No. 3** — Buy One Lunch or Dinner, Get One Lunch or Dinner Entrée – up to $7

**Jack N' Grill** — Buy One Lunch or Dinner, Get One Lunch or Dinner Entrée – up to $12

**Billy's Inn** — 25% off the Total Bill – up to $25

# Experience Las Vegas

## PLAN YOUR TRIP

**Save up to $20 OFF our Service Fees on Flights.**
1-888-645-9758 and use promo code COA2017.
www.CheapOAir.com

**Up to 35% OFF base rates.**
1-800-245-8572 and use AWD# B790094.
www.avis.com/eplasvegas

**Up to 30% OFF base rates.**
1-888-724-6212 and use offer code (BCD) X443052.
www.budget.com/eplasvegas

## WHILE YOU'RE THERE —— Find the local savings

featured attractions

FIND IT ON THE APP!

**CSI: The Experience** — Buy One, Get One Admission

**Papillon Grand Canyon Helicopters** — Buy One, Get One Strip Highlighters Tour

**Vegas Indoor Skydiving** — $25 off a Single Flight

**Beatle Show** — Buy One, Get One Ticket

Please see each individual offer for additional conditions and restrictions. Merchants and offers are subject to change.

## FEATURED HOTELS:

Book online at **www.entertainment.com/IHG16**. For reservations call **(877) 580-2943**.

**InterContinental Alliance Resorts** - **The Palazzo**
3325 Las Vegas Blvd. South, Las Vegas

**InterContinental Alliance Resorts** - **The Venetian**
3355 Las Vegas Blvd. South, Las Vegas

**Holiday Inn Club Vacations** - **Desert Club Resort**
3950 Koval Lane, Las Vegas

**Candlewood Suites**
4034 Paradise Rd., Las Vegas

**Holiday Inn Express** - **Nellis**
4035 North Nellis Blvd., Las Vegas

**Staybridge Suites**
5735 Dean Martin Dr., Las Vegas

below on your mobile app while you're in Las Vegas, plus 100s more!

featured dining

FIND IT ON THE APP!

**El Sombrero Mexican Bistro** — Buy One, Get One Entrée – up to $32

**Pampas Brazilian Grille** — Buy One, Get One Entrée – up to $52

**Urban Turban** — Buy One, Get One Entrée – up to $19

**Cafe Mayakovski** — Buy One, Get One Entrée – up to $15

# Experience Los Angeles

## PLAN YOUR TRIP

**Save up to $20 OFF our Service Fees on Flights.**
1-888-645-9758 and use promo code COA2017.
www.CheapOAir.com

**Up to 35% OFF base rates.**
1-800-245-8572 and use AWD# B790092.
www.avis.com/epla

**Up to 30% OFF base rates.**
1-888-724-6212 and use offer code (BCD) X443054.
www.budget.com/epla

## WHILE YOU'RE THERE — Find the local savings

featured attractions

FIND IT ON THE APP!

**Pacific Park on the Santa Monica Pier**
— 20% off an Unlimited Ride Wristband (good for up to 4 eople)

**Kapowui** — 50% off any Surf or Paddleboard Lesson

**Hollywoodland Tours** — 30% off Regular price

**USS IOWA** — $4 off Admission

Please see each individual offer for additional conditions and restrictions. Merchants and offers are subject to change.

**ON VACATION**

## FEATURED HOTELS:

To make your reservation, book online at **www.wyndhamhotelgroup.com/ent** or call **(877) 670-7088** and use **ID# 1000000181.**

# WYNDHAM
### HOTEL GROUP

**Howard Johnson Anaheim Hotel And Water Playground**
1380 S. Harbor Blvd., Anaheim

**Ramada Plaza West Hollywood Hotel And Suites**
8585 Santa Monica Blvd., West Hollywood

**Ramada Anaheim Maingate North**
921 S. Harbor Drive, Anaheim

**Ramada Plaza Anaheim**
515 W. Katella Ave., Anaheim

**Wyndham Anaheim Garden Grove**
12021 Harbor Blvd., Anaheim

**Wyndham Santa Monica At The Pier**
120 Colorado Ave., Santa Monica

below on your mobile app while you're in Los Angeles, plus 100s more!

featured dining

FIND IT ON THE APP!

**Gladstones** — 25% off the Total Bill – up to $25

**Pig 'N Whistle** — Buy One, Get One Entrée – up to $14

**Figtree's Cafe** — Buy One, Get One Entrée – up to $13

**Chalet Edelweiss Restaurant & Bar** — 25% off the Total Bill – up to $25

# Experience Orlando

## PLAN YOUR TRIP

**Save up to $20 OFF our Service Fees on Flights.**
1-888-204-1645 and use promo code OT2017.
www.OneTravel.com

---

**AVIS**®

**Up to 35% OFF base rates.**
1-800-245-8572 and use AWD# B790090.
www.avis.com/eporlando

---

**Up to 30% OFF base rates.**
1-888-724-6212 and use offer code (BCD) X443057.
www.budget.com/eporlando

## WHILE YOU'RE THERE — Find the local savings

featured attractions

FIND IT ON THE APP!

**Boggy Creek Airboat Rides** — Buy One, Get One Airboat Ride 50% off

**Walt Disney World** — Save on Walt Disney World Resort Tickets

**Chocolate Kingdom** — 20% off a Regular Priced Admission

**Universal Orlando** — Save on Universal Orlando Park Tickets

Please see each individual offer for additional conditions and restrictions. Merchants and offers are subject to change.

entertainment.com/travel

## ON VACATION

## FEATURED HOTELS:

To make your reservation, book online at **www.wyndhamhotelgroup.com/ent** or call **(877) 670-7088** and use **ID# 1000000181**.

# WYNDHAM
### HOTEL GROUP

**Hawthorn Suites by Wyndham Lake Buena Vista**
8303 Palm Pkwy., Orlando

**Ramada Plaza Resort and Suites**
6500 International Dr., Orlando

**Hawthorn Inn and Suites International Drive**
7975 Canada Ave., Orlando

**Wyndham Grand Orlando Resort Bonnet Creek**
14651 Chelonia Pkwy., Orlando

**Wyndham Orlando Resort International Drive**
8001 International Dr., Orlando

**Wyndham Lake Buena Vista Resort**
1850 Hotel Plaza Blvd., Lake Buena Vista

below on your mobile app while you're in Orlando, plus 100s more!

**Sleuths Mystery Dinner Shows** — $16 off one Adult Dinner Admission

**Chez Vincent** — $10 off $40

**Vines Grille & Wine Bar** — Buy One, Get One Entrée 50% off – up to $15

**BB King's Blues Club** — $10 off $50

# Experience Phoenix

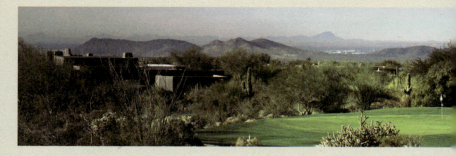

## PLAN YOUR TRIP

**Save up to $20 OFF our Service Fees on Flights.**
1-888-645-9758 and use promo code COA2017.
www.CheapOAir.com

**Up to 35% OFF base rates.**
1-800-245-8572 and use AWD# B790081.
www.avis.com/epphoenix

**Up to 30% OFF base rates.**
1-888-724-6212 and use offer code (BCD) X44064.
www.budget.com/epphoenix

## WHILE YOU'RE THERE —— Find the local savings

featured attractions

FIND IT ON THE APP!

**Arizona Science Center** — Buy One Get One Admission

**Phoenix Art Museum** — Buy One, Get One Admission

**Wildlife World Zoo & Aquarium** — Buy One, Get One Admission

**San Marcos Golf Resort** — Buy Three, Get One Green Fee

**Phoenix Zoo** — Buy One, Get One Admission

entertainment.
ON VACATION

## FEATURED HOTELS:

Book online at **www.entertainment.com/choicehotels** or call **(800) 533-2100** and mention Special Rate ID: **00803210**.

**BlueGreen Vacations Cibola Vista Resort & Spa**
27501 N. Lake Pleasant Pkwy., Peoria

**Comfort Suites - University of Phoenix Stadium**
9824 W. Camelback Rd., Glendale

**Comfort Suites - Old Town Scottsdale**
3275 N. Drinkwater Blvd., Scottsdale

**Comfort Inn - Phoenix Airport**
1625 S. 52nd St., Tempe

**Comfort Inn - West**
1344 N. 27th St., Phoenix

**Sleep Inn - North Scottsdale Road**
16630 N. Scottsdale Rd., Scottsdale

below on your mobile app while you're in Phoenix, plus 100s more!

featured dining

FIND IT ON THE APP!

**Arriverderci Ristorante** — 25% off the Total Bill – up to $25

**La Ristra New Mexican Kitchen** — Buy One, Get One Entrée – up to $12

**Marcello's Pasta Grill** — Buy One, Get One Entrée – up to $15

**Santisi Brothers** — Buy One, Get One Entrée – up to $16

# Experience San Diego

## PLAN YOUR TRIP

**OneTravel**
**Save up to $20 OFF our Service Fees on Flights.**
1-888-204-1645 and use promo code OT2017.
www.OneTravel.com

**AVIS®**
**Up to 35% OFF base rates.**
1-800-245-8572 and use AWD# B790091.
www.avis.com/epsandiego

**Budget®**
**Up to 30% OFF base rates.**
1-888-724-6212 and use offer code (BCD) X443053.
www.budget.com/epsandiego

## WHILE YOU'RE THERE — Find the local savings

featured attractions

FIND IT ON THE APP!

**Maritime Museum** — Buy One, Get One Admission

**Belmont Park** — Buy One, Get One Premium Attraction

**Birch Aquarium at Scripps** — 50% off up to 2 Admissions

**Flagship Cruises and Events** — 50% off Regular Price

Please see each individual offer for additional conditions and restrictions. Merchants and offers are subject to change.

## FEATURED HOTELS:

Book online at **www.entertainment.com/choicehotels** or call **(800) 533-2100** and mention Special Rate ID: **00803210**.

**Comfort Inn & Suites** - San Diego Zoo SeaWorld Area (CA462)
2485 Hotel Circle Place, San Diego

**Comfort Inn** - Chula Vista San Diego South (CAD71)
91 E. Bonita Rd., Chula Vista

**Comfort Inn** - San Diego at the Harbor (CA768)
5102 N. Harbor Dr., San Diego

**Comfort Inn** - Gaslamp Convention Center
660 G Street, San Diego

**Econo Lodge** - Encinitas Moonlight Beach
410 N. Coast Hwy. 101, Encinitas

**Quality Inn** - San Diego I-5 Naval Base
3878 Dalbergia Court, San Diego

below on your mobile app while you're in San Diego, plus 100s more!

featured dining

FIND IT ON THE APP!

**Humphrey's Grill** — Buy One, Get One Entrée – up to $21

**Blue Wave Bar & Grill** — $10 off $50

**Dublin Square Pub** — Buy One, Get One Entrée – up to $21

**Hunter Steakhouse** — 20% off the Total Bill – up to $25

# Experience San Francisco

## PLAN YOUR TRIP

**Save up to $20 OFF our Service Fees on Flights.**
1-888-645-9758 and use promo code COA2017.
www.CheapOAir.com

**Up to 30% OFF base rates.**
1-888-724-6212 and use offer code (BCD) X443055.
www.budget.com/epsanfran

**Entertainment® members save 5% OFF base rates on rentals in the U.S. and Canada.**
1-800-PAYLESS and use promo code A067700.
www.paylesscar.com/entertainment

## WHILE YOU'RE THERE — Find the local savings

featured attractions

FIND IT ON THE APP!

**City Sightseeing San Francisco** — Buy One, Get One Downtown Loop

**GoCar Tours** — Buy One, Get One Hour GoCar Tour

**All About Chinatown Tours** — Buy One, Get One Tour

**Bike and Roll** — Buy One, Get One Guided Tour

## FEATURED HOTELS:

Book online at **www.entertainment.com/IHG16**. For reservations call **(877) 580-2943**.

**InterContinental**
888 Howard Street, San Francisco

**Holiday Inn** - **Golden Gateway**
1500 Van Ness Avenue, San Francisco

**Holiday Inn Express & Suites** - **Fishermans Wharf**
550 North Point Street, San Francisco

**Crowne Plaza** - **San Francisco Airport**
1177 Airport Boulevard, Burlingame

**Holiday Inn Express & Suites**
1175 University Avenue, Berkeley

**InterContinental** - **Mark Hopkins San Francisco**
999 California Street, San Francisco

below on your mobile app while you're in San Francisco, plus 100s more!

**Rainforest Café** — $5 off $20

**North India Restaurant** — Buy One, Get One Entrée – up to $13

**Clement Street Bar & Grill** — Buy One, Get One Entrée – up to $13

**Marrakech Moroccan Restaurant** — $20 off Two Full Dinners

# Experience Seattle

## PLAN YOUR TRIP

**Save up to $20 OFF our Service Fees on Flights.**
1-888-204-1645 and use promo code OT2017.
www.OneTravel.com

**Up to 30% OFF base rates.**
1-888-724-6212 and use offer code (BCD) X443056.
www.budget.com/epseattle

**Entertainment® members save 5% OFF base rates on rentals in the US and Canada.**
1-800-PAYLESS and use promo code A067700.
www.paylesscar.com/entertainment

## WHILE YOU'RE THERE — Find the local savings

featured attractions

FIND IT ON THE APP!

**Seattle Art Museum** — Buy One, Get One Admission

**Outer Island Expeditions** — Buy One, Get One Whale Watching Tour

**Seattle Aquarium** — Buy One, Get One Admission

**Alki Kayak Tours** — Buy One, Get One Sunset Kayak Tour

Please see each individual offer for additional conditions and restrictions. Merchants and offers are subject to change.

## FEATURED HOTELS:

Book online at **www.entertainment.com/choicehotels** or call **(800) 533-2100** and mention Special Rate ID: **00803210**.

**Sleep Inn** - Sea Tac Airport
20406 International Blvd., Sea Tac

**Quality Inn and Suites** - Seattle Center
618 John St., Seattle

**Comfort Inn** - by the Bay
1121 Bay St., Port Orchard

**Comfort Inn** - Bothell Seattle North
1414 228th St., Southeast, Bothell

**Quality Inn**
1850 SE Maple Valley Hwy., Renton

**Comfort Inn** - Federal Way Seattle
31622 Pacific Hwy. S., Federal Way

below on your mobile app while you're in Seattle, plus 100s more!

**LloydMartin** — 25% off the Total Bill – up to $50

**Hook & Plow** — 20% off the Total Bill – up to $25

**Maxwell's** — Buy One, Get One Entrée – up to $20

**Plaza Garibaldi** — Buy One, Get One Entrée – up to $13

# Experience Southern Florida

## PLAN YOUR TRIP

**Save up to $20 OFF our Service Fees on Flights.**
1-888-645-9758 and use promo code COA2017.
www.CheapOAir.com

**Save on Everyday Low Rates.**
Reference Customer # ENBKDC7. Book now at
enterprise.com/ent167or call 1-888-446-9952.

**$15 OFF**
Reference Customer # 7016629 and Coupon Code
AD2827JAB. Book now at alamo.com/offer/ent17
or call 1-800-237-0984.

## WHILE YOU'RE THERE — Find the local savings

**featured attractions**

**FIND IT ON THE APP!**

**Zoo Miami** — Buy One, Get One Admission

**Jungle Island** — Buy One, Get One Admission

**Key Largo Princess** — Buy One, Get One Glass Bottom Boat Tour

**Bass Museum of Art** — Buy One, Get One Admission

Please see each individual offer for additional conditions and restrictions. Merchants and offers are subject to change.

## FEATURED HOTELS:

To make your reservation, book online at www.wyndhamhotelgroup.com/ent or call (877) 670-7088 and use ID# 1000000181.

**Shelborne Wyndham Grand South Beach**
1801 Collins Ave., Miami Beach

**Ramada Plaza Marco Polo Beach Resort**
19201 Collins Ave., North Miami Beach

**Wyndham Boca Raton**
1950 Glades Rd., Boca Raton

**Wyndham Deerfield Beach Resort**
2096 NE Second St., Deerfield Beach

**Wyndham Garden Fort Myers Beach**
6890 Estero Blvd., Fort Myers Beach

**Wyndham Garden Clearwater Beach**
691 S. Gulfview Blvd., Clearwater Beach

below on your mobile app while you're in Southern Florida, plus 100s more!

featured dining

FIND IT ON THE APP!

**Tradewinds Waterfront Bar & Grill** — 10% off Total Bill – up to $25

**Bistro 1902** — Buy One, Get One Entree – up to $28

**Latin American** — Buy One, Get One Entree – up to $12

**Green Plate Asian Bistro** — 10% off Total Bill – up to $25

## UP TO $400 CASH BACK

**UP TO $ 400 VALUE**

Enjoy top values like:

· Exclusive Prices

· 110% Best Price Guarantee

Visit: entertainment.cruises.com/norwegian

Call: 1-800-887-9042

**NCL NORWEGIAN CRUISE LINE®**

0000000PNDK

G14

## UP TO $400 CASH BACK

**UP TO $ 400 OFF**

Enjoy top values like:

· Free Upgrades

· 110% Best Price Guarantee

Visit: entertainment.cruises.com/carnival

Call: 1-800-887-9042

0000000PNE7

G15

## UP TO $200 TO SPEND ON BOARD

**UP TO $ 200 VALUE**

Just for you:

· Exclusive Prices

· 110% Best Price Guarantee

Visit: entertainment.cruises.com/royal

Call: 1-800-887-9042

0000000PNEL

G16

NATIONAL TRAVEL & HOTELS

# On land and on sea, Entertainment® helps you save!

# Gain Access To Wholesale Travel Pricing!

## Save up to 75% on Top Destinations Worldwide

Visit **www.entdeals.com/SnazzyTraveler** to start saving!

**Hotels**

Snazzy Traveler provides wholesale pricing on hotels guaranteeing you find the lowest prices with no blackout dates or travel restrictions. Find exactly what you need with more than 400,000 hotels and resorts worldwide, including the top brands you love.

**Cruises**

Snazzy Traveler also has the best prices on top cruise lines including Carnival, Royal Caribbean, Norwegian, Celebrity and many more. With hundreds of sailings everyday and itineraries to fit your needs you will find the perfect cruise for your next departure.

**SPECIAL OFFER**

## Save Up To 75% on Hotels and Cruises!

Free Unlimited Access to Wholesale Travel Prices

Visit www.entdeals.com/SnazzyTraveler for details

49784612

# Members Get
## 25% Off*†
### Over 200,000
### Vacation Rentals Worldwide

- Prices start at $397*† USD per week with your Entertainment® 25% off*† discount
- Units Range from Studios to 3 Bedrooms
- Most have Kitchens, Living Rooms, Spas and On-site Fitness Centers
- Many Destinations - Florida, Mexico, Caribbean, Europe, Canada and More!
- Easy Online Booking at: www.endlessvacationdeals.com/ent17

NATIONAL TRAVEL & HOTELS

---

| | **25% OFF** |

## Members get 25% OFF Vacation Rentals Worldwide.

Price does not include tax. Other restrictions may apply. Offer excludes All-Inclusive Resorts and selected other resorts. All prices are based in U.S. dollars (USD). Offer cannot be combined with any other offer or discount. Destinations and travel times are subject to availability and confirmed on a first come, first served basis.

Easy Online Booking at:
www.endlessvacationdeals.com/ent17

**ENT 17**

0000000PLU1

*entertainment.* presents
**EntertainmentHotelBucks**

# CLAIM YOUR
# 300
## Hotel Bucks

**SAVE UP TO 40%
INSTANTLY**

**LOWEST RATES
GUARANTEED**

**THOUSANDS
OF PROPERTIES
WORLDWIDE**

Located in the
front of your book

**1** **VISIT**
EntertainmentHotelBucks.com

**2** **LOG IN**
using your membership number

**3** **BOOK & SAVE
INSTANTLY**

**NATIONAL TRAVEL & HOTELS**

**SPECIAL OFFER**

## Save on Hotels & Condos instantly!

As an Entertainment®member, we've deposited 300 Hotel Bucks for you.

Hotel Bucks may only be used online at www.EntertainmentHotelBucks.com™. Only a designated portion of your Hotel Bucks may be used per reservation; balance must be paid with a major credit card at time of booking. This is not a gift card and may not be redeemed for cash. See website for information on Low Price Guarantee and other terms and conditions that apply to this offer. All transactions are in U.S. Funds. One email address per Entertainment Hotel Bucks™ account.

To book, visit EntertainmentHotelBucks.com

**Use Your Membership #**

**Entertainment
Hotel Bucks™**

0000000QS54

**Promotion valid now thru 12/31/2017**
This promotional offer is not valid with any other discount/promotion. See Rules of Use or visit www.entertainment.com/rulesofuse

G24

NATIONAL TRAVEL & HOTELS

# DRIVE. STAY. SAVE.

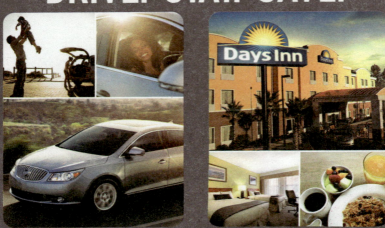

👑 We'll help you save on both!

---

## Save on Everyday Low Rates.

Reserve online at enterprise.com/ent17 or call 1 888 446-9952.

**Reference Customer #ENBKWX7**    49784648

## Up to 20% OFF*

Get up to 20% Off* Best Available Rate.

Book online at:
www.wyndhamhotelgroup.com/entdaysinn
or call (877) 670-7088.

**Mention your special ID#: 1000008029**    0000000R037

# Choice Hotels

With more than 6,400 hotels worldwide, and a range of brands from upscale to economy, Choice Hotels has a hotel to fit every need.* And travel is even more rewarding with the Choice Privileges® Rewards Program, with points that add up fast so you can earn stays around the world. You can always count on Choice Hotels® properties for a warm welcome and real value, wherever your journey takes you.

## Book Now and Save up to **10%**!**

### Three Simple Ways to Book:

**Web**
Visit EntDeals.com/
ChoiceHotels

**Phone**
Call 800.4CHOICE and
quote Rate ID #00803210

**Mobile**
Download the Choice Hotels app
and enter Rate ID #00803210

*Amenities vary by location.
**To receive discount, reservations must be made as stated above. Based on availability and location. Other terms and conditions may apply.
 Hotels are individually owned and operated.

© 2016 Choice Hotels International, Inc. All rights reserved. 16-280/04/16

---

## 10% OFF

### Save 10% OFF your next stay when you book online at www.EntDeals.com/ChoiceHotels.

Advance reservations required. Offer is subject to availability. Certain restrictions and some blackout dates may apply. Offer cannot be used with group rates.

**Book online at www.EntDeals.com/ChoiceHotels or call 800-533-2100 and mention Special Rate ID: 00803210.**

0000000PUKV

**Promotion valid now thru 12/31/2017**
This promotional offer is not valid with any other discount/promotion. See Rules of Use or visit www.entertainment.com/rulesofuse.

G29

NATIONAL TRAVEL & HOTELS

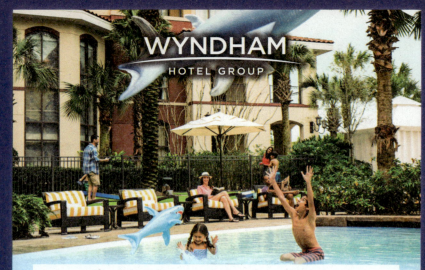

# WYNDHAM
### HOTEL GROUP

**NATIONAL TRAVEL & HOTELS**

## WYNDHAM
### REWARDS®
*You've earned this.*℠

# Start traveling like a *hotellionaire!*

With over 7,700 hotels around the globe, Wyndham Hotel Group can help your family create memorable vacation getaways!

Make your stay even more enjoyable by experiencing the magic of Wyndham Rewards! Enroll today at WyndhamRewards.com/gsous

© 2016 Wyndham Rewards, Inc. All rights reserved.

**NATIONAL TRAVEL & HOTELS**

# BW | Best Western.
## Hotels & Resorts

## Wherever Life Takes You, Best Western Is There.®

Each Best Western® branded hotel is independently owned and operated. Best Western and the Best Western marks are service marks or registered service marks of Best Western International, Inc. ©2016 Best Western International, Inc. All rights reserved.

## 10% OFF

### 10% OFF Best Available Rate

Book online at www.bestwestern.com/entertainment. For reservations, call (800) 441-1114 and request the Entertainment LC Rate. Your special LC number is 00162370.

**Valid only at participating locations.**
Discount rates apply to regular (rack) non-discounted rates and are subject to program room availability. Savings vary by chain. Advance reservation required. Blackout dates and other restrictions may apply.

BW | Best Western.
Hotels & Resorts

0000000PJSZ

## Two ways to stay.
## It's a great value either way.

### 1. Red Roof

Discover why Red Roof is **#1 in online guest reviews** – for four years running – with **FREE Wi-Fi, flat-screen TVs** in every room, and all the **conveniences** you'll need for a clean, comfortable and affordable stay. We even welcome your **family pet at no charge!**

### 2. Red Roof Plus+

Want to add a little **more WOW** to your Red Roof stay? Experience **Red Roof Plus+**. Discover an enhanced experience with all new rooms, and our most requested higher-end amenities. It's a completely remodeled and upgraded stay! A little more pampering, all at an affordable rate you expect from Red Roof.

**For reservations visit entdeals.com/redroof or call (800) 733-7663 and mention ID# 534795**

---

## 15% OFF

## Save 15% OFF Best Available Rate.

Advance reservations required. Blackout dates and other restrictions may apply. The toll-free number listed is valid only for booking the promotional rate that accompanies the ID # listed. Discount rates apply to regular (rack) non-discounted room rates and are subject to program room availability. This program cannot be used in conjunction with any other discount promotional room rate. Not valid for group travel. Valid only at participating locations.

For advance reservations, call (800) 733-7663 and mention ID # 534795.

**ID# 534795**

0000000PJP5

G33

NATIONAL TRAVEL & HOTELS

## Capture Life

**Collect stories, not selfies.**

You won't remember the time you spent staring at your screen, but you'll never forget your time with us in Hawaii.

**866·774·2924 | astonhotels.com**

A**ston**
HOTELS & RESORTS
*welcome home*

NATIONAL TRAVEL & HOTELS

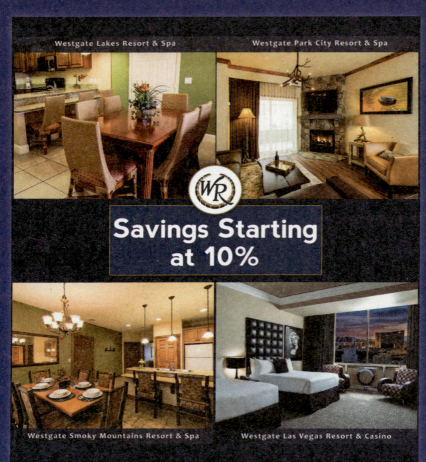

SAVE UP TO
**30% OFF**

Mercure Paris Centre Tour Eiffel

Sofitel New York

Novotel Toronto North York

Sofitel Moorea la Ora Beach Resort

BOOK EARLY AND SAVE ON YOUR NEXT HOTEL STAY!

**Save up to 30% off worldwide, when you book at least 30 days in advance.**

Book now on **www.entdeals.com/accorhotels**

*With over 3,700 hotels in 92 countries and 12 hotel brands from economy to luxury, Accorhotels.com proposes accommodation suitable to all budgets, whether you are traveling for business or leisure, weekend getaways, long stays or family vacations.*

 |

UP TO **30% OFF**

### Book 30 Days in Advance and Save up to 30%*.

Book 30 days in advance and save up to 30% on hotel rates on over 2,500 hotels worldwide. Must be booked online at www.entdeals.com/accorhotels.

*Subject to availability and conditions.

0000000PK3R

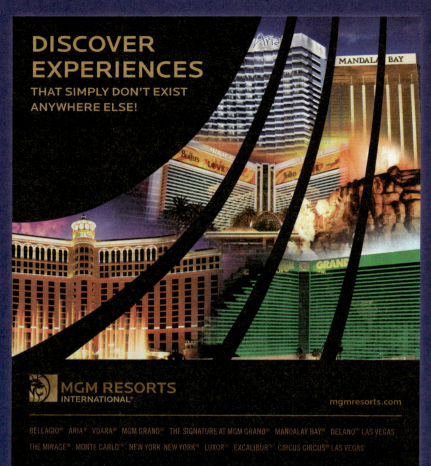

NATIONAL TRAVEL & HOTELS

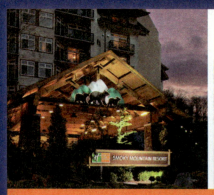

# Discover Your Next Great Getaway

**UBER**

# Go here, there or anywhere

Get a reliable ride in minutes with the Uber app.

FREE RIDE

## First ride FREE up to $20.

Get a reliable ride in minutes with the Uber app.
Not valid on uberTAXI. First-time riders only.

Sign up with the code ENTERTAINMENT
at Uber.com/app

# UBER

49783043

# All signs point to fun.

Pair the coupons below with even more offers at **budget.com/entertainment**. Entertainment members always save up to 25% off base rates. More savings means more fun.

©2016 Budget Rent A Car System, Inc.

# Ride with benefits.

**Fastbreak®**
Skip the lines and get going faster.
Join for free.

**Garmin GPS***
Get around like a local.

**Satellite Radio by SiriusXM®**
Roll out. Rock on.

**eToll™**
Save your pocket change,
pay electronically.

**Fuel Plans**
Don't stress about stopping for gas.

**Locations**
We're waiting in your neighborhood.

 **Budget®**

©2016 Budget Rent A Car System, Inc.

## $50 OFF a Monthly Rental

Get up to 25% off base rates
plus an extra $50 off a minimum monthly
rental with this reusable coupon.

Visit budget.com/entertainment
or call 1-888-724-6212.

**Mention BCD X443000 and: CPN # MUGZ144**

 **Promotion valid now thru 12/31/2017**
See reverse side for additional conditions or restrictions. **G46**

## $25 OFF Minimum
## 10-Day Rental

Get up to 25% off base rates plus an extra
$25 off a minimum ten consecutive day rental
with this reusable coupon.

Visit budget.com/entertainment
or call 1-888-724-6212.

**Mention BCD X443000 and: CPN # MUGZ143**

 **Promotion valid now thru 12/31/2017**
See reverse side for additional conditions or restrictions. **G47**

$**15** VALUE

## $15 OFF a 3-Day Weekend Rental

Get up to 25% off base rates plus $15 off a 3-day weekend rental.
Visit budget.com/entertainment or call 1-888-724-6212.

### Mention BCD X443000 and CPN # MUGZ141

**Promotion valid now thru 12/31/2017**
See reverse side for additional conditions or restrictions.  G48

**NATIONAL TRAVEL & HOTELS**

### Free Day on
### Weekly Rental

Get up to 25% off base rates
plus your 5th day free on a weekly rental
with this reusable coupon.

Visit budget.com/entertainment
or call 1-888-724-6212.

**Mention BCD X443000 and: CPN # TUGZ067**

 **Promotion valid now thru 12/31/2017**
See reverse side for additional conditions or restrictions. **G49**

## $20 OFF a
## Weekly Rental

Get up to 25% off base rates
plus $20 off a minimum weekly rental.

Visit budget.com/entertainment
or call 1-888-724-6212.

**Mention BCD X443000 and: CPN # MUGZ142**

 **Promotion valid now thru 12/31/2017**
See reverse side for additional conditions or restrictions. **G50**

Coupon valid on an intermediate (group C) and above vehicle, excluding specialty (group X). Dollars off applies to the time and mileage charges only on a minimum ten day rental period. Fuel charges are extra. All taxes, fees (including but not limited to Air Conditioning Excise Recovery Fee, Concession Recovery Fee, Vehicle License Recovery Fee, Energy Recovery Fee, Tire Management Fee, and Frequent Traveler Fee) and surcharges (including but not limited to Customer Facility Charge and Environmental Fee Recovery Charge) are extra. Optional products such as LDW and refueling are extra. One coupon per rental. An advance reservation is required. May not be used in conjunction with any other coupon, promotion or offer. Coupons cannot be transferred, sold and we reserve the right to change terms anytime at our sole discretion. Please mention **BCD X443000** to take advantage of this offer. Coupon valid at participating Budget locations in the Contiguous U.S. and Canada. Offer subject to vehicle availability at time of reservation and may not be available on some rates at some times. Dollars off coupons presented/entered during reservation are calculated at time of reservation. Renter must meet Budget age, driver and credit requirements. Minimum age may vary by location. An additional daily surcharge may apply for renters under 25 years old. *This offer is based on the currency of the location of check-out and subject to applicable exchange rates. Rental must begin by **12/31/17**.

This promotional offer is not valid with any other discount/promotion. See Rules of Use or visit www.entertainment.com/rulesofuse.          49782526

Coupon valid for $50 USD off a monthly or mini-lease rental at participating Budget locations in the Contiguous U.S. and Canada. Offer applies to a minimum 30 day rental period of an intermediate (group C) through a full-size four-door (group E) car. Offer of $50 USD off a long term rental applies to the time and mileage charges on the first month of a minimum 30 and maximum 330 consecutive day rental. Fuel charges are extra. All taxes, fees (including but not limited to Air Conditioning Excise Recovery Fee, Concession Recovery Fee, Vehicle License Recovery Fee, Energy Recovery Fee, Tire Management Fee, and Frequent Traveler Fee) and surcharges (including but not limited to Customer Facility Charge and Environmental Fee Recovery Charge) are extra. Optional products such as LDW and refueling are extra. In Canada, all taxes (including Air Conditioning Excise Tax), fees (including Vehicle License Recovery Fee), and optional items (such as LDW) are additional. One coupon per rental period. Coupons cannot be transferred, sold and we reserve the right to change terms anytime at our sole discretion. Please mention **BCD X443000** to take advantage of this offer. An advance reservation is required. Offer is subject to vehicle availability at time of reservation and may not be available on some rates at some times. May not be used in conjunction with any other coupon, promotion or offer. Dollars off coupons presented/entered during reservation are calculated at time of reservation. Renter must meet Budget age, driver and credit requirements. Minimum age may vary by location. An additional daily surcharge may apply for renters under 25 years old. *This offer is based on the currency of the location of check-out and subject to applicable exchange rates. Rental must begin by **12/31/17**.

This promotional offer is not valid with any other discount/promotion. See Rules of Use or visit www.entertainment.com/rulesofuse.          49782533

Coupon valid at participating Budget locations in the Contiguous U.S. and Canada on an intermediate (group C) through a full-size four-door (group E) car. Dollars off applies to the time and mileage charges only on a minimum three day weekend rental. A Saturday night keep is required. Fuel charges are extra. All taxes, fees (including but not limited to Air Conditioning Excise Recovery Fee, Concession Recovery Fee, Vehicle License Recovery Fee, Energy Recovery Fee, Tire Management Fee, and Frequent Traveler Fee) and surcharges (including but not limited to Customer Facility Charge and Environmental Fee Recovery Charge) are extra. Optional products such as LDW and refueling are extra. One coupon per rental. Coupons cannot be transferred, sold and we reserve the right to change terms anytime at our sole discretion. Please mention **BCD X443000** to take advantage of this offer. May not be used in conjunction with any other coupon, promotion or offer. Weekend rental period begins Thursday and car must be returned by Monday 11:59 p.m. or higher rate may apply. Offer subject to vehicle availability at the time of reservation and may not be available on some rates at some times. An advance reservation is required. Dollars off coupons presented/entered during reservation are calculated at time of reservation. Renter must meet Budget age, driver and credit requirements. Minimum age may vary by location. An additional daily surcharge may apply for renters under 25 years old. *This offer is based on the currency of the location of check-out and subject to applicable exchange rates. Rental must begin by **12/31/17**.

This promotional offer is not valid with any other discount/promotion. See Rules of Use or visit www.entertainment.com/rulesofuse.          49782536

Get $20 USD off at checkout when you spend $200 USD or more on a rental. Coupon valid on all car groups, excluding the Signature Series (group X). Coupon valid on an intermediate (group C) through a full-size four door (group E) car. Dollars off applies to the time and mileage charges only on a minimum five, maximum 28 consecutive-day weekly rental period. Fuel charges are extra. All taxes, fees (including but not limited to Air Conditioning Excise Recovery Fee, Concession Recovery Fee, Vehicle License Recovery Fee, Energy Recovery Fee, Tire Management Fee, and Frequent Traveler Fee) and surcharges (including but not limited to Customer Facility Charge and Environmental Fee Recovery Charge) are extra. Optional products such as LDW and refueling are extra. One coupon per rental. An advance reservation is required. May not be used in conjunction with any other coupon, promotion or offer. Coupons cannot be transferred, sold and we reserve the right to change terms anytime at our sole discretion. Please mention **BCD X443000** to take advantage of this offer. Coupon valid at participating Budget locations in the Contiguous U.S. and Canada. Offer subject to vehicle availability at time of reservation and may not be available on some rates at some times. Dollars off coupons presented/entered during reservation are calculated at time of reservation. Renter must meet Budget age, driver and credit requirements. Minimum age may vary by location. An additional daily surcharge may apply for renters under 25 years old. *This offer is based on the currency of the location of check-out and subject to applicable exchange rates. Rental must begin by **12/31/17**.

This promotional offer is not valid with any other discount/promotion. See Rules of Use or visit www.entertainment.com/rulesofuse.          49782522

Offer applies to one day free of the daily time and mileage charges on a minimum five, maximum 28 consecutive day rental period on weekly rates with a Saturday night keep on an intermediate (group C) through a full-size four door (group E) car. Fuel charges are extra. All taxes, fees (including but not limited to Air Conditioning Excise Recovery Fee, Concession Recovery Fee, Vehicle License Recovery Fee, Energy Recovery Fee, Tire Management Fee, and Frequent Traveler Fee) and surcharges (including but not limited to Customer Facility Charge and Environmental Fee Recovery Charge) are extra. Optional products such as LDW and refueling are extra. Coupon cannot be used for one-way rentals; one coupon per rental. Coupons cannot be transferred, sold and we reserve the right to change terms anytime at our sole discretion. Please mention **BCD X443000** to take advantage of this offer. Offer valid at participating Budget locations in the Contiguous U.S. (excluding the New York Metro area) and Canada. An advance reservation is required. Offer may not be available during holiday and other blackout periods. Offer subject to vehicle availability at the time of reservation and may not be available on some rates at some times. Days off coupons presented/entered during reservation are calculated at time of reservation. Renter must meet Budget age, driver and credit requirements. Minimum age may vary by location. An additional daily surcharge may apply for renters under 25 years old. Rental must begin by **12/31/17**.

This promotional offer is not valid with any other discount/promotion. See Rules of Use or visit www.entertainment.com/rulesofuse.          49782529

# DRIVE ON

Weekend getaways or weeklong vacations - save every time you rent. Use the coupons below and visit **avis.com/entertainment** to save **up to 25%** off base rates plus additional great offers.

**AVIS**®

© 2016 Avis Rent A Car System, LLC.

**AVIS**®

### Free Single Upgrade

Enjoy up to 25% off base rates plus a free one-car group upgrade with this reusable coupon.

Visit avis.com/entertainment or call 1-800-245-8572.

**Mention AWD B790000 and CPN # UUGA043**

 Promotion valid now thru 12/31/2017
See reverse side for additional conditions or restrictions. **G51**

**AVIS**®

### $25 OFF Weekly Rental

Enjoy up to 25% off base rates plus an extra discount of $25 off a minimum weekly rental.

Visit avis.com/entertainment or call 1-800-245-8572.

**Mention AWD B790000 and CPN# MUGA170**

 Promotion valid now thru 12/31/2017
See reverse side for additional conditions or restrictions. **G52**

# Make the most of your trip.

**Avis Preferred**   A complimentary membership, you'll travel better, saving time and money and gain access to exclusive offers.

**Garmin GPS***   Find the sights. Lose the traffic with voice navigation.

**eToll™**   Take the fast lane to your destination using electronic tolls.

**Signature Series**   Featuring luxury vehicles from BMW to Lincoln Navigator - rides that are just your style.

**Locations**   Right in your neighborhood for total convenience.

## AVIS®

*These services are optional and may be subject to availability at select locations, some for an additional fee.
©2016 Avis Rent A Car System, LLC

# AVIS®

## $30 OFF a Weekly Rental

Enjoy up to 25% off base rates
plus an extra discount of $30 when you
rent for a minimum of 5 consecutive days
with this reusable coupon.

Visit avis.com/entertainment or
call 1-800-245-8572.

**Mention AWD B790000 and CPN# MUGA171**

 Promotion valid now thru 12/31/2017
See reverse side for additional conditions or restrictions. **G53**

# AVIS®

## $50 OFF a Long Term Rental

Enjoy up to 25% off base rates
plus $50 off a minimum 30 day rental.

Visit avis.com/entertainment or
call 1-800-245-8572.

**Mention AWD B790000 and CPN# MUGA173**

 Promotion valid now thru 12/31/2017
See reverse side for additional conditions or restrictions. **G54**

**FREE WEEKEND DAY**

# AVIS®

## Third Weekend Day Free

Enjoy up to 25% off base rates plus get a free weekend day
with a 3 day weekend rental.

Visit avis.com/entertainment or call 1-800-245-8572.

**Mention AWD B790000 and CPN# TUGA008**

 Promotion valid now thru 12/31/2017
See reverse side for additional conditions or restrictions. **G55**

# AVIS®

## $30 OFF a 10-Day Rental

Enjoy up to 25% off base rates
plus an extra discount of $30 when you
rent for a minimum of ten consecutive days
with this reusable coupon.

Visit avis.com/entertainment or
call 1-800-245-8572.

**Mention AWD B790000 and CPN# MUGA172**

 Promotion valid now thru 12/31/2017
See reverse side for additional conditions or restrictions. **G56**

# AVIS®

## $20 OFF a 4 Day Weekend Rental

Enjoy up to 25% off base rates
plus an extra discount of $20 on your
next 4 day weekend rental.

Visit avis.com/entertainment or
call 1-800-245-8572.

**Mention AWD B790000 and CPN# MUGA169**

 Promotion valid now thru 12/31/2017
See reverse side for additional conditions or restrictions. **G57**

# AVIS®

# Make your way to an awesome deal.

Visit paylesscar.com/entertainment
for special offers like:

- 🕐 **Deals of the Hour**
- ☼ **Early Bird Savings**
- ⧗ **Last Minute Deals**

Payless CAR RENTAL

© 2016 Payless Car Rental, Inc.

# Entertainment® Members Drive a Great Deal!

NATIONAL TRAVEL & HOTELS

# Entertainment® Members
# Drive a Great Deal!

# Need a rental?

# Need a rental?

NATIONAL TRAVEL & HOTELS

## Save on Everyday Low Prices.

Book now at enterprise.com/ent17
or call 1-888-446-9952.

**Reference Customer #: ENBKDA7**

 Promotion valid now thru 6/30/2018
See reverse side for additional conditions or restrictions. G67

## FREE Upgrade

Book now at enterprise.com/ent17
or call 1-888-446-9952.

**Reference Customer #: ENBK2N7**

 Promotion valid now thru 6/30/2018
See reverse side for additional conditions or restrictions. G68

## Save on Everyday Low Rates.

Book now at enterprise.com/ent17
or call 1-888-446-9952.

**Reference Customer #: ENBKWR7**

 Promotion valid now thru 6/30/2018
See reverse side for additional conditions or restrictions. G69

## Save on Everyday Low Rates.

Book now at enterprise.com/ent17
or call 1-888-446-9952.

**Reference Customer #: ENBKDJ7**

 Promotion valid now thru 6/30/2018
See reverse side for additional conditions or restrictions. G70

## FREE Upgrade

Book now at enterprise.com/ent17
or call 1-888-446-9952.

**Reference Customer #: ENBK2U7**

 Promotion valid now thru 6/30/2018
See reverse side for additional conditions or restrictions. G71

## Save on Everyday Low Rates.

Book now at enterprise.com/ent17
or call 1-888-446-9952.

**Reference Customer #: ENBKDL7**

 Promotion valid now thru 6/30/2018
See reverse side for additional conditions or restrictions. G72

NATIONAL TRAVEL & HOTELS

Rent a compact through standard vehicle in the U.S. and Canada. Offer valid for a one-car-class upgrade applied at the time of reservation. Valid through June 30, 2018. Offer subject to availability and valid only at participating U.S. and Canadian Enterprise locations. Offer not valid in Manhattan, NY. One coupon per Enterprise rental and void once redeemed. Offer is subject to standard rental conditions. 24-hour advance reservation required. This offer cannot be combined with any another coupon and it is not valid for one-way, open, or previous rentals. Standard rental qualifications apply. Check your auto policy and/or credit card agreement for rental vehicle coverage. Subject to availability. This offer may change without notice and is void where prohibited. Availability is limited. Coupon subject to blackout periods, including holidays and other dates and times. Void where prohibited. Coupon is not exchangeable, refundable, transferable or redeemable for cash. Must present original coupon at time of rental. Cash value 1/100¢. ©2016 Enterprise Rent-A-Car. All rights reserved.

Offer entitles renter to a discount off of the publicly available, retail rate. Discount applies to base retail rate only and is valid at participating U.S. and Canadian Enterprise locations. Discount varies from time to time as determined by the applicable participating location. Taxes, other governmentally-authorized or imposed surcharges (including GST/VAT), license and concession recoupment fees, airport and airport facility fees, fuel, one-way rental charge and optional items (such as CDW up to US $30 per day) are extra. Rates are as posted at time of reservation at enterprise.com/ent17 or by calling 1 888 446-9952 and referencing customer number ENBKDA7. Weekly rates may apply depending on length of rental or for longer rental needs. Rental must end by June 30, 2018. Original coupon must be redeemed at the time of rental and may not be used with any other coupon, offer or discounted rate, including weekend special rates. Normal rental qualifications apply. Vehicles subject to availability. Other restrictions, including holiday and blackout dates, may apply. Pick-up and drop-off service is subject to geographic and other restrictions. Void where prohibited. Cash value: 1/100¢. © 2016 Enterprise Rent-A-Car. Subject to Rules of Use. Coupons VOID if purchased, sold or bartered for cash.

Offer entitles renter to a discount off of the publicly available, retail rate. Discount applies to base retail rate only and is valid at participating U.S. and Canadian Enterprise locations. Discount varies from time to time as determined by the applicable participating location. Taxes, other governmentally-authorized or imposed surcharges (including GST/VAT), license and concession recoupment fees, airport and airport facility fees, fuel, one-way rental charge and optional items (such as CDW up to US $30 per day) are extra. Rates are as posted at time of reservation at enterprise.com/ent17 or by calling 1 888 446-9952 and referencing customer number ENBKDJ7. Weekly rates may apply depending on length of rental or for longer rental needs. Rental must end by June 30, 2018. Original coupon must be redeemed at the time of rental and may not be used with any other coupon, offer or discounted rate, including weekend special rates. Normal rental qualifications apply. Vehicles subject to availability. Other restrictions, including holiday and blackout dates, may apply. Pick-up and drop-off service is subject to geographic and other restrictions. Void where prohibited. Cash value: 1/100¢. © 2016 Enterprise Rent-A-Car. Subject to Rules of Use. Coupons VOID if purchased, sold or bartered for cash.

Offer entitles renter to a discount off of the publicly available, retail rate. Discount applies to base retail rate only and is valid at participating U.S. and Canadian Enterprise locations. Discount varies from time to time as determined by the applicable participating location. Taxes, other governmentally-authorized or imposed surcharges (including GST/VAT), license and concession recoupment fees, airport and airport facility fees, fuel, one-way rental charge and optional items (such as CDW up to US $30 per day) are extra. Rates are as posted at time of reservation at enterprise.com/ent17 or by calling 1 888 446-9952 and referencing customer number ENBKWR7. Weekly rates may apply depending on length of rental or for longer rental needs. Rental must end by June 30, 2018. Original coupon must be redeemed at the time of rental and may not be used with any other coupon, offer or discounted rate, including weekend special rates. Normal rental qualifications apply. Vehicles subject to availability. Other restrictions, including holiday and blackout dates, may apply. Pick-up and drop-off service is subject to geographic and other restrictions. Void where prohibited. Cash value: 1/100¢. © 2016 Enterprise Rent-A-Car. Subject to Rules of Use. Coupons VOID if purchased, sold or bartered for cash.

Offer entitles renter to a discount off of the publicly available, retail rate. Discount applies to base retail rate only and is valid at participating U.S. and Canadian Enterprise locations. Discount varies from time to time as determined by the applicable participating location. Taxes, other governmentally-authorized or imposed surcharges (including GST/VAT), license and concession recoupment fees, airport and airport facility fees, fuel, one-way rental charge and optional items (such as CDW up to US $30 per day) are extra. Rates are as posted at time of reservation at enterprise.com/ent17 or by calling 1 888 446-9952 and referencing customer number ENBKDL7. Weekly rates may apply depending on length of rental or for longer rental needs. Rental must end by June 30, 2018. Original coupon must be redeemed at the time of rental and may not be used with any other coupon, offer or discounted rate, including weekend special rates. Normal rental qualifications apply. Vehicles subject to availability. Other restrictions, including holiday and blackout dates, may apply. Pick-up and drop-off service is subject to geographic and other restrictions. Void where prohibited. Cash value: 1/100¢. © 2016 Enterprise Rent-A-Car. Subject to Rules of Use. Coupons VOID if purchased, sold or bartered for cash.

Rent a compact through standard vehicle in the U.S. and Canada. Offer valid for a one-car-class upgrade applied at the time of reservation. Valid through June 30, 2018. Offer subject to availability and valid only at participating U.S. and Canadian Enterprise locations. Offer not valid in Manhattan, NY. One coupon per Enterprise rental and void once redeemed. Offer is subject to standard rental conditions. 24-hour advance reservation required. This offer cannot be combined with any another coupon and it is not valid for one-way, open, or previous rentals. Standard rental qualifications apply. Check your auto policy and/or credit card agreement for rental vehicle coverage. Subject to availability. This offer may change without notice and is void where prohibited. Availability is limited. Coupon subject to blackout periods, including holidays and other dates and times. Void where prohibited. Coupon is not exchangeable, refundable, transferable or redeemable for cash. Must present original coupon at time of rental. Cash value 1/100¢. ©2016 Enterprise Rent-A-Car. All rights reserved.

GET TO THE FUN
FASTER!

Alamo®
Drive Happy

$25 off a minimum three (3) day minivan rental in the U.S. and Canada (exclusive of applicable taxes (including GST), fees, surcharges, refueling, drop-off, delivery, youthful driver, additional driver, or pickup charges or one-way charges or any optional products or services such as damage waiver and liability protection). Valid for rentals now through June 30, 2018, unless a longer period is required by law. 24-hour advance reservation required. Offer valid at participating Alamo locations in the United States and Canada. Not valid in Manhattan, NY and Stamford, CT. Renter and additional driver(s) must meet standard age, driver and credit requirements. This offer cannot be combined with any other coupon and it is not valid for one-way, open, or previous rentals. Standard rental qualifications apply. In the U.S., check your auto policy and/or credit card agreement for rental vehicle coverage. Subject to availability. This offer may change without notice and is void where prohibited. Coupon subject to blackout periods, including holidays and other dates and times. Coupons are limited by pickup date, location, and car type. Void where prohibited. Coupon is not exchangeable, refundable, transferable or redeemable for cash. Must present original coupon at time of rental. Cash value 1/100¢.

©2016 Alamo Rent A Car. All rights reserved.

This promotional offer is not valid with any other discount/promotion. See Rules of Use or visit www.entertainment.com/rulesofuse.      49784530

Rent a compact through standard vehicle in the U.S. Offer valid for a one car-class upgrade applied at the time of reservation. Valid through June 30, 2018. Offer subject to availability and valid only at participating Alamo locations in the United States and Canada. Offer not valid in Manhattan, NY and Stamford, CT. One coupon per Alamo rental and void once redeemed. Offer is subject to standard rental conditions. In the U.S., please check your insurance and/or credit card for rental vehicle coverage. 24-hour advance reservation required. This offer cannot be combined with any other coupon and it is not valid for one-way, open, or previous rentals. Subject to availability. Coupon subject to blackout periods, including holidays and other dates and times. Coupons are limited by pickup date, location, and car type. Coupon VOID if bought, bartered or sold for cash. Void where prohibited. Coupon is not exchangeable, refundable, transferable or redeemable for cash. Must present original coupon at time of rental. Cash value 1/100¢.

©2016 Alamo Rent A Car. All rights reserved.

This promotional offer is not valid with any other discount/promotion. See Rules of Use or visit www.entertainment.com/rulesofuse.      49784539

$15 off a minimum three (3) day, maximum four (4) day, rental with a Saturday overnight keep in which the base rate charge (exclusive of applicable taxes (including GST), fees, surcharges, refueling, drop-off, delivery, youthful driver, additional driver, or pickup charges or one-way charges or any optional products or services such as damage waiver and liability protection) is at least $75. Valid for rentals on any size car now through June 30, 2018, unless a longer period is required by law. 24-hour advance reservation required. Offer valid at participating Alamo locations in the United States and Canada. Not valid in Manhattan, NY and Stamford, CT. Renter and additional driver(s) must meet standard age, driver and credit requirements. This offer cannot be combined with any other coupon and it is not valid for one-way, open, or previous rentals. Standard rental qualifications apply. In the U.S., check your auto policy and/or credit card agreement for rental vehicle coverage. Subject to availability. This offer may change without notice and is void where prohibited. Coupon subject to blackout periods, including holidays and other dates and times. Coupons are limited by pickup date, location, and car type. Void where prohibited. Coupon is not exchangeable, refundable, transferable or redeemable for cash. Must present original coupon at time of rental. Cash value 1/100¢.

©2016 Alamo Rent A Car. All rights reserved.

This promotional offer is not valid with any other discount/promotion. See Rules of Use or visit www.entertainment.com/rulesofuse.      49784518

$25 off a minimum five (5) day, maximum eleven (11) day, rental in which the base rate charge (exclusive of applicable taxes (including GST), fees, surcharges, refueling, drop-off, delivery, youthful driver, additional driver, or pickup charges or one-way charges or any optional products or services such as damage waiver and liability protection) is at least $175. Valid for rentals on any size car now through June 30, 2018, unless a longer period is required by law. 24-hour advance reservation required. Offer valid at participating Alamo locations in the United States and Canada. Not valid in Manhattan, NY and Stamford, CT. Renter and additional driver(s) must meet standard age, driver and credit requirements. This offer cannot be combined with any other coupon and it is not valid for one-way, open, or previous rentals. Standard rental qualifications apply. In the U.S., check your auto policy and/or credit card agreement for rental vehicle coverage. Subject to availability. This offer may change without notice and is void where prohibited. Coupon subject to blackout periods, including holidays and other dates and times. Coupons are limited by pickup date, location, and car type. Void where prohibited. Coupon is not exchangeable, refundable, transferable or redeemable for cash. Must present original coupon at time of rental. Cash value 1/100¢.

©2016 Alamo Rent A Car. All rights reserved.

This promotional offer is not valid with any other discount/promotion. See Rules of Use or visit www.entertainment.com/rulesofuse.      49784545

## $15 OFF
### When The Base Rate Is At Least $75.

Book now at alamo.com/offer/ent17
or call 1-800-237-0984.

Mention Customer# 7016629 and
Coupon Code AD2828JAZ.

## Free Upgrade

Book now at alamo.com/offer/ent17
or call 1-800-237-0984.

Mention Customer# 7016629 and
Coupon Code AU2673AHT.

## $15 OFF
### When The Base Rate Is At Least $75.

Book now at alamo.com/offer/ent17
or call 1-800-237-0984.

Mention Customer# 7016629 and
Coupon Code AD2827JAB.

## $25 OFF SUV

Book now at alamo.com/offer/ent17
or call 1-800-237-0984.

Mention Customer# 7016629 and
Coupon Code AD8392SDE.

## $25 OFF Convertible

Book now at alamo.com/offer/ent17
or call 1-800-237-0984.

Mention Customer# 7016629 and
Coupon Code AD8392SDE.

## $15 OFF
### When The Base Rate Is At Least $75.

Book now at alamo.com/offer/ent17
or call 1-800-237-0984.

Mention Customer# 7016629 and
Coupon Code AD2826JAA.

NATIONAL TRAVEL & HOTELS

NATIONAL TRAVEL & HOTELS

### FREE Day

Book now at nationalcar.com/offer/ent17
or call 1-888-575-6279.

Mention Contract ID 5031479 and
Coupon Code NF5337ZDN.

 **Promotion valid now thru 6/30/2018**
See reverse side for additional conditions or restrictions. **G83**

### FREE Weekend Day

Book now at nationalcar.com/offer/ent17
or call 1-888-575-6279.

Mention Contract ID 5031479 and
Coupon Code NF83Z6AAN.

 **Promotion valid now thru 6/30/2018**
See reverse side for additional conditions or restrictions. **G84**

### $20 OFF

Book now at nationalcar.com/offer/ent17
or call 1-888-575-6279.

Mention Contract ID 5031479 and
Coupon Code ND5291AAA.

 **Promotion valid now thru 6/30/2018**
See reverse side for additional conditions or restrictions. **G85**

### $30 Off (Any Size Car) when the base rate is at least $180

Book now at nationalcar.com/offer/ent17
or call 1-888-575-6279.

Mention Contract ID 5031479 and
Coupon Code ND9349JAJ.

 **Promotion valid now thru 6/30/2018**
See reverse side for additional conditions or restrictions. **G86**

GO LIKE A PRO.

**≋National** Car Rental™

Requires a 3-day minimum (5-day maximum) rental with a Saturday overnight keep. Valid on a compact through full-size vehicle through June 30, 2018. Offer subject to availability and valid only at participating National locations in the United States and Canada. Offer not valid in Manhattan, NY and Stamford, CT. One coupon per National rental and void once redeemed. Free day is prorated against base rate for entire rental period, which does not include applicable taxes (including GST), fees, surcharges, refueling, drop-off, delivery, youthful driver, additional driver, or pickup charges or one-way charges or any optional products or services such as damage waiver and liability protection, which are the responsibility of the renter. Offer is subject to standard rental conditions. In the U.S., please check your insurance and/or credit card for rental vehicle coverage. 24-hour advance reservation required. This offer cannot be combined with any other coupon and it is not valid for one-way, open, or previous rentals. Subject to availability. This offer may change without notice. Coupon subject to blackout periods, including holidays and other dates and times. Coupons are limited by pickup date, location, and car type. Coupon VOID if bought, bartered or sold for cash. Void where prohibited. Coupon is not exchangeable, refundable, transferable or redeemable for cash. Must present original coupon at time of rental. Cash value 1/100¢. ©2016 National Car Rental. All rights reserved.

This promotional offer is not valid with any other discount/promotion. See Rules of Use or visit www.entertainment.com/rulesofuse.          49784422

Requires a 5-day minimum rental with a Saturday overnight keep. Valid on a compact through full-size vehicle through June 30, 2018. Offer subject to availability and valid only at participating National locations in the United States and Canada. Offer not valid in Manhattan, NY and Stamford, CT. One coupon per National rental and void once redeemed. Free day is prorated against base rate for entire rental period, which does not include applicable taxes (including GST), fees, surcharges, refueling, drop-off, delivery, youthful driver, additional driver, or pickup charges or one-way charges or any optional products or services such as damage waiver and liability protection, which are the responsibility of the renter. Offer is subject to standard rental conditions. In the U.S., please check your insurance and/or credit card for rental vehicle coverage. 24-hour advance reservation required. This offer cannot be combined with any other coupon and it is not valid for one-way, open, or previous rentals. Subject to availability. This offer may change without notice. Coupon subject to blackout periods, including holidays and other dates and times. Coupons are limited by pickup date, location, and car type. Coupon VOID if bought, bartered or sold for cash. Void where prohibited. Coupon is not exchangeable, refundable, transferable or redeemable for cash. Must present original coupon at time of rental. Cash value 1/100¢. ©2016 National Car Rental. All rights reserved.

This promotional offer is not valid with any other discount/promotion. See Rules of Use or visit www.entertainment.com/rulesofuse.          49784413

$30 off a minimum five (5) day, maximum eleven (11) day, rental in which the base rate charge (exclusive of applicable taxes (including GST), fees, surcharges, refueling, drop-off, delivery, youthful driver, additional driver, or pickup charges or one-way charges or any optional products or services such as damage waiver and liability protection) is at least $180. Valid for rentals on any size car now through June 30, 2018, unless a longer period is required by law. 24-hour advance reservation required. Offer valid at participating National locations in the United States and Canada. Not valid in Manhattan, NY and Stamford, CT. Renter and additional driver(s) must meet standard age, driver and credit requirements. This offer cannot be combined with any other coupon and it is not valid for one-way, open, or previous rentals. Standard rental qualifications apply. In the U.S., check your auto policy and/or credit card agreement for rental vehicle coverage. Subject to availability. This offer may change without notice and is void where prohibited. Coupon subject to blackout periods, including holidays and other dates and times. Coupons are limited by pickup date, location, and car type. Void where prohibited. Coupon is not exchangeable, refundable, transferable or redeemable for cash. Must present original coupon at time of rental. Cash value 1/100¢. ©2016 National Car Rental. All rights reserved.

This promotional offer is not valid with any other discount/promotion. See Rules of Use or visit www.entertainment.com/rulesofuse.          49784418

$20 off a minimum three (3), maximum four (4) day rental with a Saturday overnight keep in the U.S. and Canada (exclusive of applicable taxes (including GST), fees, surcharges, refueling, drop-off, delivery, youthful driver, additional driver, or pickup charges or one-way charges or any optional products or services such as damage waiver and liability protection). Valid for rentals now through June 30, 2018, unless a longer period is required by law. 24-hour advance reservation required. Offer valid at participating National locations in the United States and Canada. Not valid in Manhattan, NY and Stamford, CT. Renter and additional driver(s) must meet standard age, driver and credit requirements. This offer cannot be combined with any other coupon and it is not valid for one-way, open, or previous rentals. Standard rental qualifications apply. In the U.S., check your auto policy and/or credit card agreement for rental vehicle coverage. Subject to availability. This offer may change without notice and is void where prohibited. Coupon subject to blackout periods, including holidays and other dates and times. Coupons are limited by pickup date, location, and car type. Void where prohibited. Coupon is not exchangeable, refundable, transferable or redeemable for cash. Must present original coupon at time of rental. Cash value 1/100¢. ©2016 National Car Rental. All rights reserved.

This promotional offer is not valid with any other discount/promotion. See Rules of Use or visit www.entertainment.com/rulesofuse.          49784407

### $30 Off (Any Size Car) when the base rate is at least $180

Book now at nationalcar.com/offer/ent17 or call 1-888-575-6279.

Mention Contract ID 5031479 and coupon code ND9349JAR.

 **Promotion valid now thru 6/30/2018**
See reverse side for additional conditions or restrictions. G87

### $25 OFF Specialty Vehicle

Book now at nationalcar.com/offer/ent17 or call 1-888-575-6279.

Mention Contract ID 5031479 and Coupon Code NDA2274BF

 **Promotion valid now thru 6/30/2018**
See reverse side for additional conditions or restrictions. G88

$**25** VALUE

### $25 OFF Specialty Vehicle

Book now at nationalcar.com/offer/ent17 or call 1-888-575-6279.

Mention Contract ID 5031479 and coupon code NDA2284BM.

**Promotion valid now thru 6/30/2018**
See reverse side for additional conditions or restrictions. G89

### FREE Day

Book now at nationalcar.com/offer/ent17 or call 1-888-575-6279.

Mention Contract ID 5031479 and coupon code NF5327ZDQ.

 **Promotion valid now thru 6/30/2018**
See reverse side for additional conditions or restrictions. G90

### FREE Upgrade

Book now at nationalcar.com/offer/ent17 or call 1-888-575-6279.

Mention Contract ID 5031479 and coupon code NU5137AAY.

**Promotion valid now thru 6/30/2018**
See reverse side for additional conditions or restrictions. G91

NATIONAL TRAVEL & HOTELS

Save up to 25% each time you rent using Entertainment® Discount Code CDP 205521

Combine CDP 205521 with included offers for even MORE savings!!

CDP 205521 + Coupon Offers Below = $$

Reserve at **www.hertz.com/entertainment** or call 888-999-7125 and say "Entertainment" to reserve your vehicle today

**Want to earn free days?**
see back for details

*Hertz.*

### Free Weekend Day

Enjoy up to 25% OFF <u>plus</u> a
**FREE Day** on a Weekend Rental
At Airport Locations
Compact through Fullsize Car Class
**PC# 109060 and
CDP# 205521**

 Promotion valid now thru 12/31/2017
See reverse side for additional conditions or restrictions.　G92

### $25 OFF Weekly Rentals

Enjoy up to 25% OFF <u>plus</u> a
**$25 OFF** Weekly Rentals at
Airport Locations
Economy Car Class and Above
**PC# 109001 and
CDP# 205521**

 Promotion valid now thru 12/31/2017
See reverse side for additional conditions or restrictions.　G93

### Up to $20 OFF on Weekend Rentals

Enjoy up to 25% off <u>plus</u>
**$5 off** a Day up to $20 off Weekend Rentals
Economy Car Class and Above
**PC# 109211 and
CDP# 205521**

 Promotion valid now thru 12/31/2017
See reverse side for additional conditions or restrictions.　G94

### Free Week Day

Enjoy up to 25% OFF <u>plus</u> a
**FREE Day** on a 5 Day Rental
Economy Car Class and Above
**PC# 109082 and
CDP# 205521**

 Promotion valid now thru 12/31/2017
See reverse side for additional conditions or restrictions.　G95

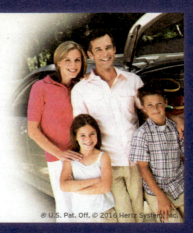

**PC 109001:** Promotion Code must be provided at time of reservation or offer is void. **Advance reservation required.** Reservation must include Entertainment's CDP # 205521 along with the PC# 109001 for this offer. Modifying your reservation may result in a change in your rate and/or invalidate this offer. Twenty-four (24) hour advance reservations required. Offer valid for Airport location only. Offer valid for a minimum rental of 5 days for weekly rentals. Offer is valid on all car classes except Dream cars. This offer has no cash value, may not be used with Contract Rates, Pre-pay Rates, Tour Rates, Insurance Replacement Rates or hourly rentals and cannot be combined with any other certificate, voucher, offer or promotion. Hertz age, driver, credit, qualifying weekly and weekend rate restrictions for the renting location apply. Taxes, tax reimbursement, age differential charges, fees and optional service charges, such as refueling, are not included. Discounts apply to time and mileage charges only. Discounts in local currency on redemption. Blackouts may apply. Offer valid for vehicle pickup through 12-31-17.

This promotional offer is not valid with any other discount/promotion.
See Rules of Use or visit www.entertainment.com/rulesofuse.        49783919

**PC 109060:** Promotion Code must be provided at time of reservation or offer is void. **Advance reservations required.** Reservation must include Entertainment's CDP # 205521 along with the PC# 109060 for this offer. Twenty-four (24) hour advance reservations required. Subject to availability, this offer is redeemable at participating airport Hertz locations in the U.S, Canada, and Puerto Rico. Modifying your reservation may result in a change in your rate and/or invalidate this offer. Offer valid for a minimum rental of 3 day for weekend rentals. Saturday night keep is required. Offer is valid Intermediate through Full-size car classes. This offer is available at participating airport Hertz locations in the U.S., Canada and Puerto Rico. This offer has no cash value, may not be used with Contract Rates, Pre-pay Rates, Tour Rates, Insurance Replacement Rates or hourly rentals and cannot be combined with any other certificate, voucher, offer or promotion. Hertz age, driver, credit, qualifying weekly and weekend rate restrictions for the renting location apply. Taxes, tax reimbursement, age differential charges, fees and optional service charges, such as refueling, are not included. Discounts apply to time and mileage charges only. Discounts in local currency on redemption. Blackouts may apply. Offer valid for vehicle pickup through 12-31-17.

This promotional offer is not valid with any other discount/promotion.
See Rules of Use or visit www.entertainment.com/rulesofuse.        49783927

**PC 109082:** Promotion Code must be provided at time of reservation or offer is void. **Advance reservations required.** Reservation must include Entertainment's CDP # 205521 along with the PC# 109082 for this offer. Twenty-four (24) hour advance reservations required. This offer is redeemable on Economy Car Class and above, excluding dream cars at participating Hertz locations. Modifying your reservation may result in a change in your rate and/or invalidate this offer. Rate subject to increase or fees may apply in the event of early / late vehicle return. Vehicle must be returned to renting location to avoid change in rate or drop charge. Subject to availability, this offer is available at participating Hertz locations in the U.S., Canada and Puerto Rico. Free Day offer requires a five (5) day minimum vehicle keep. Saturday Night Keep is required. Free Day offer is valid on all car classes except Dream cars. Offer has no cash value, may not be used with Pre-Pay Rates, Tour Rates, Insurance Replacement Rates or Hourly Rentals and cannot be combined with any other certificate, voucher, offer or promotion. Age, driver, credit and qualifying rate restrictions for the renting location apply. Taxes, tax reimbursement, age differential charges, fees, surcharges and optional service charges, such as refueling, are not included. Offer valid for vehicle pick-up on or before 12-31-17.

This promotional offer is not valid with any other discount/promotion.
See Rules of Use or visit www.entertainment.com/rulesofuse.        49783922

**PC 109211:** Promotion Code must be provided at time of reservation or offer is void. **Advance reservations are required.** Reservation must include Entertainment's CDP # 205521 along with the PC# 109211 for this offer. Twenty-four (24) hour advance reservations required. Modifying your reservation may result in a change in your rate and/or invalidate this offer. Rate subject to increase or fees may apply in the event of early / late vehicle return. Vehicle must be returned to renting location to avoid change in rate or drop charge. Minimum keep for a weekend rental is one (1) day, Saturday keep is required. Subject to availability, this offer is redeemable at participating Hertz locations in the US, Canada and Puerto Rico. Offer has no cash value and may not be used with Pre-Pay Rates, Tour Rates, Insurance Replacement Rates or Hourly Rentals and cannot be combined with any other CDP#, certificate, voucher, offer or promotion. Age, driver, credit and qualifying rate restrictions for the renting location apply. Taxes, tax reimbursement, age differential charges, fees, surcharges and optional service charges, such as refueling, are not included. Discounts apply to time and mileage charges only. Discounts in local currency upon redemption. Blackout periods may apply. Offer valid for vehicle pick-up on or before 12-31-17.

This promotional offer is not valid with any other discount/promotion.
See Rules of Use or visit www.entertainment.com/rulesofuse.        49783928

# A Fundraiser With Over 50 Years of Success.

**Your Group Profits. Families Save. Your Community Wins.**

# Join the thousands of groups that are using Entertainment® to meet their fundraising goals.

- Quick and easy fundraiser with no upfront cost
- Earn high-dollar profit per unit, so you can get to your goal quickly
- Popular and in demand year after year
- **NEW:** Raise even more funds with a FREE storefront website created just for your group. Supporters can order online directly through your site, while your group gets credit!

# Start Your Fundraiser Today!

Visit **learnmore.entertainment.com** for more information.

# Neighborhood Index

**Get these offers, and thousands more, on the mobile app!**
Search for "Entertainment® Coupons" in your app store to download.

# Neighborhood Index

**Get these offers, and thousands more, on the mobile app!**
Search for "Entertainment® Coupons" in your app store to download.

# Neighborhood Index

**Get these offers, and thousands more, on the mobile app!**
Search for "Entertainment® Coupons" in your app store to download.

NEIGHBORHOOD INDEX

# Neighborhood Index

**NEIGHBORHOOD INDEX**

## Get these offers, and thousands more, on the mobile app!
Search for "Entertainment® Coupons" in your app store to download.

# Neighborhood Index

**Get these offers, and thousands more, on the mobile app!**
Search for "Entertainment® Coupons" in your app store to download.

# Alphabetical Index

**Get these offers, and thousands more, on the mobile app!**
Search for "Entertainment® Coupons" in your app store to download.

# Alphabetical Index

**ALPHABETICAL INDEX**

**Get these offers, and thousands more, on the mobile app!**
Search for "Entertainment® Coupons" in your app store to download.

# Alphabetical Index

ALPHABETICAL INDEX

**Get these offers, and thousands more, on the mobile app!**
Search for "Entertainment® Coupons" in your app store to download.

# Alphabetical Index

**Get these offers, and thousands more, on the mobile app!**
Search for "Entertainment® Coupons" in your app store to download.

ALPHABETICAL INDEX

# Alphabetical Index

# Alphabetical Index

**Get these offers, and thousands more, on the mobile app!**
Search for "Entertainment® Coupons" in your app store to download.

# Alphabetical Index

**ALPHABETICAL INDEX**

# Get More

## Get thousands more discounts to use at home or when traveling.

Download the mobile app now, included with this membership.
Search for "Entertainment® Coupons" in your app store.

**Get these offers, and thousands more, on the mobile app!**
Search for "Entertainment® Coupons" in your app store to download.

# Entertainment® Membership Information

## To Activate Your Mobile and Online Benefits:

Go to **www.entertainment.com/getstarted** and have your membership card number ready. If you placed your order online and already activated your membership using the activation code provided at checkout, simply sign in using the email address you used during activation.

## Member Services

- **To download the Entertainment® mobile app to your phone:**
  Search for "Entertainment® coupons" in your app store, or visit **www.entertainment.com/mobile** for more information.

- **To purchase additional Entertainment® book memberships at member-only prices (great for gifts):**
  Go to **shop.entertainment.com**
  You must be signed in to receive special member pricing.

- **For our hotel programs:**
  Go to **www.entertainment.com/travel**

## Fundraiser Services

- **Since 1962, Entertainment® has helped raise millions of dollars for schools, charities and fundraising groups each year. To see how an Entertainment® fundraiser can help your group raise needed funds:**
  Go to **learnmore.entertainment.com**

## Business and Corporate Marketing Services

- **If you are a merchant interested in participating in the Entertainment® program:**
  Go to **www.entertainment.com/advertise**

- **If you are a corporate marketer looking for targeted and relevant rewards to increase customer acquisition, retention and loyalty:**
  Go to **cms.entertainment.com**

- **If you are a business interested in creating a custom coupon book or online savings program:**
  Go to **www.entertainment.com/pmd**

## Questions Regarding Your Membership?

- **To access your comprehensive source for customer support:**
  Go to **answers.entertainment.com**

Published by: Entertainment®, 1401 Crooks Road, Suite 150, Troy, Michigan 48084

# Entertainment® Offer Rules of Use

- **READ EACH OFFER CAREFULLY** for any conditions, restrictions and exclusions. When an offer has additional stated conditions, those conditions supersede the Rules of Use.

- Present your coupon, mobile device and/or Membership Card to a participating merchant at the time you request your bill.

- The merchant will retain your coupon. You will be asked to show your phone when redeeming mobile offers.

- Frequent Values® offers are "percentage-off" discounts that may be used on an ongoing basis. Present your Membership Card at participating Frequent Values® merchants each time you visit.

- Discounts exclude tax, tip and/or alcohol unless expressly stated otherwise and allowed by law.

- Offers expire December 30, 2017, unless otherwise indicated. Printable offers expire 14 days from the date of print or as stated on the coupon.

- Offers are not valid with other discounts and are nontransferable.

- Special discounts for car rentals, airfare and select hotels are available by using codes printed on offers and/or by identifying yourself as an Entertainment® member when making reservations.

- One Membership Card, coupon or mobile device offer may be used for every two people. Up to three coupons, Membership Cards or mobile offers may be used per party unless the offer states otherwise.

- Some offers state that they allow 1–4 people; others up to 8. When an offer is for a specific percentage off the total dining bill, one bill per table will be totaled and only one card/coupon per table is allowed.

- Offers are subject to the maximum dollar value stated. The least expensive item(s), up to the maximum value stated, will be deducted from your bill, or you will receive a percentage off the designated item(s), up to the maximum value stated.

- When dining, tipping for satisfactory service should be 15–20% of the **total** bill before the discount amount is subtracted.

- For restaurants offering a complimentary "*menu item*" when a second is purchased, a "*menu item*" is a main course or entrée item.

- Dining offers are not valid on children's menu items, discount-priced daily specials, senior citizen rates, early bird specials, carryout/takeout, and buffets, unless otherwise noted.

- Major holidays are excluded: New Year's Eve/Day, Valentine's Day, St. Patrick's Day, Easter, Mother's Day, Father's Day, Thanksgiving and Christmas Eve/Day. Additionally, for **Canada**: Victoria Day, Canada Day, Labour Day and Boxing Day. *Please check with the merchant regarding other regional or local holidays that might be excluded.*

- Coupons and Entertainment® Membership Cards are not gift cards.

- **EDITION SPECIFIC RULES**
  **Louisville:** Offers not valid during Derby Week of Derby-related events.

  **San Diego:** Limitations of liability stated above may not apply in the city of San Diego. See San Diego Municipal Code 33.2713.

  **WI/TN:** Redemption may be subject to certain conditions and limitations, which must be stated on the coupon. You are entitled to inspect the coupon before purchase.

- Refer to the Rules of Use section at **answers.entertainment.com** for more detailed examples and additional clarification.

# Entertainment® Makes a Great Gift!
## Available in Most Major Cities

You can order additional books* and receive special pricing when you log on as a member!
Order online at shop.entertainment.com

**ARIZONA**
047 Phoenix
068 Tucson

**CALIFORNIA**
055 East Bay
086 Fresno
097 Inland Empire
016 Los Angeles &
    Long Beach
014 Orange County
110 Reno & Lake Tahoe
042 Sacramento
017 San Diego
012 San Fernando Valley
073 San Francisco Bay Area
096 San Gabriel Valley
010 San Jose
088 Santa Barbara
    & Ventura

**COLORADO**
141 Colorado Springs
038 Denver

**CONNECTICUT**
080 Fairfield County
046 Hartford & New Haven

**DELAWARE**
157 Delaware

**FLORIDA**
035 Ft. Lauderdale
    & Palm Beach
075 Ft. Myers & Naples
036 Jacksonville
154 Miami & Florida Keys
153 Orlando
118 Sarasota & Bradenton
045 Tampa Bay &
    St. Petersburg

**GEORGIA**
028 Atlanta

**HAWAII**
146 Hawaii

**IDAHO**
085 Boise

**ILLINOIS**
008 Chicago North
015 Chicago South & West

**INDIANA**
078 Ft. Wayne
039 Indianapolis
056 Louisville &
    Southern Indiana
058 Northwest Indiana

**IOWA**
053 Des Moines

**KANSAS**
105 Kansas City
057 Wichita

**KENTUCKY**
056 Louisville &
    Southern Indiana

**LOUISIANA**
121 New Orleans

**MARYLAND**
024 Baltimore
022 Maryland &
    Washington, D.C.

**MASSACHUSETTS**
030 Boston
124 Springfield
108 Worcester County

**MICHIGAN**
001 Detroit Area
150 Grand Rapids
303 Saginaw

**MINNESOTA**
091 Twin Cities &
    Twin Ports

**MISSOURI**
105 Kansas City
013 St. Louis

**NEBRASKA**
138 Omaha

**NEVADA**
149 Las Vegas
110 Reno & Lake Tahoe

**NEW HAMPSHIRE**
128 Southern New
    Hampshire & Maine

**NEW JERSEY**
048 NJ Central
026 NJ North
076 NJ South

**NEW MEXICO**
083 Albuquerque
    & Santa Fe

**NEW YORK**
060 Albany
011 Buffalo
033 Long Island
087 Mid-Hudson Valley
034 New York City
044 Rochester
074 Syracuse
040 Westchester

**NORTH CAROLINA**
043 Charlotte
112 Raleigh & Durham

**OHIO**
006 Akron
069 Canton
002 Cincinnati Area
004 Cleveland
003 Columbus
005 Dayton
018 Toledo
131 Youngstown

**OKLAHOMA**
160 Oklahoma City
151 Tulsa

**OREGON**
051 Oregon
029 Portland

**PENNSYLVANIA**
162 Harrisburg
072 Lancaster & York
062 Lehigh Valley
156 Pennsylvania
    Northeast
031 Philadelphia
007 Pittsburgh

**RHODE ISLAND**
155 Providence

**SOUTH CAROLINA**
600 South Carolina

**TENNESSEE**
116 Memphis
064 Nashville

**TEXAS**
142 Austin
145 Dallas
147 Ft. Worth
019 Houston Area
152 San Antonio

**UTAH**
092 Utah

**VIRGINIA**
063 Hampton Roads
070 North Virginia &
    Washington, D.C.
158 Richmond

**WASHINGTON**
050 South Puget Sound
023 Seattle &
    North Puget Sound
090 Spokane

**WEST VIRGINIA**
115 Charleston
117 Huntington

**WISCONSIN**
077 Appleton & Green Bay
049 Madison
032 Milwaukee

**CANADA**
065 Calgary
601 Canadian Prairies
066 Edmonton
059 Hamilton
089 Montréal et environs
067 Ottawa/Outaouais
054 Toronto Area
025 Vancouver &
    Fraser Valley
107 Vancouver Island